Fundamental Concepts of Biology

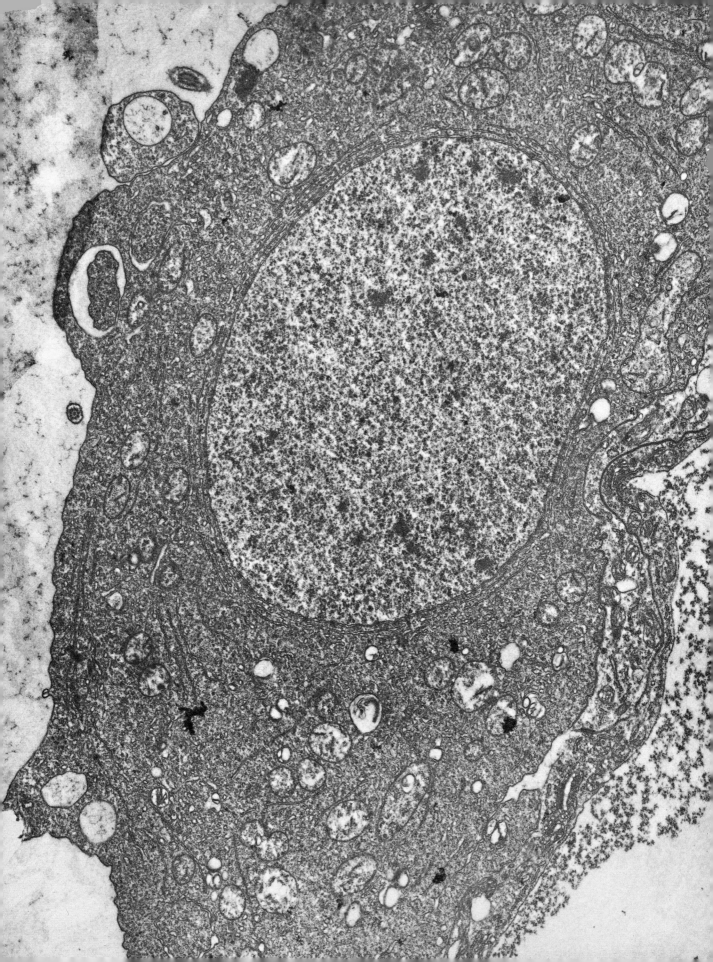

Fundamental Concepts of Biology

GIDEON E. NELSON
University of South Florida

GERALD G. ROBINSON
University of South Florida

RICHARD A. BOOLOOTIAN
BSCS at University of Colorado

John Wiley & Sons, Inc. New York • London • Sydney

Illustrated by Geraldine Beye

Library of Congress Catalog Card Number: 66–27897
Printed in the United States of America

SECOND PRINTING, APRIL, 1967

The frontispiece is an electron micrograph of a European corn borer spermatocyte ($\times 14,000$), reproduced courtesy of Dr. L. Evans Roth.

The photograph of an owl on the title page and cover was taken by Ron Austing (Photo Researchers, Inc.).

The photograph of a cell on the cover is reproduced courtesy of Dr. L. Evans Roth.

Preface

This textbook was written with two primary objectives. The first is to help students develop an understanding of the operation of biological systems through acquaintance with selected basic biological concepts and principles. The topics chosen are, in our experience and judgment, those that are most important to the understanding of biological systems as a whole. Some of the material is presented in a fairly traditional manner, but more of it, we hope, breaks away from conventional treatments which present surveys of the field of biology.

The second objective, which also influenced the selection of topics included in this book, is to provide a foundation of subject matter that enables students to achieve a better interpretation and evaluation of the types of biological information they encounter in newspapers, magazines, and semiscientific journals—in short, in everyday life. The value of this type of activity to an informed citizenry seems obvious in this age of rapid scientific advance.

The scheme of presentation we have followed starts with the smallest fundamental units of living material and gradually progresses toward the largest functioning biological system, the world of living things. Chapters II and III deal with the structural features of living matter, commencing with its basic chemical and physical composition and then examining in considerable detail the unit called the cell. These chapters are followed by three devoted to photosynthesis, respiration, and transport, the key metabolic processes which are so characteristic of life.

The subject of regulation dominates Chapters VII through XI. Here we treat the coordination of cellular activities, the coordination and control among cells by hormones and the nervous system, the maintenance of the entire organism, and finally, the integration of behavior made possible by communication among organisms. We then proceed to the subjects of reproduction and development, which are discussed in Chapters XII–XIV. This leads logically to a consideration of the genetics of individuals and populations (Chapters XV–XVIII). We devote four chapters to this important topic because we believe that every educated

person should have a broad knowledge of heredity and its many applications to human society.

Darwin's contribution to the principles of evolution has been termed the major unifying principle in biology. The significant subject of evolution together with its evidence and mechanisms occupy the next two chapters, XIX and XX. The final five chapters of the book examine organisms, their environments, and the relationships between the two. The last of these chapters selects a major habitat type, aquatic environments, and applies to it the major principles presented in the preceding four.

A book such as this presents a number of opportunities for the introduction of outside readings. Many teachers of biology prefer two types of readings: those of a historical and classical nature, and material such as *Scientific American* offprints which present recent information on various topics. Many references of this sort are available at reasonable cost to be utilized as individual instructors see fit.

We would like to acknowledge the assistance of those who have contributed to the clarity and accuracy of this text by reading all or part of the manuscript and suggesting possible modifications. These include Mr. James Campbell, Dr. Marvin Cantor, Dr. Elof Carlson, Dr. Jack E. Fernandez, Dr. John W. Hall, Dr. Joe R. Linton, Dr. Knut Norstog, Dr. Eugene Odum, and Dr. James D. Ray, Jr. In addition we would like to recognize the assistance of Mrs. Janice Duncan, Mr. Arthur Hepner, Miss Joyce McKee, and Mr. Thomas L. Sears in the preparation of the manuscript.

We wish to thank especially the General Biological Supply House, Inc., for the use of prepared microscope slides, from which we made many of the photomicrographs appearing in this book.

Gideon E. Nelson
Gerald G. Robinson
Richard A. Boolootian

June, 1966

Contents

Life: Its Characteristics and Study

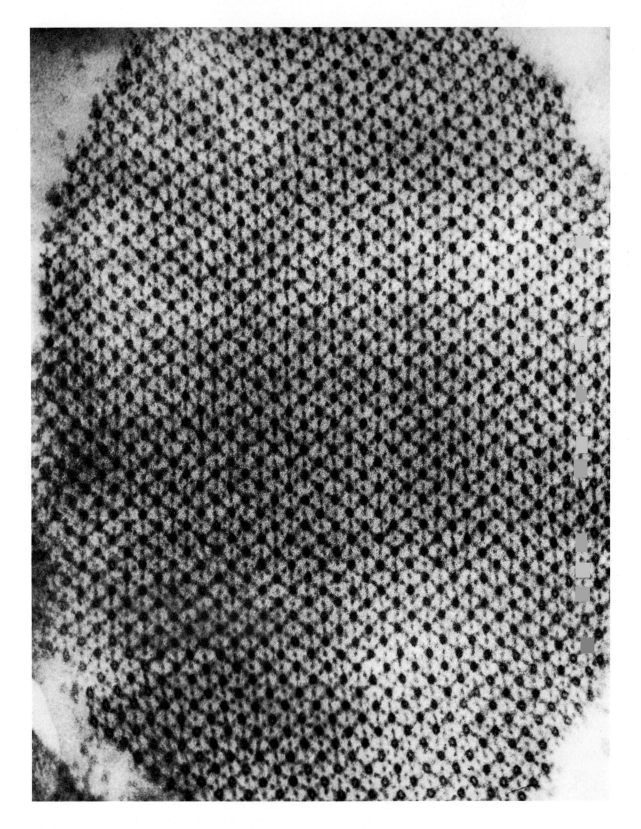

An electron micrograph of cross section of muscle (×11,000). (Dr. H. E. Huxley.)

Life: Its Characteristics and Study

Man turns to science to fathom the mysteries of the universe. For knowledge of the living world he relies on biology, the science of life itself. A tiny acorn grows into a massive oak tree, a bougainvillea plant that lends rich coloring to a tropical isle cannot survive the northern Minnesota climate, a child cannot easily be told apart from his identical twin, a quarterback throws a touchdown pass three weeks after bone surgery. What actually makes each of them possible becomes clear from an understanding of the fundamentals of modern biology.

To many students biology suggests dissection of tiny animals in a laboratory, collecting leaves and flowers, and memorizing obscure Latinized names for the myriad plants and animals. These activities no more characterize the whole field of biology than heating chemicals in a test tube typifies the science of chemistry. The true scope of biology is all of life, which the science treats as a series of processes whose natures may be discovered through experimentation or microscopic investigation. These processes cover a vast range of phenomena from how cells develop into tissues and organisms to the changes that occur in organisms over a period of time. They include such matters as how living organisms obtain their energy from chemical sources, how certain mechanisms control and regulate the functioning of plant and animal parts, how organisms reproduce and pass on their traits from one generation to the next. Our knowledge of the living world gains perspective from a description of its features and behavior, and from extensive study of biological principles.

In a broad sense biology deals with two sets of living things, plants and animals. Both plant and animal kingdoms contain millions of organisms in an almost limitless variety of sizes and shapes. These differ as widely as the single-celled bacterium and the million-celled poinsettia plant or the microscopic amoeba and the six-foot, one-inch man. Despite the profusion of different organisms, all share certain features to some degree. The study of biology seeks to explain the basis of these similarities and disparities.

Characteristics of Living Things

All living things have structure, experience metabolism, engage in regulation and control, reproduce and develop, inherit from their forebears, and adapt to their surroundings ultimately participating in an evolutionary process. These many areas point to some of the major characteristics of life which have occupied biologists for years. Since we believe that these topics will continue to be important, we shall have much to say about them in the course of this book.

Structure. Most flowering plants, like the cherry tree and the rose bush, consist of several principal parts called organs. All of us are familiar with their names—root, stem, leaf, flower. Each of these organs performs an important function in the plant. If we

3

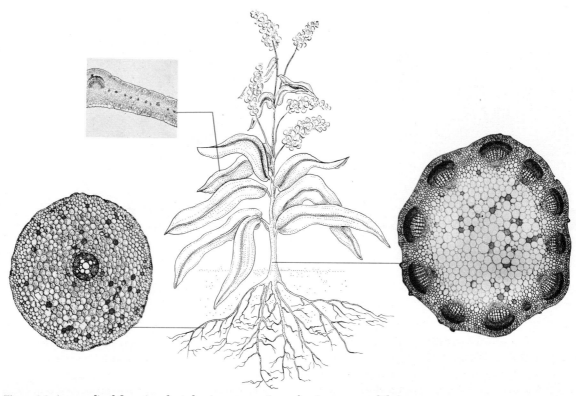

Figure 1.1. A generalized flowering plant showing cross sections of major organs and their structural components.

take a close look at them under laboratory conditions we see that they are composed of many groups of tissues, each having a job of its own (Figure 1.1). In the stem, for example, one tissue may conduct the passage of water and minerals, another may supply storage facilities, and there are also supporting tissues and an outer protective tissue. If we place any of these tissues under a microscope for a still closer look we observe that it consists of a mass of cells, which are the basic units of biological organization.

When we turn this hierarchy the other way around, in the realm of the so-called higher plants we note that a group of similar cells with a similar function forms a tissue, a group of tissues forms an organ, and a group of organs composes the plant itself. The location and arrangement of the tissues and organs are generally similar in all plants even though their structures may differ. For example, a cactus plant and a pear tree may share many internal features while having quite different external appearances.

The so-called lower plants like mosses, algae, or fungi are less complex in structure than higher plants. Some, like liverworts, may consist only of cells and tissues, and many of the algae are single celled (Figure 1.2).

The structural—or *morphological*—plan of animals follows the same course as in plants, except that the level of complexity is often greater. Thus the cat is composed of many *systems* of organs, such as the nervous, glandular, and muscular systems. Each of these systems is a composite of many organs. For example, the upper bone of the leg is an organ of the

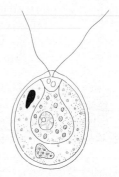

Figure 1.2. A single-celled alga, Chlamydomonas.

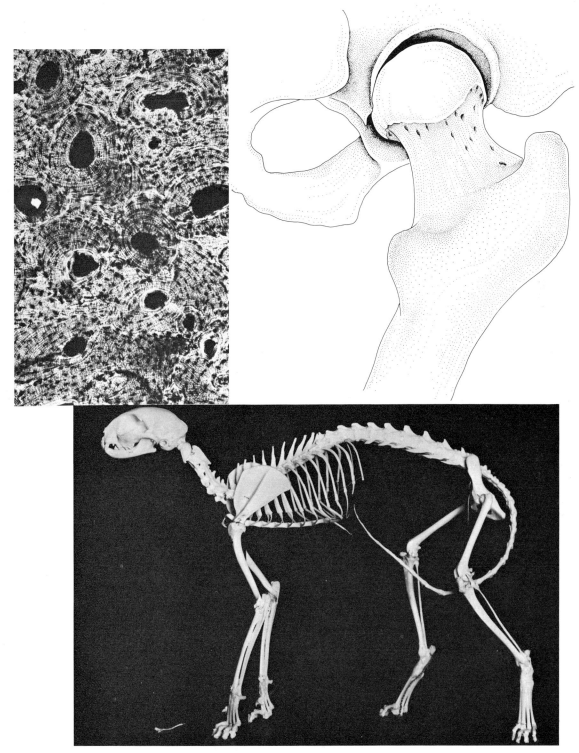

Figure 1.3. The skeletal system of the cat showing parts of two organs, the upper leg bone and a pelvic bone, and a cross section of the bone tissues. (Ward's Natural Science Establishment, Inc., for bone tissue.)

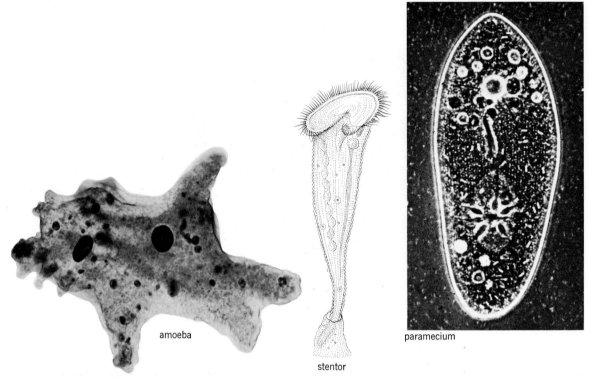

amoeba

stentor

paramecium

Figure 1.4. A variety of protozoans. (Ward's Natural Science Establishment, Inc.)

skeletal system (Figure 1.3). As in plants, the organs of animals are groups of tissues, which, in turn, are clusters of cells.

The parallel continues with lower animals having less complex structural formations than higher forms of animal life. *Hydra,* for example, may barely get beyond the cell-tissue arrangement, and most of the minuscule animals called protozoans consist only of single cells (Figure 1.4).

All living things, from the smallest to the largest, thus share structure as a common characteristic. In reality, an organism's structure is inseparable from its function since each of them influences and modifies the other. Nevertheless, we separate them for convenience in discussion and description.

Metabolism. Living organisms acquire and utilize the energy they need through intricate chemical changes which take place mostly within the cells. These important processes constitute metabolism, a second significant characteristic of living things. Although quite varied, the chemical reactions involved in metabolism show marked similarities among a wide range of organisms. In their own unique ways two organisms as unlike as lotus flowers and porcupines

obtain nourishment, strength, hardiness, and other requisites for survival through similar chemical action.

Every biological activity—whether growth, reproduction, movement, or production of chemical products—demands an expenditure of energy. For maintenance and repair of its biological structure alone, every form of life continually consumes an enormous amount of energy. The chemical process that manufactures this energy occurs mostly in the cells and is much the same in most instances. For all living organisms the ultimate energy supply, in the form of carbon compounds, derives from *photosynthesis,* a metabolic process dependent on sunlight and the green coloring matter of plants (Figure 1.5).

Research into metabolism occurs for the most part in the field of biochemistry. Biologists have attempted to identify the enzymes, which are crucial to metabolism, and to find out exactly where they function in various biochemical reactions in the cell. They have also sought to discover the structure of proteins—in particular the sequences of amino acids, the basic chemical units from which proteins are built.

Photosynthesis has been subjected to extensive research. Use of new research tools like the electron

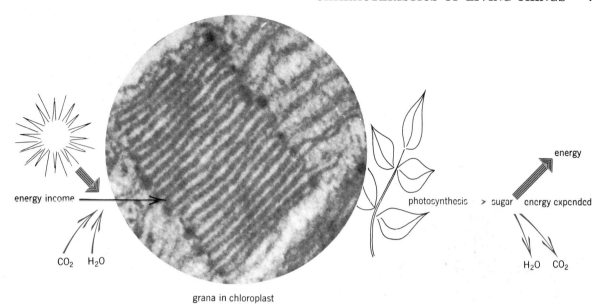

energy income

CO_2 H_2O

grana in chloroplast

energy

photosynthesis   >   sugar   energy expended

H_2O CO_2

Figure 1.5. A generalized scheme of energy capture and expenditure.

microscope has acquainted man with the structure of the *chloroplasts* (Figure 1.5), the site where photosynthesis occurs in the cell. In addition, biochemical studies have unearthed many details about the sequence of chemical reactions, the nature of the substances involved, and their relationship to the visible structure of the particular specimen.

Regulation.   Just as engineers have devised intricate systems of automatic controls for the operation of huge assembly lines, organisms have developed their own regulatory mechanisms. Such activity, through many self-regulatory control systems, is essential if all the biological processes are to function effectively in organisms. The control mechanisms must execute their roles not only within cells but also among the cells composing an organism, and in the integration of an organism with its surroundings. The study of two well-known examples of control mechanisms, the nervous and hormonal systems, has been part of biology for a long time. The study of other areas, like behavior and intracellular chemical control, is relatively new.

Reproduction and Development.   Every living thing reproduces and grows. In every organism the first step in reproduction occurs at the cellular level. This step is *cell division*. It may lead to the formation of a new organism—as in the single-celled plant or animal, to the formation of specialized sex cells and hence new organisms—as in the ovary of a woman, or to an increase in the size of an individual—as in a growing pine tree. Cell division is a complex process for which the inanimate world has no counterpart.

Growth is unique. It results from cell division and chemical activities within cells. Nonliving, or inanimate, objects like crystals may increase in size, but their growth follows from an addition of new atoms to the outside of the object rather than from internal events.

The study of developmental biology is called *embryology.* This is one of the most fascinating areas of biological investigation. New techniques have taught scientists to grow plant and animal embryos outside of their normal environment and to apply biochemical methods to problems of development. These advances have inspired new research into how the fertilized egg gives rise to an adult organism (Figure 1.6).

One urgent aspect of studies on reproduction in today's heavily populated world is the question of birth control among human beings. New drugs have demonstrated a capacity to alter the normal hormonal system which affects reproduction. Such drugs may eventually be useful everywhere to slow down the population explosion which threatens the world's food resources.

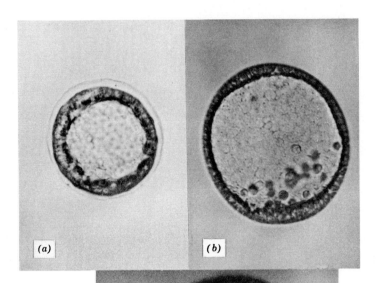

Figure 1.6(a–e). Successive stages in the development of sea urchins. The embryos of these animals have been extensively used as subjects in developmental biology. (Dr. P. Denny and Mr. D. Kaplan.)

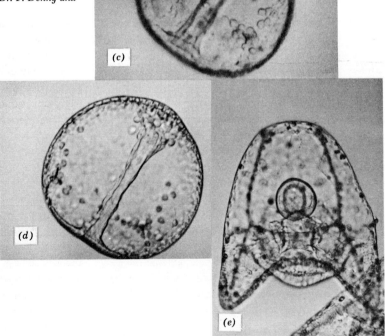

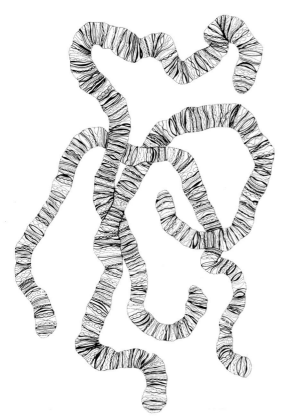

Figure 1.7. Giant chromosomes from the salivary gland of the fruit fly, Drosophila.

4 *Heredity.*   Any mention of biological reproduction necessarily leads to the subject of heredity. Nearly all of our knowledge of heredity—or *genetics,* as this area of biology is usually called by biologists—dates from the beginning of this century. Genetics is one of the newer areas of biology.

The general mechanisms of transfer from parents to offspring are well known (Figure 1.7). But the center of greatest interest at this time is a giant molecule called DNA (deoxyribonucleic acid). All hereditary information seems evidently coded into this basic hereditary material located in all the cells of living things. DNA not only serves as an hereditary mechanism but also controls all biochemical events in the cell. Indeed, studies on metabolism, for example, often become involved with functions related to DNA. We shall have much to say about DNA in the course of this book. Some biologists predict that the discovery of its significance may eventually rank as the foremost biological advance of the century.

5 *Adaptation and Evolution.*   The last of the major characteristics of life to require our attention are adaptation and evolution. Anyone who travels from North to South immediately becomes aware of a marked change in plant and animal life. Fir trees may be seen against the snow in one clime and live oak among the marshes in another. In both places plants and animals are adjusted to their surroundings. This adaptation is accomplished through the interaction of hereditary materials with the environment. As the adaptation continues over a long period of time it becomes part of a gradual process of evolution.

Life has doubtless existed on earth for a longer time than we can readily conceive, perhaps for at least two billion years. The origin and early evolution of life remains one of the baffling puzzles of biological science. Recent discoveries of primitive microscopic organisms indicate they may be nearly two billion years old. The knowledge obtained from studying them provides a basis for making inferences about the environment in which these plants thrived. These inferences, in turn, shed light on the kinds of events that could have occurred in earlier epochs.

Many important factors bear on the adaptation and evolution of living organisms. Some of the major ones are the flow of energy from producers (plants) to consumers (animals), the interaction of populations of organisms with their environment, and the distribution of principal communities of living things (Figure 1.8). Studies on these subjects belong to the branch of biology called *ecology.* Ecological research is particularly heavy in the areas of energy flow and population dynamics (Figure 1.9). The findings may someday enable man to achieve a better adjustment of his growing numbers to the available resources on the earth. From all this, it is evident that the numerous areas of biology are not disjoined, but are parts of one whole. Through their linkage, the smallest development in the cell, for example, may directly affect the study of the organism and its habitat or, for that matter, any other biological endeavor. Modern biology is not standing still. Indeed, this highly diversified though fully integrated science continues to probe further for greater knowledge and more exact answers to the profound question, "What is life?"

Methods of Study

Like other scientists, biologists approach their investigations within a broad framework of what is termed scientific methodology, but it would be

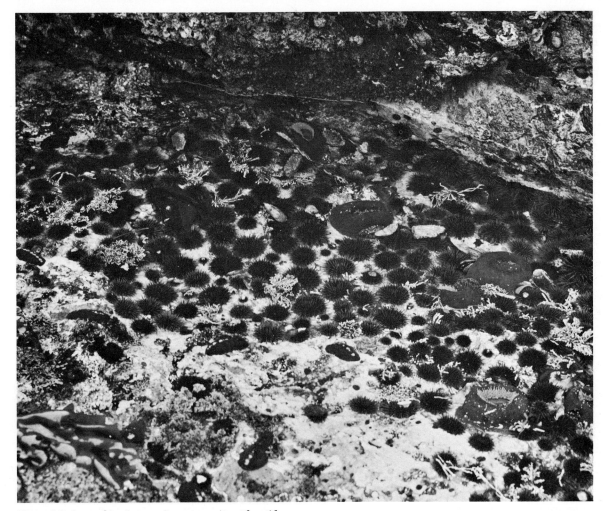

Figure 1.8. Sea urchins in a marine community at low tide.

erroneous to assume that all biologists, or all scientists, utilize this approach in the same manner.

Before an individual can really begin an investigation he must be familiar with previous studies regarding his topic. He can then avoid needless duplication of effort and utilize the data from other studies in his own work. This is frequently accomplished by a thorough review of the appropriate scientific literature, especially journals that report research studies in his field. With this knowledge the investigator is ready to proceed with his own work. From this point on the sequence of steps varies considerably, depending on the investigator and the nature of the material with which he is working.

Let us say that a researcher has decided approximately what he wants to study and knows how he is going to do it. He may have a tentative hypothesis and perhaps some general ideas about how the investigation will turn out. He proceeds to gather data by making observations; these may originate in nature or in the laboratory. In addition, his observations are usually aided by scientific equipment: camera, microscope, chemical apparatus, etc. Eventually he takes his observations (facts) and proposes a statement that relates them or summarizes their significance. This is an hypothesis, a working statement. If possible, additional observations or experiments are performed to test the validity of the hypothesis.

Scientists rely heavily on experimentation as a method for verifying an hypothesis when the material

Figure 1.9. Part of a dense population of squid. These marine organisms feed on many animals which in turn feed on plants.

is suitable to this technique. Experiments are designed to discover which of the variables in a situation are significant. In other words, experimentation is a method for discovering the true cause-and-effect relationship. The experimenter is bound by only two rules. His experiments must be conducted in such a way that one set of tests differs from another set of tests by only one factor: that is, they must have proper controls. Further, they must be of such a nature that they may be repeated by other individuals. *Repeatability* is one of the most crucial aspects of the scientific method, for it is the major basis for the acceptance or rejection of many hypotheses.

If the hypothesis is supported (verified) by whatever tests the experimenter applies, then it reaches a level of greater certainty. There is now a higher probability that it correctly interprets a set of facts. In a way, this is the essence of science—not to "prove" or "disprove,"

but to indicate levels of certainty or probability.

At this point the investigator has contributed two kinds of knowledge: the facts he has gathered, and the hypotheses or theories he has derived from the facts. These are important additions to the field of biology.

Theories are useful not only for synthesizing data but also because predictions can frequently be made from them, thus leading to entirely new lines of investigation. For example, from Darwin's observation on the way in which young plants grew toward light, he constructed the hypothesis that the influence of light on the stem tip was transmitted to the rest of the plant by a chemical factor. This hypothesis led to experiments which proved him correct, as we shall see in Chapter VIII.

A theory that has been repeatedly verified and appears to have wide application in biology may become a biological principle. These are sometimes called biological laws, although this does not change their status as statements that apply with a high degree of probability to a wide range of biological events. They are still man-made and subject to change if additional facts emerge in the future. Throughout this book the term *principle* is used in this sense.

An important aspect of scientific investigation is the imagination, the creativity of the scientist. The proper interpretation of data, the design of experiments, and the formulation of useful new theories frequently involve a certain amount of intuition—a hunch about how to proceed. This may sound quite unscientific, yet many scientists admit that it is important in their investigatory work.

In addition to gathering facts, hypothesizing, and testing hypotheses, someone must at intervals attempt to bring together the research efforts of other biologists in order to present the current status or progress being made in a biological field. Frequently this type of material appears as a monograph or an extensive review article in a scientific journal. The knowledge presented in the chapters to follow was acquired through the techniques described.

Principles

1. Life is a series of processes that can be studied scientifically. Living things are characterized by the combination of their structure, metabolism, regulatory devices, reproduction, heredity, and evolutionary history.

2. Scientists employ a variety of techniques and approaches in acquiring new knowledge. Such knowledge must be capable of verification by others.

Suggested Readings

Beveridge, W. I. B., *The Art of Scientific Investigation.* Revised edition. W. W. Norton and Co., New York. 1957.

Wald, George, "Innovation in Biology," *Scientific American,* Vol. 199 (September, 1958). Offprint No. 48, W. H. Freeman and Co., San Francisco.

Questions

1. How is life defined in this chapter?

2. Would you say that this is a definition which emphasizes a structural or a functional approach? Why?

3. In your own experience, how do you separate living from nonliving entities?

4. List the differences between living and nonliving objects using the characteristics of living things from this chapter. How does this compare with your ideas from question 3?

5. Why is there not a single scientific method, i.e., a list of steps, which all scientists follow in their investigations?

6. List one possible sequence of steps one might follow in a scientific investigation. In what ways could you change the sequence of steps and still accomplish the same investigation?

7. Why is it erroneous to state that science can prove or disprove a hypothesis?

8. Can science prove or disprove a fact? Why?

Life: Its Chemical Basis

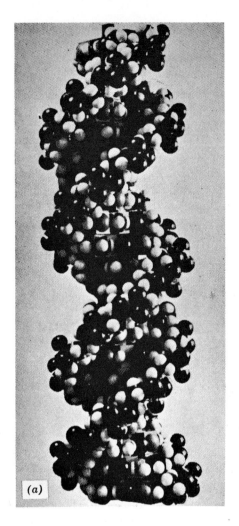

Models of molecular structures depicting (a) *deoxyribonucleic acid (from Dr. Christian B. Anfinsen,* The Molecular Basis of Evolution, *Wiley, New York, 1959, through the courtesy of Dr. M. H. F. Wilkins); (b) ethane (Russ Kinne, Photo Researchers, Inc.); (c) terramycin (courtesy of Chas. Pfizer and Co., Inc.).*

Life: Its Chemical Basis

Every organism, as we have seen, has a number of characteristics that help us to identify it as living. The more important of these include the chemical activities that occur in the organisms. If we look at the general structure of the atom and then turn to some of the types of atoms that are common to living things, we can acquire a general understanding of these vital chemical processes.

(A) ***Atomic Structure.*** Atoms are the smallest particles of elements which enter into chemical reactions. Nevertheless, atoms are not indivisible. Each atom consists of a relatively heavy, compact central nucleus and lighter particles called electrons, which orbit the nucleus at some distance from its center. Electrons are virtually weightless and each one carries a negative electrical charge. The nucleus is composed of protons and neutrons, each proton and neutron having one (B) unit of atomic weight (an arbitrary unit) and being about 1,800 times heavier than the electron. An atom's weight results almost entirely from its protons and neutrons. A proton's charge is positive, whereas a neutron is neutral.

Looking at the structure of atoms of different elements, we see that each element has a distinctive number of protons (Figure 2.1). An element is a substance whose atoms all contain the same number of protons and the same number of electrons. Furthermore, since the number of protons equals the number of electrons, an atom is electrically neutral.

From the illustration of atoms we might have the impression that the number of neutrons present is the same in every atom of an element. This is not always true. In the atoms of some elements the number of neutrons may vary. Atoms of carbon, for example, may have one of three different atomic weights, 12, 13, or 14, depending on the number of their neutrons. These different kinds of atoms of the same element are called *isotopes,* and in this instance are designated C^{12}, C^{13}, and C^{14} (Figure 2.2). Each of these contains six protons, but has six, seven, or eight neutrons, respectively.

Any substance created by the chemical combination of the atoms of two or more elements is called a *compound.* The compound will have different characteristics from those of the elements forming it.

(B) ***Bonds and Energy.*** When atoms react chemically to form a *molecule* (the smallest particle retaining all the properties of the substance itself), they may gain, lose, or share electrons. Atoms that gain electrons become negatively charged, whereas those that lose them become positively charged, having originally been electrically neutral. These charged particles are called *ions.* Negatively charged ions are attracted to positively charged ions because the opposite charges attract each other. The resulting force that binds these ions together is an *ionic bond* (Figure 2.3).

When immersed in water, compounds held together

15

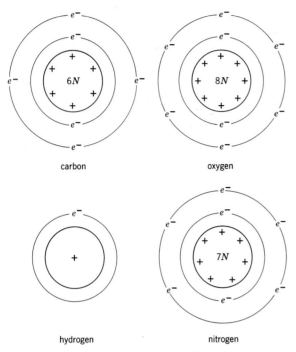

carbon   oxygen

hydrogen   nitrogen

Figure 2.1. A schematic representation of four atoms important in biology. The circle represents the nucleus of the atom containing protons (indicated by the plus signs) and neutrons (N). The electrons are represented by e⁻. The distance of e⁻ from the nucleus represents the various energy levels of different electrons. Carbon, for example, has six neutrons and six protons in the nucleus and six electrons in rapid motion around the nucleus.

by ionic bonds tend to separate, or dissociate, into their constituent ions because of the action of the water. Many substances required by biological systems exist in nature in ionic form. Such mineral salts as sodium (Na^+), chloride (Cl^-), potassium (K^+), calcium (Ca^{++}), phosphate ($PO_4^=$), etc., are good examples. The minus and plus signs indicate the kind and size of charge on each ion.

Another type of bond found in many molecules is the *covalent bond* (Figure 2.3). Here the atoms share electrons. Molecules containing covalent bonds do not dissociate when placed in water but remain intact. Carbon (C), oxygen (O), hydrogen (H), and nitrogen (N), which constitute about 95 per cent of the material in cells, engage in this type of bonding. All of the cell's larger molecules and many of its smaller ones contain such bonds.

The importance of electrons in bonds and in reactions—the changing of bonds—make it convenient to classify molecules according to their role in these changes. Molecules furnishing electrons during a reaction are called electron *donors*. Those that gain electrons during the process are called electron *acceptors*. Some molecules gain electrons only to lose them to some other molecule in a very short time; these are designated electron *carriers*.

Bonds contain energy, the ability to do work. This results from the interaction of the atoms linked by the bond. If we measure the amount of energy present between two atoms, we find that this amount varies as the distance between the atoms changes. The amount of energy is high when two atoms are close because

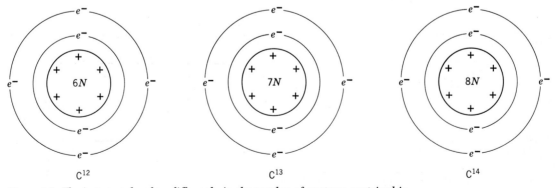

C^{12} C^{13} C^{14}

Figure 2.2. The isotopes of carbon differ only in the number of neutrons contained in the nucleus. The numbers of protons and electrons in these three isotopes are the same, making them chemically identical. C^{14} is synthetically prepared and has been extensively used in clarifying metabolic pathways.

their two nuclei which have like charges repel each other. As the distance between the atoms grows, the amount of energy decreases markedly, and then increases somewhat to a level that remains constant (Figure 2.4). Point *A* on the graph represents the distance separating the atoms in a molecule; this is the point at which there is the least energy.

In order to break a bond we must move its atoms farther apart. To do so we must add energy. Generally,

when one bond is broken another forms. If the new bond contains more energy than the first, we assume energy must have been added. On the other hand, if the new bond contains less energy, we assume energy has been released, which may be used to change bonds elsewhere or which may escape as heat. In either case a certain amount of energy, the *activation energy* (Figure 2.5), must be initially added to move the atoms apart so that the reaction may proceed. If the new

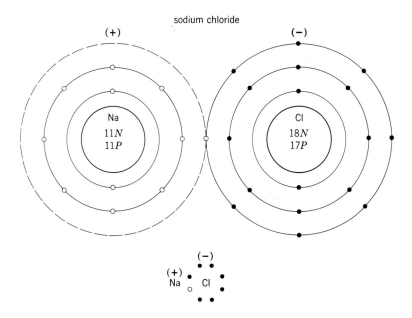

Figure 2.3. Representation of two types of bonding. In sodium chloride (NaCl), the common table salt, the chlorine atom and the sodium atom are held together by an ionic bond. The water molecule (H₂O) contains covalent bonds.

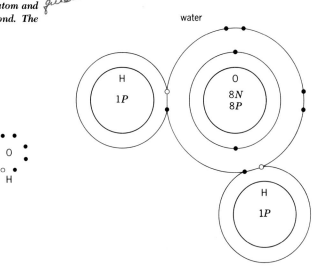

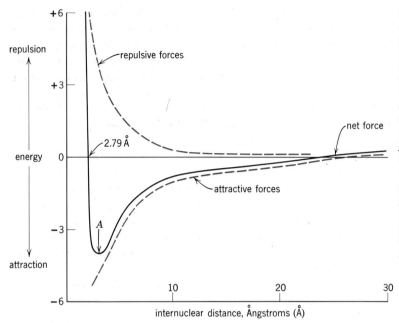

Figure 2.4. Diagram illustrating the amount of energy between two atoms. There is an electrostatic attraction between two charged ions such as K$^+$ and Cl$^-$. Owing to this attraction the two ions will approach one another. When the two ions get very close together their electron orbitals will begin to overlap, and this causes a strong repulsion. The point at which the attractive and repulsive forces are balanced is indicated by the intersection of the solid curve with the horizontal denoting zero energy. In KCl this point occurs where the average internuclear distance is 2.79 Ångstroms (Å) or about 0.00000001 inch. The solid line indicates the net force, and the two dashed lines indicate the repulsive and attractive forces.

Figure 2.5. The activation energy required for the reaction from A to B is represented by E_a; for the reverse reaction it is represented by E_a'. In both directions the reaction proceeds through the activated complex X. ΔE signifies the difference in energy between compounds A and B.

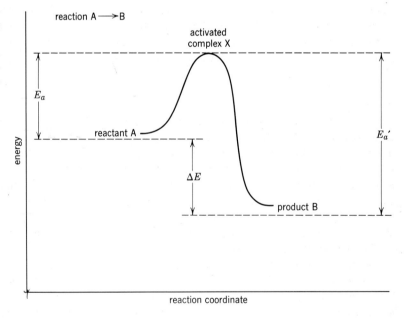

bond contains less energy, the reaction will continue because the energy released serves to activate changes in other molecules. This kind of reaction supplies energy to be utilized in the cell's varied activities.

Common Substances in Living Systems

Small Molecules. Water is the most abundant substance in living cells. It consists of small, simple molecules composed of two hydrogen atoms attached to one oxygen atom (H_2O). The three distinct parts that water plays in cells underline its importance. It takes part in some reactions (see Chapters IV and V), it serves as a medium (or solvent) for other reactions, and it serves as a basis for the transport of materials. In reality the chemistry of life is dominated by the chemistry of water.

Chemical reactions occur between individual atoms, ions, or molecules, and not between large aggregations of these particles. Most substances placed in water separate into small particles. As these particles move about in the water, they come into contact with other particles and a reaction occurs.

Carbon dioxide (CO_2) is composed of another kind of small molecule. Each molecule contains one carbon atom and two oxygen atoms. The role of carbon dioxide in living systems is not nearly as diverse as that of water, but it plays a part in both respiration and photosynthesis, two processes of great importance. All the carbon in the larger carbon-containing (organic) compounds found in living systems comes directly or indirectly from carbon dioxide.

Molecular oxygen (O_2) is required by almost all organisms. It is utilized in respiration, the releasing of energy in the cell (see Chapter V). Since oxygen is a product of photosynthesis (see Chapter IV), the supply in the atmosphere is maintained at a nearly constant level. The small size of the oxygen molecule lessens the problems involved in its transport between the environment and the cells (Chapter VI).

The last small molecule we shall mention is the ammonia molecule (NH_3). A common source of ammonia molecules is the decomposition of proteins. The organism must have a method of disposing of ammonia because even a moderate concentration is injurious to cells.

Larger Molecular Substances. The other classes of compounds that we shall survey, carbohydrates, lipids, proteins, and nucleic acids, are characterized by larger molecules. At least a major portion of each of these kinds of molecules is composed of carbon atoms bonded to each other. In many plants these molecules may be produced inside the cell from simple molecules such as CO_2, H_2O, and NH_3, whereas in other organisms simpler carbon-containing compounds brought into the cell serve as a raw material for synthesis of the larger molecules.

Carbohydrates are composed of carbon, hydrogen, and oxygen. All molecules of carbohydrates contain the atoms of hydrogen and oxygen in a two-to-one ratio. Each molecule is composed of a chain of carbon atoms with hydrogen and oxygen bonded to them. The smallest carbohydrates, called *simple sugars,* are those that cannot be made to react with water to produce a simpler form. These vary in size; the smallest have a chain of three carbon atoms, whereas the largest have seven. More complex carbohydrates are formed by the joining of two or more of the simple sugars.

The commonest of the simple sugars is *glucose* ($C_6H_{12}O_6$). Its structure is

The connecting lines represent molecular bonds. Note the repetitions of the H—C—OH unit. This is typical of sugars. *Starch, glycogen,* and *cellulose* in common with many other complex carbohydrates are formed by bonding a number of glucose molecules. Besides glucose there are other six-carbon sugars. Combinations of these with glucose result in another series of sugars. Common table sugar, sucrose, is one (Figure 2.6).

Carbohydrates have two functions, energy storage and strengthening of the cell. Energy storage is the more common of these. Glycogen and starch, respectively, are animal and plant examples of carbohydrates used mainly for this purpose. Cellulose is a carbohydrate used to strengthen the structure of the cell. In most plants it constitutes the cell wall. Animals do not commonly use carbohydrates in this way.

Fats are members of a large group of compounds called *lipids.* The structures of most other lipids are

glucose   fructose   sucrose

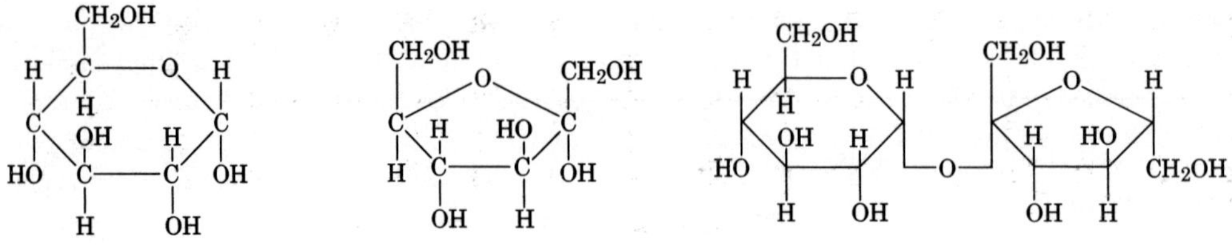

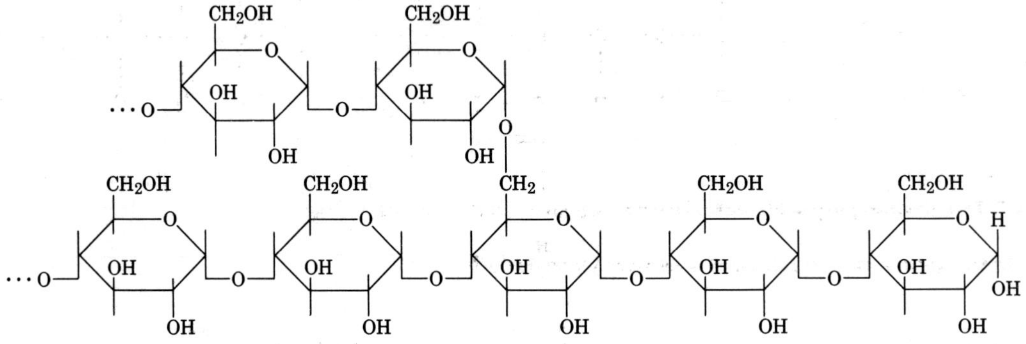

glycogen

Figure 2.6. One molecule of glucose and one molecule of fructose compose the table sugar sucrose, a disaccharide. Glycogen is comprised of many glucose units and is termed a polysaccharide.

similar to that of fats. We shall describe only the general structure for the fats. One molecule of *glycerol*, a three-carbon relative of the sugars (note the H—C—OH), is combined with three molecules of *fatty acids* to form a molecule of fat.

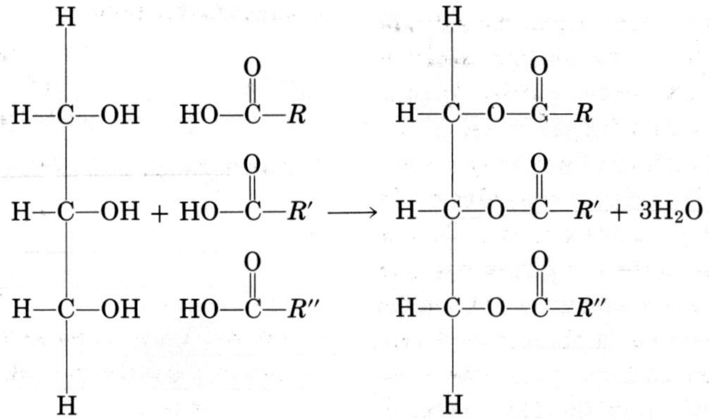

The letters R, R', and R'' represent chains of different lengths. These chains consist of carbon atoms and their attached hydrogen atoms, but the letters R, R', and R'' do not specify the lengths of the chains or their exact structures. One fat, for example, might contain three

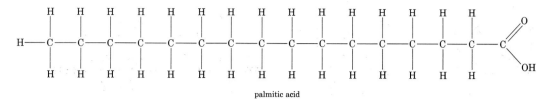

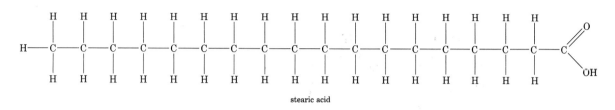

Figure 2.7. *Two common fatty acids. Note the repeating* —C— *unit. This long hydrogen-carbon (hydrocarbon) chain imparts the characteristic properties of the lipids.*

fatty-acid molecules of the same structure. Another fat might have fatty acids of different structures. Two of the commonest fatty acids are palmitic and stearic acids (Figure 2.7). For these, the letter *R* would represent chains having lengths of 15 and 17 carbon atoms, respectively.

Fatty acids contain the *carboxyl group*, —C—OH. This group is characteristic of the most important kind of organic acids occurring in living systems. Many such simple acids play an important role in respiration in cells. We shall be referring frequently to *acetic acid* (a two-carbon acid), *pyruvic acid,* and *lactic acid* (the latter two are three-carbon acids). These three do not actually exist as acids in the cell but as the dissociated salts, acetate, pyruvate, and lactate, which are the products of reactions between acids and bases.

The lipids serve four functions. First, they are important in the structure of the cell, as we shall mention in discussing the makeup of membranes (see Chapter III). Second, lipids are important energy reserves; any intake of food in excess of the amount needed at the time may result in an increase in the body's fat reserves, as many people realize from first-hand experience. Third, the waxes, another group of lipids, serve a protective role on the leaves of plants and the skin or fur of animals. Fourth, in the form of steroids, they serve as chemical coordinating agents.

Whether we examine the carbohydrates or the lipids, we find similar molecules in all organisms. Some variations exist, but they are minor compared with the variation in proteins and nucleic acids, the other two groups of carbon-containing compounds common in living things. These latter compounds show tremendous diversity partly because of their large size and also because the smaller molecules from which they are synthesized may be arranged in any order. Remember that although there is a wide variety of fatty acids, a maximum of three can be combined with glycerol to form any particular fat. This limits the number of possible combinations.

Amino acids are the units from which *proteins* are built. The word acid in the name indicates the presence of the carboxyl group.

The word amino tells us that an *amino group*

is present. Each amino acid has at least one amino group and one carboxyl group. We represent a generalized amino acid as

H—C—NH$_2$ (with H above C and COOH below)

(a) glycine

COOH
|
CH$_2$
|
CH$_2$
|
H—C—NH$_2$
|
COOH

(b) glutamic acid

NH$_2$
|
CH$_2$
|
CH$_2$
|
CH$_2$
|
CH$_2$
|
H—C—NH$_2$
|
COOH

(c) lysine

OH (on benzene ring)
CH$_2$
|
H—C—NH$_2$
|
COOH

(d) tyrosine

SH
|
CH$_2$
|
H—C—NH$_2$
|
COOH

(e) cysteine

Figure 2.8. Five amino acids. (a) *The simplest amino acid, glycine, where* R *in the general formula is equivalent to a hydrogen atom.* (b) *The acidic amino acid glutamic acid.* (c) *The basic amino acid lysine.* (d) *The amino acid tyrosine containing the six-membered benzene ring.* (e) *Cysteine, an amino acid containing a sulfhydryl group, a sulfur with a hydrogen attached.*

The part of the molecule symbolized by the letter R varies from one hydrogen atom to a group of carbon atoms with hydrogen and other atoms attached. Each amino acid is characterized by the nature of the R-group. Figure 2.8 shows some of the known amino acids. Many amino acids are interconvertible with fatty acids through exchange of the amino group. Removal of this group from an amino acid results in a fatty acid and ammonia.

The reaction between the amino group of one amino acid and the carboxyl group of another amino acid results in the formation of a *peptide* bond between them. This is a carbon-to-nitrogen bond (Figure 2.9). A large number of amino acids held together by peptide bonds form a protein. There are about two dozen different amino acids found in various proteins. Since the amino acids may be linked together in any order, and each different order of amino acids is a different protein, the variety of possible proteins approaches infinity. This variety is so great, in fact, that each organism has its unique protein combination.

In addition to peptide bonds, other bonds give each protein a distinctive shape because they link portions of the amino acid chain. An example of these bonds is the sulfur-to-sulfur bond which forms between two sulfhydryl groups.

Individuals normally build up antibodies against any foreign proteins introduced into the body. Antibodies are proteins that help to inactivate foreign proteins and render them harmless. Although this mechanism is usually helpful, it may pose a drastic problem in certain artificially induced cases. For example, blood transfusions and tissue transplants often fail or prove damaging because of antibody reactions.

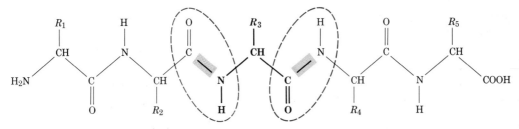

Figure 2.9. Peptide bonds link amino acids. *(A single amino acid residue is indicated by the boldface type.) Chains of amino acids are called polypeptides. Proteins are made from polypeptide chains.*

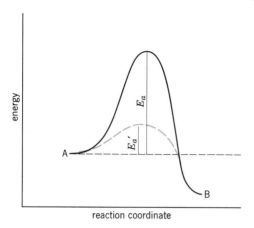

Figure 2.10. In order for A to be converted to B a certain amount of activation energy is required. This is indicated by the solid line above. E_a represents the amount of energy required. An enzyme may lower the amount of energy required for activation. This is shown by the dashed line, E_a' representing the activation energy in the presence of the proper enzyme.

In living systems many proteins, functioning differently from antibodies, may form an integral part of the structure of cells. All membranes, for example, have a protein component; in Chapter III we see how proteins in membranes contribute to many structures within the cell. In muscle cells, two proteins form the specialized contractile structure. Other proteins contribute to the structure of supporting and protective elements such as skin, hair, nails, bone, and cartilage.

3 *Enzymes* are catalysts; in biological systems they are the substances that change the rate of a reaction without themselves being changed. Remember that reactions often require activation energy (Figure 2.10). In common with many other types of catalysts, en-

zymes reduce the amount of activation energy required. As a result, many reactions that occur rapidly in cells proceed slowly in the absence of the proper enzymes.

All known enzymes are wholly or partly protein. This gives enzymes many of their characteristics. For example, they are sensitive to heat and to the relative amounts of acids and bases. Any marked change in the temperature or quantity of acid in a cell will change the activity of the enzymes and may even deactivate some.

Enzymes have complex and varied surface shapes. If they are to affect any reaction of a molecule, the surfaces of both the molecule and the enzyme must fit together (Figure 2.11). Since the surface of a given enzyme will fit with only a few different molecules, enzymes are specific in their action. Often an enzyme will act on only one kind of molecule.

4 *Nucleic acids* are the fourth group of carbon-containing molecules found in all cells. These are composed of long chains of *nucleotides*. Each nucleotide has three parts: an organic base, a sugar, and a phosphate (Figures 2.12–2.14). As in proteins, we find a large variety of nucleic acids. They have two functions: the control of cell activity and information storage. (See Chapters VII and XVII.)

Carbohydrates, lipids, proteins, and nucleic acids are similar enough in structure to be interconvertible in the cell (see Chapter V). It might seem, then, as though the intake of any one of these groups should suffice for complete nutrition. However, most animals cannot synthesize all fatty acids or amino acids, but must obtain some of them through food. In addition, other complex molecules, the vitamins, are needed in minute amounts, as are the mineral salts.

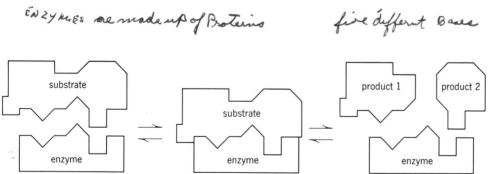

Figure 2.11. Enzymes are highly specific, as is indicated by a schematic "lock and key" model. The reaction shown is reversible. The enzyme itself remains the same and is unchanged during the course of the reaction. The word substrate is used to denote a compound which is acted upon by an enzyme.

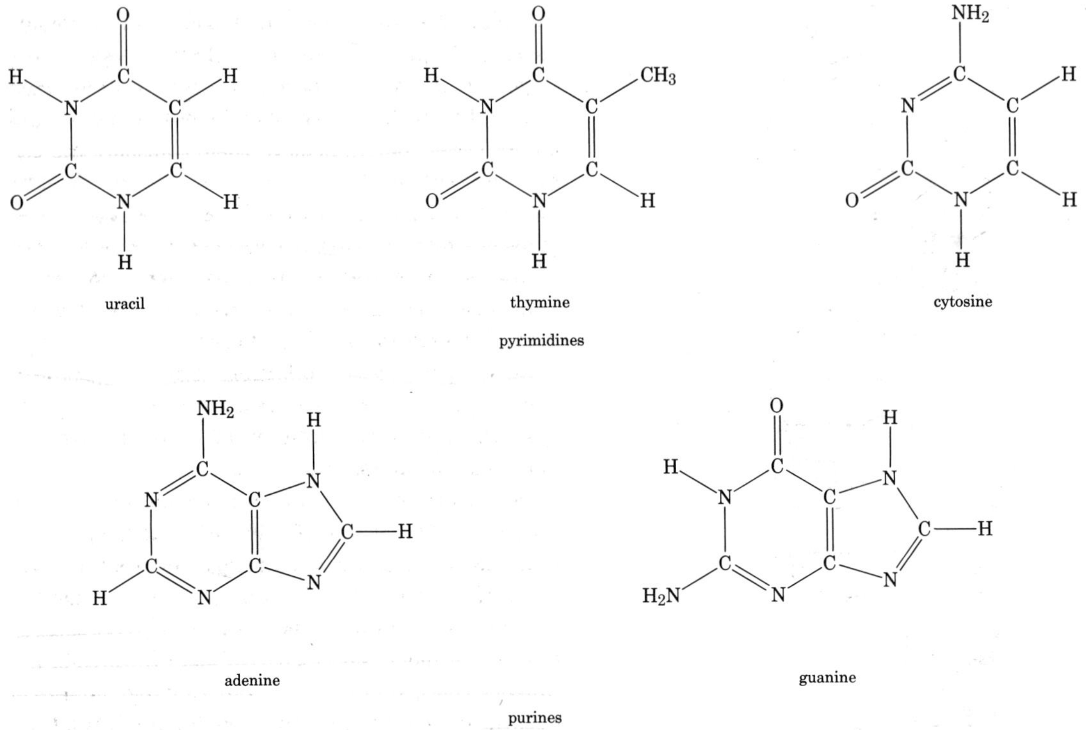

uracil

thymine

cytosine

pyrimidines

adenine

guanine

purines

Figure 2.12. The organic bases of the nucleic acids are the pyrimidines and purines. The three most common pyrimidines are uracil, thymine, and cytosine. The two most common purines are adenine and guanine.

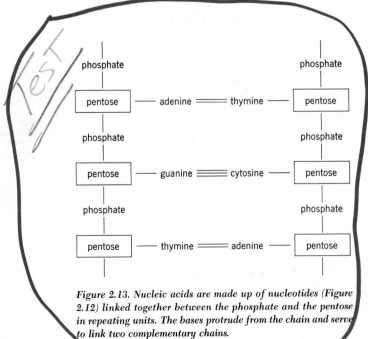

Figure 2.13. Nucleic acids are made up of nucleotides (Figure 2.12) linked together between the phosphate and the pentose in repeating units. The bases protrude from the chain and serve to link two complementary chains.

Some Physical Phenomena

Molecular Movement. All molecules are in constant, and usually random, motion. On the average, a given molecule is as likely to move in one direction as it is to move in any other. If the molecules of a substance are evenly distributed throughout a container, the movement in one direction is equaled by the movement of other molecules in the opposite direction, and no *net* movement of material results.

If we remove all the molecules from the container and then reintroduce a number of them into one corner, random movement causes them to disperse. Molecules that move toward the corner bounce off the walls of the container and each other; those that move away from the corner pass into other areas of the container. This movement of molecules from an area of higher concentration to an area of lower concentration is called *diffusion* (Figure 2.15).

Biological membranes are called *differentially* permeable membranes because they allow only certain kinds of particles to pass through. Small, uncharged

Test

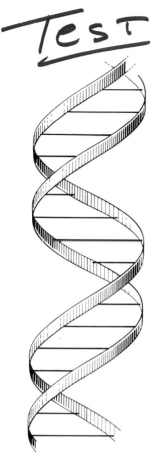

Figure 2.14. _This schematic diagram illustrates the spatial configuration of the double-stranded DNA molecule. The bars represent paired purine and pyrimidine bases while the spiral backbone is composed of alternating pentose and phosphate units._

particles like water, carbon dioxide, and ammonia move through easily. Larger molecules, such as the sugars, and charged particles pass through more slowly, if at all. These particles do indeed move in and out of cells, but to achieve their transport the cells must expend energy. Because they require the cell's active participation, both this latter transport and transport from an area of lower concentration to one of higher concentration are called _active transport_.

In strict biological usage, the diffusion of water through a _semipermeable_ membrane is called _osmosis_. This is a special case of diffusion; thus no expenditure of energy by the cell is required. For convenience, however, we refer to the diffusion of water through _any_ biological membrane as osmosis.

Osmosis is an important phenomenon for cells. An example of the effects of different concentrations of sugar solutions on sea urchin eggs demonstrates this point. If we place sea urchin eggs in a solution that has a lower concentration of dissolved particles than do the eggs, water molecules will move from the area of their higher concentration to the area of their lower concentration, namely, into the eggs (Figure 2.16). Consequently, the eggs will swell and eventually burst. If the sugar solution has a higher concentration of dissolved particles than the eggs, water will move out of the eggs. Through this loss of water, the eggs will shrink.

This movement is the _net_ movement of water molecules. In either case some of the water molecules will

Passive transport
Hight To lower concentration

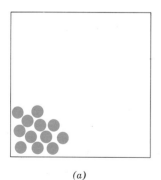 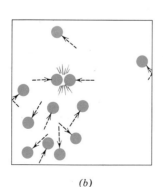 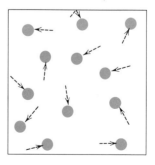

(a)   (b)   (c)

Figure 2.15. _In this diagrammatic representation of diffusion we can follow the process whereby the molecules become randomly distributed. In (a) the molecules are introduced into one corner of the container. Owing to their kinetic energy the molecules undergo random movement (b). The molecules can collide with one another and with the walls of the container. After a time, the molecules will be evenly distributed throughout the container. The random movement will continue and the molecules will remain evenly distributed, as in (c)._

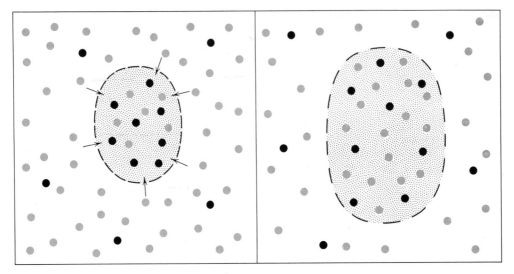

Figure 2.16. A diagrammatic example of osmosis, where the cell has a higher concentration of dissolved particles (the black dots) than does the surrounding medium. As a result of the difference in concentration, the water molecules (blue dots) move through the cell membrane to equalize the concentration. This causes the cell to swell, sometimes to a point at which it will burst.

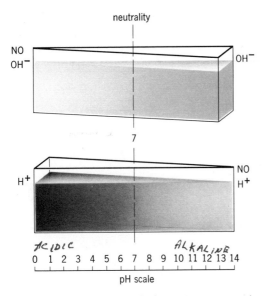

Figure 2.17. The pH scale. The hydrogen ion concentration is highest at low pH and decreases with increasing pH. The opposite holds true for the concentration of hydroxyl ion. At pH 7.0, the concentrations of hydrogen ion and hydroxyl ion are equal.

move in each direction, but many more will move in one direction than in the other. However, if we place the eggs in a sugar solution that has the same concentration of dissolved particles as the eggs, the eggs will remain unchanged in size because no *net* movement of water occurs.

pH. Careful analysis shows that not all water molecules remain as H_2O. Some ionize, producing hydrogen ions (H^+) and hydroxyl ions (OH^-). These ions will be associated with water molecules, but for simplicity we shall indicate them as H^+ and OH^-. The number of ions produced in pure water is small when compared with the number of molecules present as H_2O. However, when other substances are added to water, the number of hydrogen or hydroxyl ions change. Shifts in the concentration of these ions have important effects upon the activities of cells and cell components.

To aid our discussion, let us classify substances into two categories, acids and bases. Acids have the capacity to act as proton donors, whereas bases can act as acceptors. A hydrogen atom that has lost its electron is a proton, that is, hydrogen ion. When added to water, an acid increases the concentration of hydrogen ions. A base decreases the concentration of hydrogen ions or, in other words, increases the concentration of hydroxyl ions.

(a)

$$\underset{\text{tripeptide}}{NH_2-\overset{\overset{R}{|}}{CH}-\overset{\overset{O}{\|}}{C}-NH-\overset{\overset{R}{|}}{CH}-\overset{\overset{O}{\|}}{C}-NH-\overset{\overset{R}{|}}{CH}-COOH} \;+\; \underset{\text{water}}{2H_2O} \;\rightleftharpoons\; \underset{\text{amino acids}}{3NH_2-\overset{\overset{R}{|}}{CH}-COOH}$$

(a)

(b)

3-phosphoglyceraldehyde

$$\begin{array}{c} H\;\;\;O \\ \diagdown\!\!\diagup \\ C \\ | \\ H-C-OH \\ | \\ CH_2OPO_3H_2 \end{array}$$

$+$

dihydroxyacetone phosphate

$$\begin{array}{c} CH_2OH \\ | \\ C=O \\ | \\ CH_2OPO_3H_2 \end{array}$$

$\rightleftharpoons$

fructose–1,6–diphosphate

$$\begin{array}{c} CH_2OPO_3H_2 \\ | \\ C=O \\ | \\ HO-C-H \\ | \\ H-C-OH \\ | \\ H-C-OH \\ | \\ CH_2OPO_3H_2 \end{array}$$

(b)

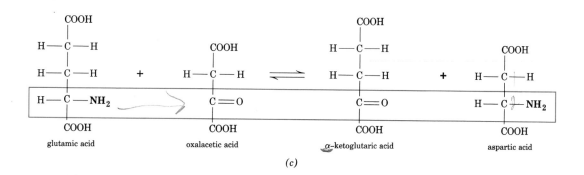

glutamic acid $+$ oxalacetic acid $\rightleftharpoons$ α–ketoglutaric acid $+$ aspartic acid

(c)

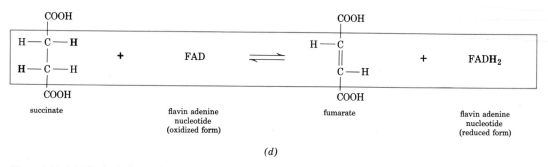

succinate $+$ flavin adenine nucleotide (oxidized form) $\rightleftharpoons$ fumarate $+$ flavin adenine nucleotide (reduced form)

(d)

Figure 2.18. (a) *The hydrolysis of proteins or peptides into amino acids is a typical digestive reaction.* (b) *The condensation of two three-carbon compounds into the six-carbon sugar fructose is an important synthetic reaction.* (c) *The transfer of an amino group from one compound to another illustrates a transfer reaction.* (d) *The oxidation of succinate by the oxidized form of flavin adenine nucleotide (FAD) is an important reaction in respiration. During the course of the reaction succinate is oxidized to fumarate and FAD is reduced to FADH₂.*

It is impractical to describe the actual numbers of hydrogen and hydroxyl ions in water because of the small number present. We would be discussing ratios of 10^{-7} (1/10,000,000) hydrogen ions for every 56 molecules of water. To cope with this problem, the pH scale (Figure 2.17) was developed by the Swedish chemist, Jönen Sørensen, who did not like negative numbers. Arbitrarily he converted the exponent -7 to a positive number and gave it the designation pH. Students who have had high school algebra will recognize this as the negative logarithm of the hydrogen ion concentration. A pH of 7 is a description of the concentration of hydrogen ions in pure water. Since the number of hydroxyl and hydrogen ions are equal, this is a neutral solution. As the pH becomes larger (8, 9, 10, etc.), the concentration of hydrogen ions decreases. As the pH becomes smaller (6, 5, 4, etc.), the concentration of hydrogen ions increases. In other words, as the pH rises, the solution becomes more basic; as the pH decreases, the solution becomes more acidic. This scale is a convenient description of the conditions in and around cells.

Types of Reaction

Know

The reactions in the cell are many and varied. They can be classed into five general groups: *digestive, synthetic, transfer, oxidative,* and *reductive* (Figure 2.18).

Molecules can be either broken down into smaller units or combined into larger ones. These reactions are called digestive and synthetic, respectively. In biological systems water plays an important role in both. In digestive reactions, water is generally added to the bond broken; hence the alternative name, *hydrolysis,* for such reactions. Conversely, water is removed in the formation of bonds in synthesis so these are also known as *dehydration* reactions.

If a small part of a molecule such as a hydrogen atom or an amino group is transferred from one molecule to another, a transfer reaction occurs.

The final pair of reactions is oxidation and reduction reactions (Figure 2.19). Both involve a change in the number of electrons which an atom controls. If the number decreases, the atom becomes more positively charged and is oxidized. If the number of electrons increases, the atom becomes more negatively charged and is reduced.

It is important to notice that when one atom loses electrons, another atom must gain them. Consequently, if oxidation occurs, reduction accompanies it, and vice versa. When we label a reaction as an oxida-

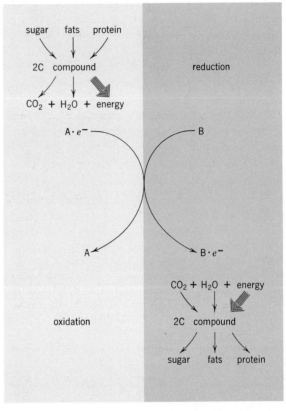

Figure 2.19. A general scheme of oxidation-reduction reactions which indicates the relation of the three classes of food to each type of reaction.

tion reaction, we are really saying that the molecule in which we are interested is the one being oxidized.

The oxidation of molecules within a cell may be identified by any of three kinds of treatment: (1) addition of oxygen, (2) removal of hydrogen, or (3) removal of electrons. In reality these are only three different indications of oxidation. All of them result in the removal of electrons from the molecule being oxidized.

The addition of oxygen is not as common in biological systems as we generally suppose. This form of oxidation is familiar to us from the burning of many compounds in air and from rusting and other slower oxidative reactions. In the cell it occurs only in the final step of cellular respiration (see Chapter V).

The removal of hydrogen (*dehydrogenation*) and the concurrent removal of electrons from the molecule are processes commonly found in cells. The importance of these processes in energy release will be noted in Chapter V.

Life can be described in part by describing the chemical makeup of living organisms. Much more is involved. These chemical substances are highly organized into structural entities which we call cells. Life is, at least in this sense, more than the sum of its parts.

Principles

1. The laws governing the chemical and physical events in living matter are the same as those acting on inanimate matter.

2. Living things are characterized by four types of complex molecules.

3. The method of transport of molecules in living matter depends on their size.

Suggested Readings

Allfrey, Vincent G. and Alfred E. Mirsky, "How Cells Make Molecules," *Scientific American,* Vol. 205 (September, 1961). Offprint No. 92, W. H. Freeman and Co., San Francisco.

Asimov, Isaac, *The Chemicals of Life.* New American Library of World Literature, New York. 1954.

Baker, Jeffrey J. W. and Garland E. Allen, *Matter, Energy, and Life.* Addison-Wesley Publishing Co., Reading, Mass., July 1965.

Holter, Heinz, "How Things Get into Cells," *Scientific American,* Vol. 205 (September, 1961). Offprint No. 96, W. H. Freeman and Co., San Francisco.

Kendrew, John C., "The Three-Dimensional Structure of a Protein Molecule," *Scientific American,* Vol. 205 (December, 1961). Offprint No. 121, W. H. Freeman and Co., San Francisco.

Moore, Frances D., *Give and Take, the Biology of Tissue Transplantation.* Doubleday and Co., Garden City, N. Y., 1965.

Roberts, John D., "Organic Chemical Reactions," *Scientific American,* Vol. 197 (November, 1957). Offprint No. 85, W. H. Freeman and Co., San Francisco.

Questions

1. What is the simplest atom from a structural viewpoint? Is this atom of importance in living matter?

2. Does the symbol H_2O represent a compound, a molecule, or both? Explain.

3. How would you test whether the atoms in a substance were held together by covalent bonds or ionic bonds?

4. Which type of bonding is found in table salt? Which type is found in table sugar?

5. What is the relation between the bonds which hold atoms together and the energy that is essential to maintaining life?

6. What three features make water vital to life?

7. Do CO_2 and NH_3 have any importance to cells except as waste products? Explain.

8. What are the chief carbon-chain compounds in living tissue? List their major functions.

9. What characteristic group of atoms always designates that an organic compound is an acid? Which of the following probably contain this group: amino acid, fatty acid, glycerol, acetic acid?

10. Review the structural arrangements found in proteins, then deduce what is meant by *polypeptide.*

11. What evidence is presented in the chapter to indicate that every living being probably has some proteins unique to it? How is this possible? (*Hint:* check on the building units of proteins.)

12. What are the (*a*) advantages, and (*b*) disadvantages to cells of diffusion and osmosis?

13. What does a pH of 7.8 signify? A pH of 5.9?

14. Name five types of chemical reactions important in cells and explain each one.

Life: Its Structural Basis

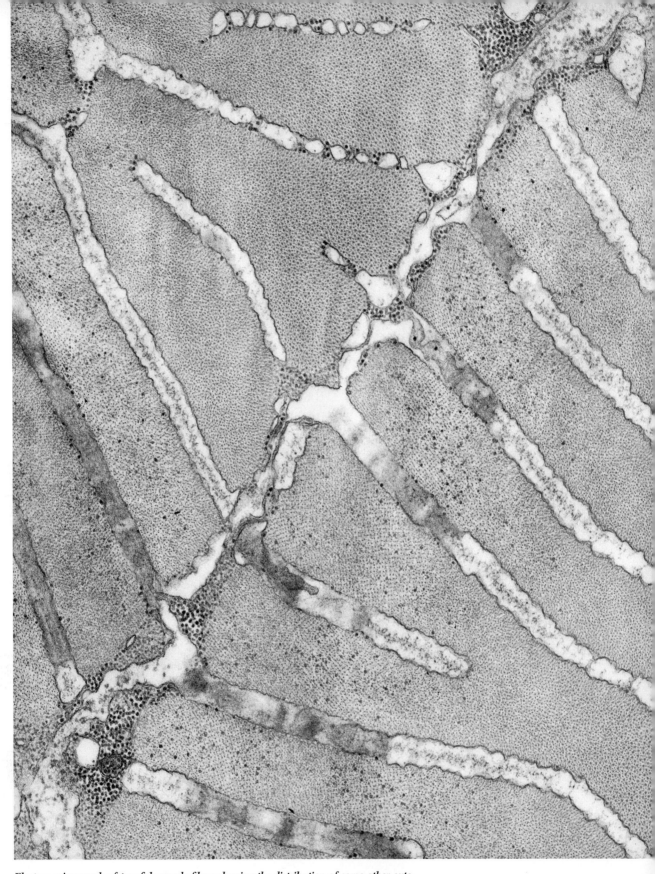

Electron micrograph of two fish muscle fibers showing the distribution of some other cyto-plasmic elements. (Dr. Keith R. Porter.)

Life: Its Structural Basis

Much significant biological knowledge has been obtained by studying the various parts of the cell, by examining it as a functional entity, and by considering its role in relation to other cells. The cell often forms the basic unit of reference for understanding the structure or function of any living entity. In this chapter we turn to *cytology,* the study of the cell, by reviewing briefly the history of the cell concept, examining the traditional or "classical" idea of cell structure, and then relating it to recent ideas concerning cells as interpreted from studies made with modern cytological "tools."

The discovery of cells and the subsequent realization of their basic importance in biology could not take place until lenses and microscopes were developed. By the beginning of the seventeenth century, various types of magnifying devices began to disclose the microscopic structure of many materials. A number of significant biological events then took place during the century. An Italian, Marcello Malpighi, performed the first microscopic studies on the embryology of plants and animals and also discovered capillaries. An Englishman, Robert Hooke, with a 30-power "microscope" noted the honeycomblike nature of a thin slice of cork and he termed the tiny spaces "cells." A Dutchman, Van Leeuwenhoek, with an improved 270-power microscope was able to describe blood cells, spermatozoa, bacteria, protozoans, and many other previously unknown objects.

Over two hundred years passed, however, before biologists began to suspect that most living matter was composed of cells. Early in the 1800s, a number of zoologists and botanists began, as a result of their observations, to suggest a principle that was eventually to become one of the most significant principles in biology, the *cell theory.* This theory together with its various ramifications proposed that all living things were composed of cells or of cells and their products, that all cells arose from pre-existing cells, that all were basically alike in chemical composition, and that the activity of an organism was the outcome of the activities of its constituent cells.

The cell theory cannot be credited to any particular individual; rather it evolved from the researches and writings of many biologists. To mention a few, Mirbel in 1802 concluded that plants were made up of cells, Lamarck in 1809 stated that cellular tissue was the general matrix of all organization, and Schwann in 1838 emphasized that entire animals and plants were aggregates of cells.

Some General Features of Cells

A majority of cells are microscopic in size and only a few, such as birds' eggs or some algae, are macroscopic. The size of a cell is limited by what might be termed a "surface-to-volume" dilemma. Small bodies have a greater ratio of surface area to volume than larger ones. Cells continually obtain materials neces-

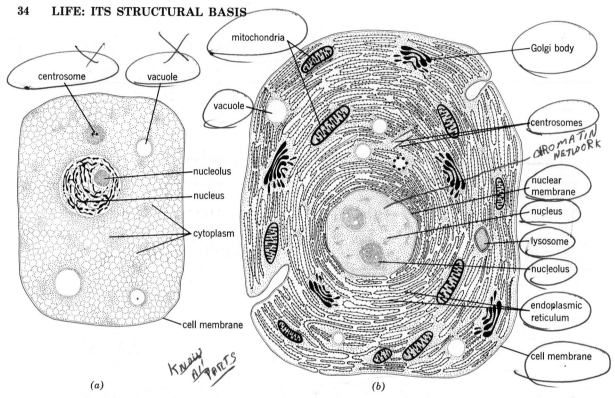

Figure 3.1. (a) *A generalized cell as shown in texts of the 1920s.* (b) *A contemporary idea of a generalized cell as shown by the electron microscope.* (Reprinted with permission, Copyright © 1961 by Scientific American, Inc. All rights reserved.)

sary for their metabolism from the surrounding environment. Since this acquisition occurs through their surface membranes, the surface-volume relationship is vitally important. A cell that is extremely active metabolically cannot have a very large volume. If a cell must be both large and active, some way must be found to increase its surface area disproportionately. The long thin processes of some nerve cells are examples.

There are other problems encountered in relation to cell size, such as the amount of cytoplasm to be controlled by the nucleus, and the matter of physical support for a cell as it increases in size. These various chemical and physical factors usually limit cell size to the microscopic level.

The size of cells has obviously affected the methods used to investigate their structure and function. Coincident with the improvement of microscopes, many techniques for staining specific parts of the cell, new ways to cut exceedingly thin slices of tissues so that various cell aggregates could be studied, and microsurgical instruments to manipulate and remove parts

within the cell were developed. Today, cells and tissues may be cultured or grown in laboratory glassware and thus studied in great detail. The development of extremely high-speed centrifuges, known as *ultracentrifuges,* has facilitated such things as separating parts of cells and obtaining concentrations of these parts for study.

The use of radioactive isotopes or "tracers" is also an important tool in the study of cells and tissues. For example, carbon 14 (C^{14}) is an isotope of ordinary carbon 12 (C^{12}) and can be used in place of it in chemical reactions. Since C^{14} is also energy-emitting (radioactive), it can be detected and followed by means of appropriate laboratory instruments as it is incorporated into a cell or passes from one cell to another. By following an atom or molecule through chemical reactions in the cell, we can often acquire information about the reactions that was formerly unobtainable.

In addition to these and other techniques, the *electron microscope* has provided new knowledge and greater detail of the structure of cells (Figure 3.1). The electron microscope uses beams of electrons rather

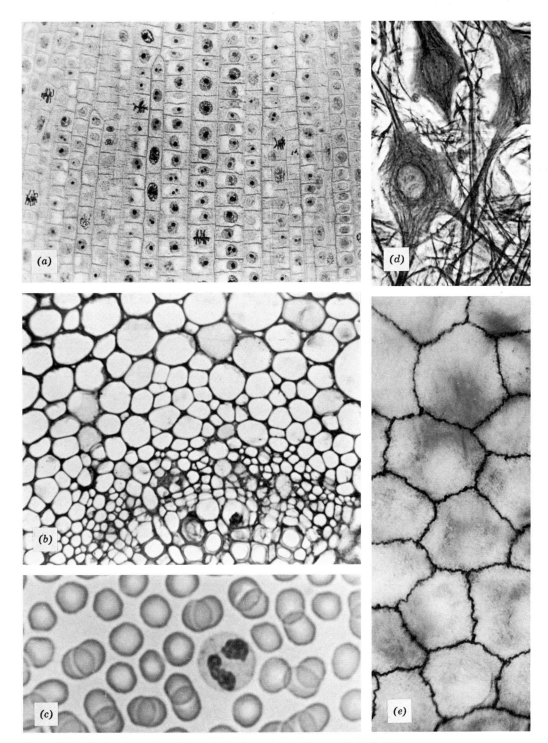

Figure 3.2. Cells showing various shapes. (a) *Onion root tip;* (b) *part of a leaf;* (c) *human blood cells;* (d) *human nerve cells;* (e) *mesothelium.* *(c and e—Ward's Natural Science Establishment, Inc.)*

35

Figure 3.3. Assorted foraminifera (top) and radiolaria. (General Biological Supply House, Inc.)

than light rays. As a result, an observer can see far more detail than is possible with conventional microscopes. By using an electron microscope a cytologist can study the minute structure of cell parts rather than just their over-all shapes and sizes.

These tools and techniques have contributed much new knowledge to the field of cytology since 1950. Concepts of cell structure, for example, have changed markedly during this time. In fact, a new area called *molecular biology* developed out of the studies on the structure and functioning of living matter at the submicroscopic—that is, molecular—level. *Ultrastructure* refers to the molecular configuration of various biological materials as revealed by the aforementioned techniques. Molecular biology is an exciting frontier in contemporary biology since new discoveries and concepts are emerging from research laboratories almost daily.

The shapes of cells vary greatly, as illustrated in Figure 3.2. Cells such as those forming tissues and organs demonstrate the existence of a close relation-

ship between a cell's form and function. Free-living cells such as protozoans (Figure 3.3) and algae show an even greater range of forms or shapes, from simple spheres to the bizarre and complex.

Structures in the Cell

If one asks a cytologist to describe the structure of a cell, he would be likely to respond, "What *kind* of cell?" There are many structural differences between a nerve cell and a blood cell, for example. What we describe here is a composite cell which contains the structures this chapter emphasizes. A cell of exactly this type probably does not exist. It is only a useful model.

In describing a cell it is convenient to consider two major regions, the *cytoplasm* and the *nucleus*. Until recently the cytoplasm was often described as a viscous, fluidlike material without definite structure, containing a number of functional bodies such as mitochondria, the Golgi bodies, chloroplasts, centrioles, and a miscellaneous assortment of granules, droplets, and pigments. Electron microscopy has disclosed additional structures, particularly the endoplasmic reticulum, indicating that the cytoplasmic region of cells can no longer be said to be "structureless." As these cytoplasmic parts are described we should note that many of them consist of membranes of essentially the same structure.

Cell Membrane. All cells are bounded by an extremely thin membrane. Although this cell membrane is not normally visible with an ordinary microscope, its presence has been known for many years as a consequence of various experimental techniques. For example, osmosis requires the presence of a membrane of some sort. Or, when a cell is poked with a microdissection needle, the surface pushes inward as though a covering were present. In recent years the membrane has been observed and studied rather intensively with the electron microscope revealing a structure that appears to be double (Figure 3.4). Various experiments have supported an hypothesis proposed by J. F. Danielli, an Englishman, that cell membranes consist of two layers of lipid molecules surrounded on the inner and outer surfaces by a layer of protein molecules (Figure 3.5). Thus in passing through this ultrathin lipoprotein membrane we would encounter, in order, the following strata of molecules: protein, fat, fat, protein.

The reason for discussing this structure in such detail is that everything that passes into or out of a cell

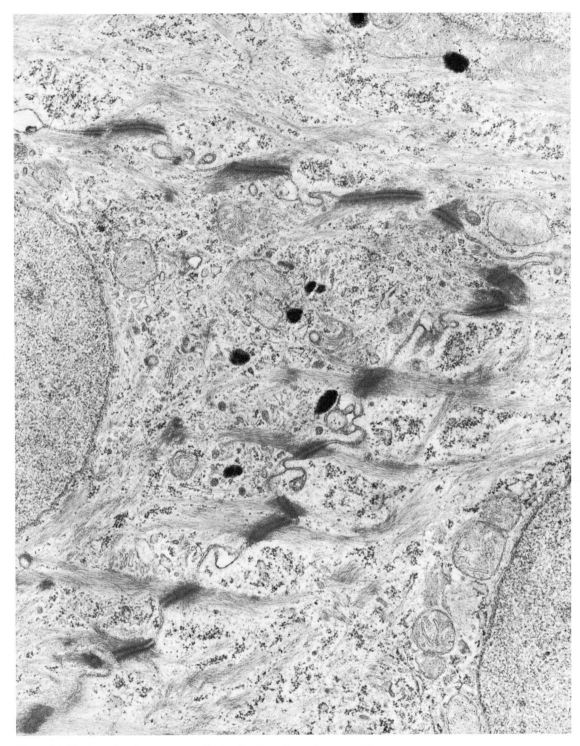

Figure 3.4. The boundary between two cells showing the cell membranes and desmosomes which form bridges between the cells (×25,000). (Dr. Keith R. Porter.)

must go through the membrane. This passage is not passive, like sand sifting through a sieve, but is highly regulated by the membrane itself. In other words, the cell membrane is selectively permeable. The consequences of this partial permeability have been discussed in Chapter II in relation to osmosis and active

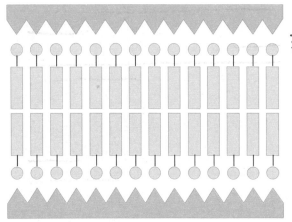

Figure 3.5. A model for the structure of membranes. The two outer layers are protein and the two medial layers are lipid.

transport. There is little conclusive evidence yet as to *how* materials pass through the four latticeworklike layers of molecules which form the membrane; this remains an important and challenging problem in biology.

The cell membrane shows many specializations and functions. For example, it frequently forms tiny canals leading into the cell. Fluids may flow into these canals and then be pinched off in the cytoplasm, a process termed *pinocytosis* (Figure 3.6). Or the membrane may surround and engulf particles of material much too large to pass through by diffusion—this is termed *phagocytosis*. Where adjacent cells meet, their membranes are often interlocked by fingerlike convolutions. In cells where absorption is a major function, their free surfaces consist of thousands of microvilli (minute projections of the cell membrane which result in a greatly increased surface area for the cell).

Endoplasmic Reticulum. The endoplasmic reticulum (sometimes called ER) refers to a system of canal-like spaces bounded by membranes and extending through the cytoplasm (Figure 3.7). The membranes appear to be continuous with the cell membrane on

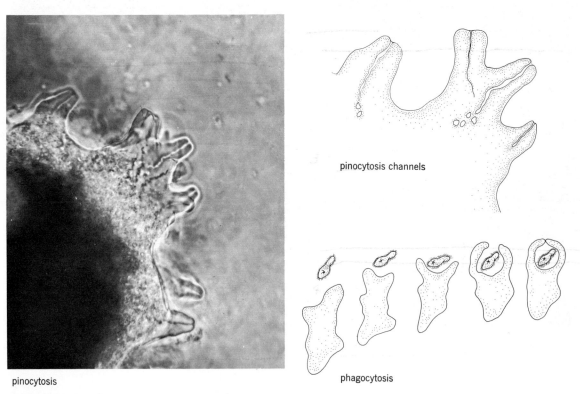

pinocytosis channels

pinocytosis

phagocytosis

Figure 3.6. Amoeba showing pinocytosis (Dr. David Prescott) and phagocytosis.

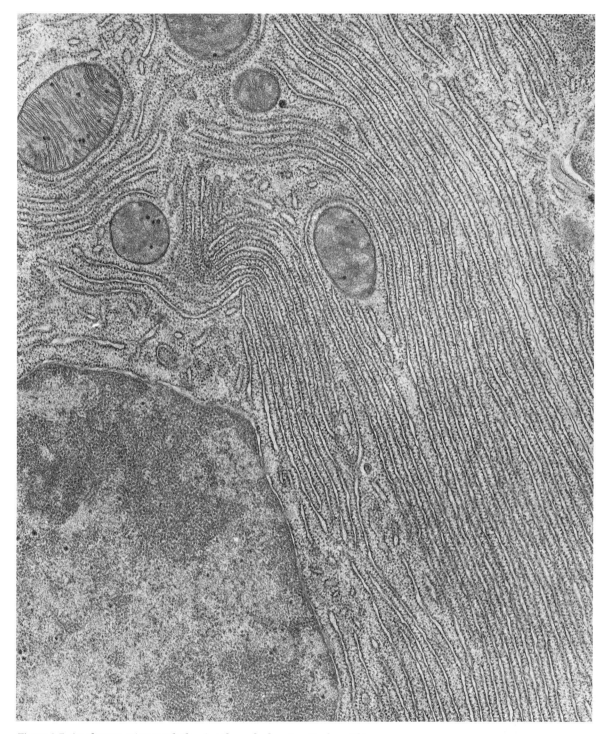

Figure 3.7. An electron micrograph showing the endoplasmic reticulum. This appears as numerous diagonal lines. The small black dots lining the diagonal lines are ribosomes (×30,000). (Dr. Keith R. Porter.)

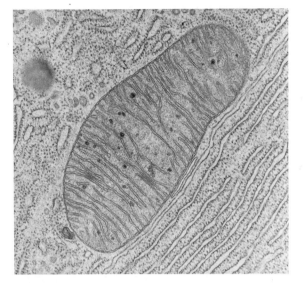

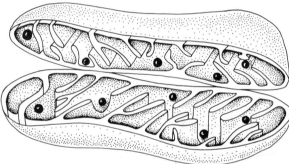

Figure 3.8. An electron micrograph of a mitochondrion in the bat pancreas cell (×53,000). (Dr. Keith R. Porter.) A three-dimensional diagrammatic representation of a mitochondrion is shown below.

the outside of the cell and with the outer nuclear membrane.

The ER is closely associated with the synthesis or making of important cellular products like proteins and lipids. In many cells, ribosomes, the sites of protein synthesis, are found adjacent to the ER. In cells where protein synthesis occurs frequently, the ER is abundant. In some cells, the endoplasmic reticulum also appears to be the site of enzymes involved in the manufacture of fatty substances.

Another function of the ER, suggested by electron photomicrographs, is that of a communication system (canals) between the external environment of the cell and the cell's interior. Pinocytosis, for example, represents this function. The ER seems to be a versatile ultrastructure which provides increased surface areas for chemical activities, localizes specific syntheses, and serves as a transport device.

FUNCTION

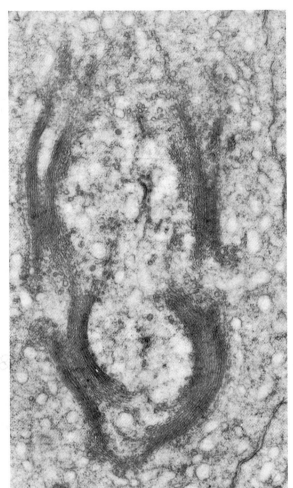

Figure 3.9. The Golgi body, made of a platelike series of membranes. Notice the association of numerous tiny droplets with these contoured membranes. (Dr. L. Evans Roth.)

3 *Ribosomes.* Frequently associated with the ER, but free in the cytoplasm in some cells, are tiny granular bodies known as ribosomes or microsomes (Figure 3.7). They are found in all cells and contain from 40 to 60 per cent ribonucleic acid (RNA). It is now well established that ribosomes function in the synthesis of proteins, a vital function which is described in detail in Chapter VII.

4 *Mitochondria.* Another membranous structure of great importance in cellular functioning is the mitochondrion, a body barely visible with the conventional microscope (Figure 3.8). Mitochondria may appear in various forms such as spheres and rods and are found in all cells, except bacteria and red blood corpuscles. Ultrastructure studies show that a mitochondrion consists of two layers—an outer and an inner mem-

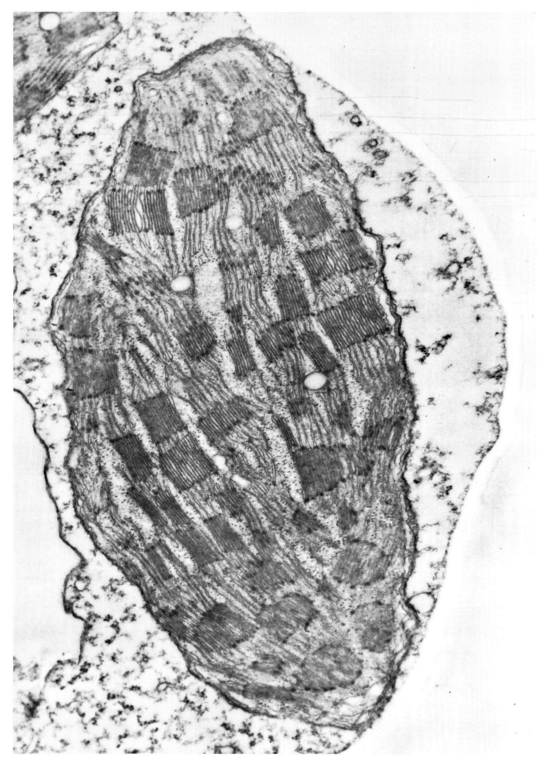

Figure 3.10. A chloroplast. The darkest areas represent the grana (×31,000). (Dr. A. Vatter.)

brane. A liquid matrix fills the body. The inner membrane is folded to form a series of shelves or plates within the mitochondrion, a feature which increases its surface area. Its membranes are known to be a lipoprotein, apparently identical to the cell membrane previously described. Mitochondria are the sites where most of the respiratory activities of a cell are located. Most energy production in the cell takes place here.

5   *Lysosomes.* Closely related in structure to mitochondria are bodies termed lysosomes. These structures contain enzymes utilized in digesting food materials within the cell. These enzymes are sometimes termed *autolytic* because they will digest and destroy the cell if released from the lysosomes. The aging of meat in cold storage is probably the consequence of the action of these enzymes on the meat.

6   *Golgi Body.* The Golgi body is still another membranous structure or series of small spaces enclosed by membranes (Figure 3.9). Some electron photomicrographs indicate that the Golgi complex and the endoplasmic reticulum are continuous, namely that the Golgi body appears to be a specialization or elaboration of the ER. The membranes forming this structure are frequently piled up in a platelike series. In cells that are active in secretion, the Golgi body is larger than usual. Evidently secretory products form within this body and pass to the outside. Moreover, the Golgi complex functions in lipid storage in some cells and possibly may be involved in the formation of endoplasmic reticulum.

7   *Chloroplast.* Plastids, associated with plant cells, are cytoplasmic bodies constructed of membranes. The chloroplast (Figure 3.10) has been studied thoroughly because it is the site of photosynthesis. It is enclosed by a membrane and, in most plants, is divided internally by numerous additional membranes which contain the chlorophyll. Areas of closely packed membranes within the chloroplast are termed *grana*. In the electron microscope, a granum has the appearance of a stack of thin disks interconnected to adjacent grana by intergrana membranes (Figure 3.11). A fluid fills the remainder of the chloroplast. Many variations in chloroplast structure exist among groups of plants. Some, for example, lack grana, but in virtually all cases the chlorophyll is associated with some membranous structure.

8   *Centrioles.* Centrioles have been known in animal cells for a long time, and appear as two dark granules

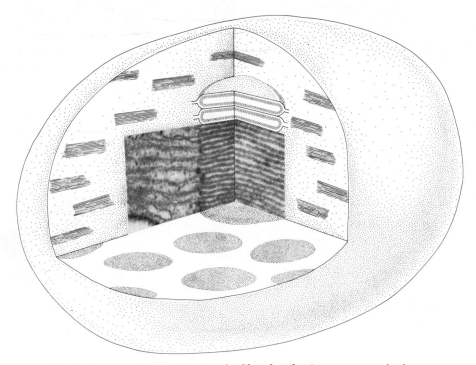

Figure 3.11. An interpretation of the structure of a chloroplast showing granum organization.

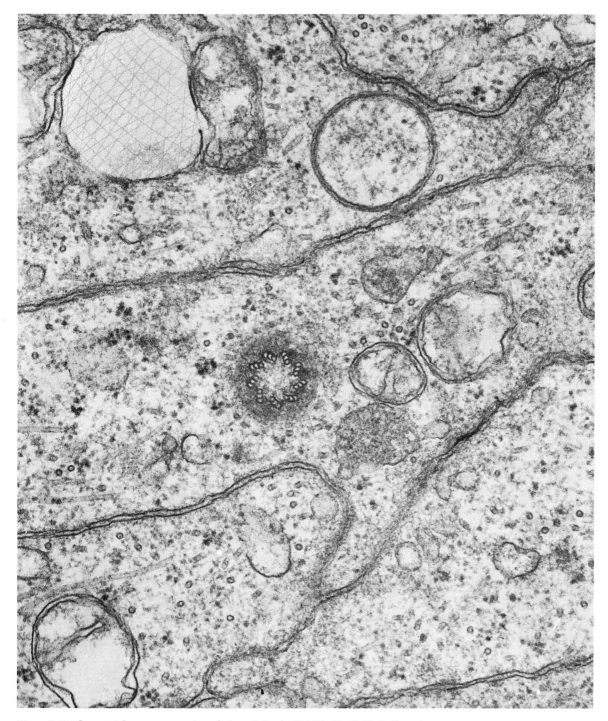

Figure 3.12. The centriole appears as a ring of nine tubules (×66,000). (Dr. Keith R. Porter.)

located adjacent to the nucleus. Electron microscopy indicates that these granules are actually tiny rods lying at right angles to each other. Each rod consists of nine tubules arranged in a circle (Figure 3.12). Each tubule may consist of one to three units. This precise arrangement has been found in all cases where centrioles have been studied but its functional significance is not known at present. Centrioles control the formation of the spindle during cell division in animals (Figure 3.13) and at least a few plants (see Chapter XII).

9   *Vacuoles.* Some cells contain fluid-filled spaces termed vacuoles, and a moment's thought should lead one to conclude, correctly, that these spaces are enclosed by membranes. It may be, as some cytologists suggest, that vacuoles are expanded portions of the endoplasmic reticulum. They are apparently quite useful (in an adaptive sense) to cells since a number of functional modifications of vacuoles have been observed in different kinds of cells. For example, many plant cells contain extremely large vacuoles which fill with fluid to support the cell. Perhaps they also act as sites where unusable chemical products can be stored or dumped.

Some animal cells use vacuoles for regulating their water content. Perhaps the reader has observed the specialized contractile vacuoles in *Paramecium* which eliminate excess water from the animal's body. Some organisms also use vacuoles to hold food particles for intracellular digestion and these are logically termed "food vacuoles."

10   *Cytoplasmic Adaptations.*   In relation to the cytoplasm, several points should be emphasized. First, the cytoplasm is that part of the cell which *differentiates* (specializes) for a particular function. Thus the functional element of a nerve cell is its cytoplasm. The same statement can be made for muscle cells, secretory cells, or specialized plant cells. Another way of stating this is to say that genetic information in the nucleus is always expressed by some type of activity or modification of structure in the cytoplasm.

Second, the adaptations, or specialization, shown by

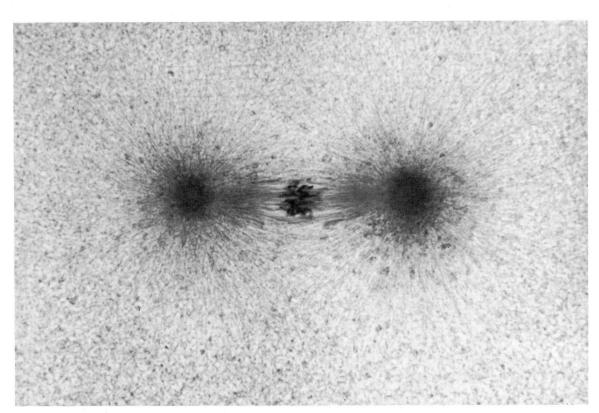

Figure 3.13. The centrioles are located within the dark circular areas which lie at the ends of the spindle during cell division. Other fibers radiate from the centrioles. (General Biological Supply House, Inc.)

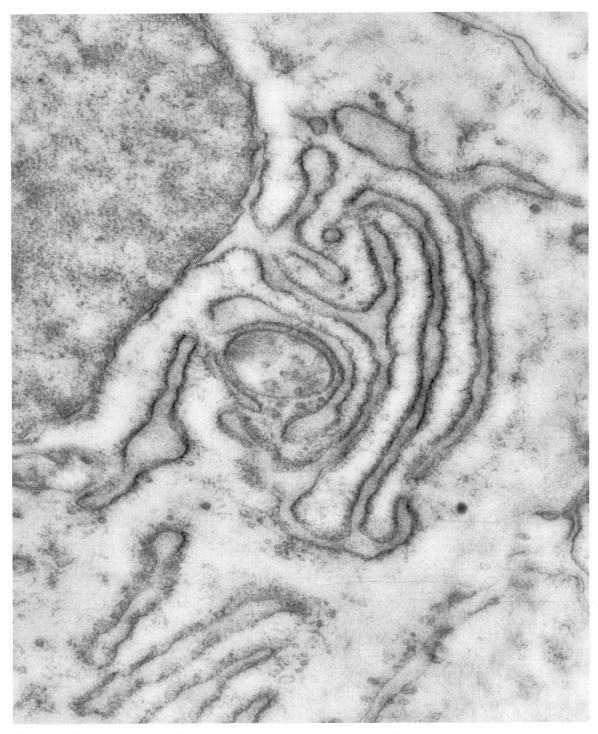

Figure 3.14. The membrane surrounding the dark spherical nucleus is continuous with the endoplasmic reticulum. (Dr. Keith R. Porter.)

the cytoplasm are a reflection of the functions performed by the cell. In other words, there is an intimate relation between the morphology of a cell and its function. This may seem too obvious to need explanation; nevertheless the form-function concept is a basic one in biology and is found not only at the molecular and cellular level but also in relation to tissues, organs, and organisms.

If one wonders why the form-function idea appears universally in biological materials, one should keep in mind that everything from molecules to organisms must exist in relation to an environment. Later we consider a process called *natural selection* which matches up the most efficient "fit" between materials and their environment (see Chapter XX). This fit we call adaptation, which, after all, is no more than form following function.

Nuclear Structures.   The nucleus is bounded by a membrane which consists of an outer portion continuous with the endoplasmic reticulum and an inner portion (Figure 3.14). Electron photomicrographs seem to indicate that these layers are porous. The pores may be related in some way to nuclear permeability since it is known that large molecules can enter and leave the nucleus. Inside the nucleus we find darkly staining, threadlike material, dense bodies of granular material termed *nucleoli,* and a nuclear sap. None of this material shows up well under the electron microscope, hence other techniques have been used to study its ultrastructure. The threadlike material is known to consist of DNA, RNA, and certain protein substances. Chromosomes, rod-shaped bodies found in the cell during cell division, are composed of these same materials and appear to satisfy the requirements as hereditary carriers. Hence it is assumed that the threadlike material represents uncoiled chromosomes containing the hereditary substance.

The nucleolus appears granular in the electron photomicrographs, and there is evidence that the granules are ribosomes which later pass into the cytoplasm. Some investigators consider the nucleolus as reserve chromosome material which is utilized in nuclear division since it disappears during this process. Nuclear sap, as the term indicates, is a fluid which likely contains a complex assortment of chemical substances employed in the nucleus.

Many experiments have indicated that the nucleus is the control center for the cell. Specifically, it appears to direct the synthesis of enzymes in the cytoplasm, which in turn regulate cellular functions. It is also the hereditary reservoir, a feature closely related to the preceding function. The nucleus, unlike the cytoplasm, seldom shows any morphological specializations. It is usually spherical or disklike, although some cells, like certain types of white blood cells, have odd-shaped nuclei.

Cells: Basic Units.   Starting with the basic molecular configurations and chemical compounds which compose the cell, we have an exceedingly plastic, adaptable, unit of structure and function in the living world. Perhaps, as some biologists contend, all of the important problems concerning life processes can be solved by studying cells. Certainly the current studies on cell biology are revealing many new facts about cell structure, which in turn will provide many new hypotheses concerning cell functions. Probably the most startling and significant consequences of studies in this new field are in relation to the DNA molecule, a topic to be taken up in detail in Chapter VII.

The concept that the basic structural units of life are cells remains valid. Some groups of microorganisms, such as bacteria and blue-green algae (groups sometimes termed the "lower protists"), do not have a definitive nucleus and therefore differ in their structure from the conventional notion of a cell. Nevertheless, they are bounded by functional cell membranes and contain proteins, nucleic acids, lipids, and carbohydrates of the same molecular structure as that found in the remainder of the living world. These organisms violate the cell principle only by lacking a highly organized nucleus. Otherwise they are cells in a functional sense.

The higher protists (algae, fungi, and protozoans) do possess a true nucleus and fit the idea of cellular structure reasonably well. Some biologists have argued that these highly organized bits of life should be termed noncellular or acellular because of their complexity, but this appears to be a semantic argument rather than one of biological import.

A considerable amount of current research is concerned with the mechanics of cell specialization. Why do cells with identical hereditary codes or messages in their nuclei differentiate into unlike bodies—for example, nerve cells and muscle cells? What keeps the process so orderly so that exactly the right amount of each tissue and organ is formed? There are dozens of related questions also unanswered.

Principles

1. A convenient basic unit of biology is the cell.

2. The form of a cell is an adaptation to its performance.

3. Many of the cell's structures are composed of membranes.

4. Specialization entails primarily amount and placement of cytoplasmic structures.

Suggested Readings

Brachet, Jean, "The Living Cell," *Scientific American,* Vol. 205 (September, 1961). Offprint No. 90, W. H. Freeman and Co., San Francisco.

de Duve, Christian, "The Lysosome," *Scientific American,* Vol. 208 (May, 1963). Offprint No. 156, W. H. Freeman and Co., San Francisco.

Gray, George W., "The Ultracentrifuge," *Scientific American,* Vol. 184 (June, 1951). Offprint No. 82, W. H. Freeman and Co., San Francisco.

Hooke, Robert, "Of the Schematisme or Texture of Cork, and of the Cells and Pores of Some Other Frothy Bodies," in *Great Experiments in Biology,* edited by M. L. Gabriel and S. Fogel. Prentice-Hall, Englewood Cliffs, N. J., 1955, pp. 3–5.

Robertson, J. David, "The Membrane of the Living Cell," *Scientific American,* Vol. 206 (April, 1962). Offprint No. 151, W. H. Freeman and Co., San Francisco.

Rustad, Ronald C., "Pinocytosis," *Scientific American,* Vol. 204 (April, 1961).

Solomon, Arthur K., "Pores in the Cell Membrane," *Scientific American,* Vol. 203 (December, 1960). Offprint No. 76, W. H. Freeman and Co., San Francisco.

Swanson, Carl P., *The Cell.* Second edition. Prentice-Hall, Englewood Cliffs, N. J., 1964, pp. 1–61.

Questions

1. Give several reasons why the cell is considered a fundamental unit in biology.

2. What are some of the fundamental units in the other sciences?

3. Describe how additions to the knowledge about cells have depended on improvements in tools and technology. Is this true of other sciences?

4. List the parts of cells which are made of membranes and the parts which are not. Which is the longest list?

5. Assign a function to each of the parts you listed.

6. Does the membranous structure of a cell part have any relation to the functioning of that part? Explain with examples.

7. What is meant by the phrase cytoplasmic adaptations? Give several examples.

8. In what way does this idea express the form-function concept in biology?

9. In what ways does the form and structure of the nucleus reflect its function?

10. Why does the nucleus, unlike the cytoplasm, seldom show any morphological specializations?

CHAPTER IV

Photosynthesis: Energy Fixation

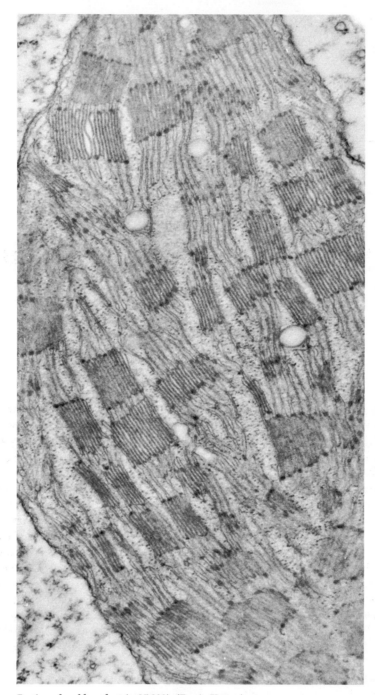

Portion of a chloroplast (×37,000). (Dr. A. Vatter.)

Photosynthesis: Energy Fixation

High school discussions of photosynthesis are often limited to the statement, "All the food energy on earth comes from the sun and is trapped by green plants," plus the chemical equation

I₁

$$6CO_2 + 6H_2O + Energy \xrightarrow{\text{Chlorophyll}} C_6H_{12}O_6 + 6O_2$$

For the most part, both expressions are true summaries of photosynthesis, for this process does transform energy from light into a universally usable form in carbon-to-carbon bonds. These summaries, however, hide much of what really occurs. Yet even these were the result of a long series of experiments and were not known until the late nineteenth century.

Historical Background

I₁ One of the earliest experiments relating to photosynthesis was carried out by Jean-Baptiste Van Helmont in the 1740s. Van Helmont weighed dried earth, placed it in a large pot, and then planted a weighed willow shoot in it. For a period of five years, only water was added to the soil. Then the willow tree and the soil were weighed. The weight of the soil had changed only slightly, but the tree had gained over 160 pounds. Van Helmont concluded that the tree had arisen from water alone. He did not realize that carbon dioxide from the air had contributed to its gain.

I₂ In the late eighteenth century Joseph Priestly, an English pastor and chemist, showed that plants could utilize carbon dioxide and produce oxygen but he did not call these substances by these names. Not long after the Priestly experiments, Jan Ingenhousz, a *I₃* Dutch scientist, demonstrated that only leaves and green stems could carry out such activity—and only when illuminated. Ingenhousz' experiments were simple. Placing different parts of plants such as leaves, green stems, older stems, wood, and seeds in separate sealed glass vessels, he left them in the dark for several hours and then tested the air by introducing a burning candle. The candle did not burn in any of the trials. He then placed the vessels in the light and found that after a few hours the candle burned in any vessel which contained green parts of the plant but would not burn in the other vessels (Figure 4.1). Ingenhousz also showed that the brighter the light, the more rapid was the evolution of oxygen.

Just after 1800, Nicholas de Saussure, a Swiss *I₄* scientist, carried out the first quantitative studies of photosynthesis and showed that the amount of oxygen produced was the same as the amount of carbon dioxide utilized by the plant. He carefully measured the amounts of oxygen, nitrogen, and carbon dioxide in the vessels before and after illuminating the plants in them. He also weighed the plants. By comparing

Figure 4.1. Ingenhousz found that the green portions of plants such as leaves, green stem, or green seeds produced oxygen when kept in light (below) but not in darkness (above).

the amounts of gases before and after the experiment he was able to show the changes that were brought about by photosynthesis.

It was possible at this time to write the following general equation for photosynthesis

$$\text{Carbon dioxide} + \text{Water} \xrightarrow[\text{Light}]{\text{Green plants}}$$

$$\text{Living material} + \text{Oxygen}$$

Notice that this does not indicate why the light was needed, what part of the green plants functioned in this reaction, or what was the organic product.

By 1875 the equation

$$6CO_2 + 6H_2O + \text{Energy from light} \xrightarrow{\text{Chlorophyll}}$$

CARBON↑   WATER
DIOXITE

$$C_6H_{12}O_6 + 6O_2$$

SUGAR

had been experimentally determined. At that time it was thought to be a simple one-step reaction. Over the next sixty years evidence slowly accumulated to the contrary. Investigators showed that many organisms

could incorporate carbon dioxide into carbohydrates without light as a source of energy. This incorporation seemed to occur in the same way as in photosynthesis, except that a different source of energy was used to drive the reaction. Shortly after 1900 F. F. Blackman, 15 an English plant physiologist, studied the rates at which photosynthesis occurred under various conditions and showed that the process had to be a composite of several different reactions. Today, it is necessary to talk of the light and dark reactions of photosynthesis in order to distinguish those reactions for which light is essential from those that take place by utilizing the products of the light reactions, but do not directly depend on light.

Until modern biochemical techniques became available, it was thought that the oxygen released in photosynthesis came from the carbon dioxide. It is now known, however, that water is the source of the oxygen. Although several studies had given indirect evidence, it was not until 1941 when Samuel Ruben, an 16 American biochemist, and his coworkers confirmed this by using isotopes as tracers in the study of photosynthesis. They grew suspensions of single-celled plants in two solutions. In one of these the water molecules contained heavy oxygen (O^{18}), while in the other bicarbonate, a source of carbon dioxide, contained the heavy oxygen. The gases released by the plants were then analyzed for heavy oxygen. If the amount of heavy oxygen in the water molecules was increased, the amount of heavy oxygen released by the plant increased. However, increased amounts of heavy oxygen in the bicarbonate did not change the amount released by the plant (Figure 4.2).

More detailed information awaited the development in 1954 of a technique for carrying out the complete process of photosynthesis in chloroplasts that were freed from the cell. This technique makes it possible to examine photosynthesis without interference from other reactions.

It has been learned that chlorophyll and the enzymes involved in photosynthesis are integral parts of the structure of the chloroplasts. The multiple layers of lipoprotein membrane composing the grana of the chloroplasts (Figure 4.3) present a large amount of chlorophyll to light while maintaining the necessary close relationship between chlorophyll and the enzymes.

Nearly all the reactions of photosynthesis have been experimentally demonstrated often enough to inspire

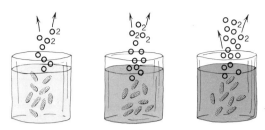

water with increased amounts of heavy oxygen

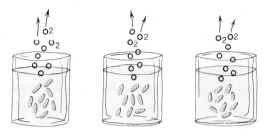

bicarbonate with increased amounts of heavy oxygen

Figure 4.2. This experiment shows that the oxygen released during photosynthesis comes from water. Compare the amount of heavy oxygen released as its concentration in the water is increased with that released as its concentration in bicarbonate is increased.

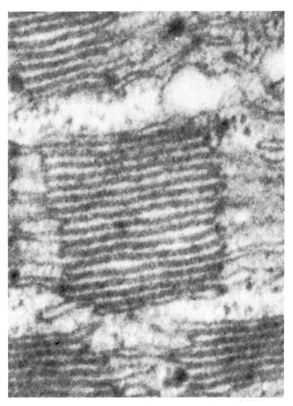

Figure 4.3. A granum of a chloroplast.

confidence in our present understanding of the general processes. However, the mechanisms by which these reactions occur are still relatively unknown.

The Photosynthetic Reactions

ADP and ATP. Before we can discuss the reactions which constitute photosynthesis, we must consider the *ADP-ATP* cycle,* which serves as the basic system for energy transfer in the cell. The high-energy bond in ATP is the immediate source of energy for all reactions in the cell (Figure 4.4). When this bond is broken, leaving ADP plus a simple inorganic phosphate group (P_i), the released energy can be used in reactions. When the right amount of energy becomes available, the high-energy bond between ADP and P_i is reconstituted, resulting in ATP. The usual sources of energy

---

*ADP (adenosine diphosphate) and ATP (adenosine triphosphate) are substances that differ by one phosphate group. This group is attached to the rest of the molecule by a bond (high-energy bond) containing a large amount of energy relative to most bonds. Adenosine is an organic base plus a five-carbon sugar. (See Chapter VII.)

are sunlight or the oxidation of some complex molecule.

Even though photosynthesis is a series of many steps, it is convenient to use the division into *light* and *dark* reactions as a starting point for our discussion. The reactions that require light and are therefore called the light reactions can be summarized by the equation

$$ADP + P_i + H_2O + Energy\ (light) \xrightarrow{Chlorophyll}$$

$$ATP + H + O_2$$

Notice that ADP, P_i, and water are used during these reactions and that ATP, hydrogen (attached to a carrier molecule), and oxygen are the products. Of these, the equation used to summarize photosynthesis shows only water as a reactant and oxygen as a product. We may then expect that the dark reactions of photosynthesis will use up the remaining products of the light reactions (ATP and hydrogen) and will produce ADP and P_i which were shown as reactants. Thus, the net changes that result from photosynthesis do not show any over-all changes in these materials.

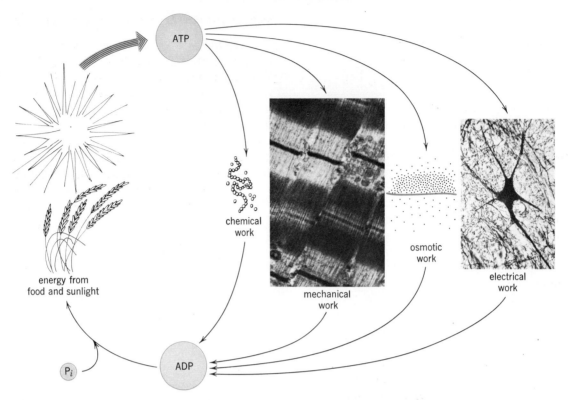

Figure 4.4. The ADP-ATP cycle, the basic pattern of energy transfer in all living systems. (Reprinted with permission, Copyright © 1961 by Scientific American, Inc. All rights reserved. Muscle photograph, Dr. H. E. Huxley.)

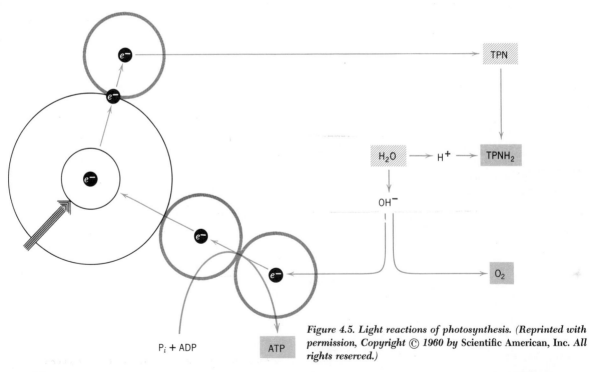

Figure 4.5. Light reactions of photosynthesis. (Reprinted with permission, Copyright © 1960 by Scientific American, Inc. All rights reserved.)

The dark reactions may be summarized by

$$ATP + CO_2 + H \longrightarrow$$
$$ADP + P_i + \text{Carbohydrate (PGAL)}$$

They occur in plants any time that the reactants for this equation, ATP, carbon dioxide, and hydrogen, are all present. ADP, inorganic phosphate, and PGAL (phosphoglyceraldehyde, a three-carbon relative of sugars) result. Notice that this equation, like the one used to summarize the light reactions, shows only what the reactants and the products are; it is not a balanced equation.

Light Reactions. Let us now look at the light and dark reactions in a little more detail. Chlorophyll absorbs energy from sunlight. This extra energy makes the chlorophyll molecule unstable. As a result an electron, which carries the excess energy, is lost. This electron is picked up by a hydrogen carrier which is then able to remove hydrogen from water, that is, split the water molecule. The product other than hydrogen is OH^-. This ion donates an electron to the cytochrome system (see p. 67) leaving OH. Several of these combine to form water and release O_2 (Figure 4.5).

The electrons that are transferred to the *cytochrome system* pass from one of the complex substances that make up this system to the next. As the transfers occur, energy is obtained which is used to form ATP from ADP and P_i. The last acceptor for these electrons is chlorophyll. The return of the electrons to the chlorophyll restores its original condition. This allows it again to absorb energy from light.

Again, the summary for the light reactions is:
(1) Energy from light is absorbed by chlorophyll.
(2) This energy is used to split water and to build ATP from ADP and P_i.
(3) The oxygen from the water is released but the hydrogen is picked up by hydrogen carrier molecules.

Dark Reactions. In the dark reactions (Figure 4.6) each of several carbon dioxide-carrier molecules (five-

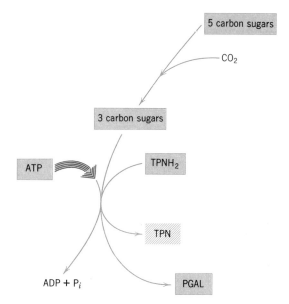

Figure 4.6. Dark reactions of photosynthesis.

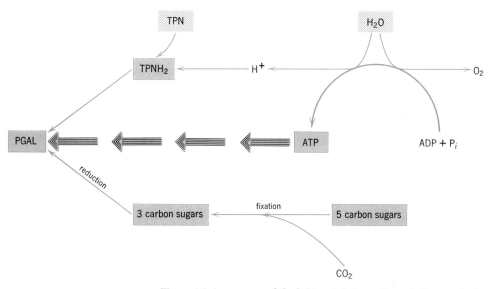

Figure 4.7. A summary of the light and dark reactions of photosynthesis.

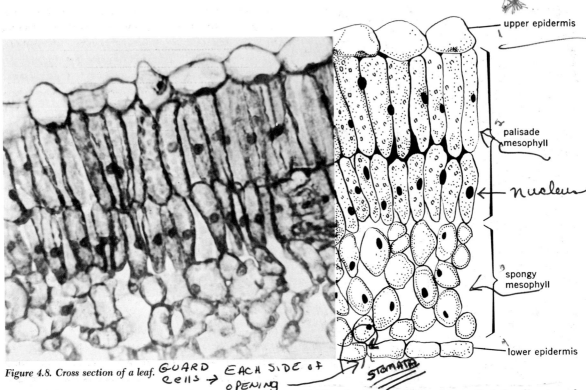

Figure 4.8. Cross section of a leaf. GUARD EACH SIDE OF ℓℓᶫˢ → OPENING

upper epidermis

palisade mesophyll

nucleus

spongy mesophyll

lower epidermis

STOMATA

carbon sugars) picks up a carbon dioxide molecule and immediately splits into two three-carbon molecules. Energy is transferred to these three-carbon molecules by splitting the high-energy bond in ATP, leaving ADP + P_i. Hydrogen is now transferred to the three-carbon molecules from the hydrogen carrier, resulting in PGAL molecules and carrier molecules which can participate in the removal of hydrogen from more water molecules. Much of the PGAL produced is used to reconstitute the five-carbon carrier molecules but some is available for the synthesis of other compounds.

In summary the dark reactions show:

(1) The incorporation of carbon dioxide by its addition to a carbohydrate molecule.

(2) The resulting molecule splits into three-carbon molecules.

(3) The ATP and the hydrogen-carrier complex produced by the light reactions are utilized to change the three-carbon molecules into PGAL.

Fate of PGAL. We have shown how each reactant in the over-all equation enters into photosynthesis and how each product is manufactured. The only difference is that we show the end product as PGAL rather than glucose. This is really more accurate. Work by Melvin Calvin and his associates at the University of California since 1948 has shown that the direct product of photosynthesis is not glucose. Rather, six-carbon sugars like glucose are produced along with many other chemicals from these three-carbon molecules, which are the actual end products of the reactions. Calvin discovered the reactions by which various compounds are produced in photosynthesis by growing illuminated suspensions of single-celled plants for short periods of time in the presence of radioactive carbon dioxide (CO_2 with C^{14}). The California group then killed the suspensions and identified the compounds in which the radioactive carbon was found.

We now know that all of the reactions of photosynthesis are complete when PGAL is formed (Figure 4.7). PGAL serves as a starting point for the synthesis of all the major groups of organic molecules in the cell. Two of these three-carbon units will produce the six-carbon sugars such as glucose and fructose, which in turn are used as the basic units for producing the more common complex carbohydrates such as sucrose, cellulose, starch, and glycogen.

In addition, PGAL may be modified to glycerol, acetate, or pyruvate. Fatty acids are formed by the combination of several of the two-carbon acetate molecules. These fatty acids and glycerol are the two sub-

TPN

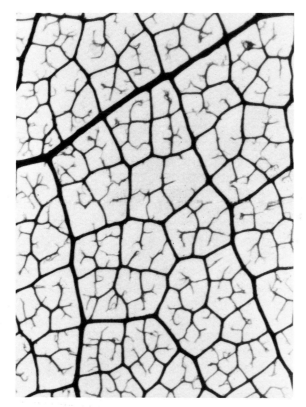

Figure 4.9. The network of vascular tissue (veins) in a leaf.

stances from which fats are formed. Fatty acids may be further modified by the addition of an amino group to form amino acids, the basic unit for protein synthesis. Thus, the energy originally captured by the chlorophyll may end up in any of these compounds.

If all these groups have the same precursor in PGAL, it would seem logical that compounds of one group could be digested and the products modified to form compounds of another group. This occurs regularly in both plant and animal cells.

Site of Photosynthesis

The leaves of green plants are the most familiar sites for photosynthesis. Because the processes of photosynthesis are the same in each leaf, all leaves have some structural similarities. The cross section of a "typical" leaf is shown in Figure 4.8. Most of the photosynthesis occurs in the *mesophyll* of the leaf.

The upper layer of the mesophyll is called the *palisade* because of its closely packed, vertically oriented cells. The concentration of chlorophyll is higher

here than anywhere else in the leaf. The rest of the mesophyll, the *spongy mesophyll,* consists of cells that have considerable space between them. Atmospheric gases circulate rather freely through these spaces.

Within the mesophyll branching cylinders of *vascular* tissue (veins) traverse the leaf (Figure 4.9). These carry water and minerals to the leaves and organic products away from the leaves.

The upper and lower surfaces of the leaf reduce water loss because they are covered by *epidermis,* a tissue with an outer layer of waxy material called cuticle. The lower surface differs from the upper because it has small openings called *stomata* which allow gases to move between the spaces in the mesophyll and the atmosphere. (See Chapter X for a description of the operation of the stomata.)

Adaptive Variations. The leaves of many plants show marked differences from our "typical" leaf, because the environments in which plants live are not the same in each case. The alfalfa leaf (Figure 4.10) is representative of leaves found in plants that require moderate or large amounts of moisture. Both the upper and lower epidermal layers contain stomata. A maximum supply of carbon dioxide is made available in this way but water loss is also maximal. If the water supply is inadequate, wilting occurs.

Plants like the Russian thistle, creosote bush, and oleander (Figure 4.11) show many adaptations to the dry conditions under which they live. Notice the increase in the thickness of the palisade layers, the reduction (in some cases, absence) of the spongy mesophyll, the thickened cuticle, the water-storage cells, and the protective location of the stomata in some or all of these plants.

The thicker palisade layer and smaller spongy mesophyll lessens the amount of cell surface exposed to the air and to evaporation inside the leaf. The thickened cuticle reduces evaporation from the outer surface of the leaf, while the protected stomata partially blocks air mixture at the stomata and further cuts water loss.

If we compare leaves from the same plant, some taken from parts of the plant that are in the shade and some from parts that are in the sun, we find considerable difference between them (Figure 4.12). Sun leaves typically show more palisade layers and a thicker cuticle on the epidermis. This indicates that the palisade may be an adaptation for exposed situations. A thicker palisade has two possible effects. First, it may concentrate more chlorophyll in the leaf and in-

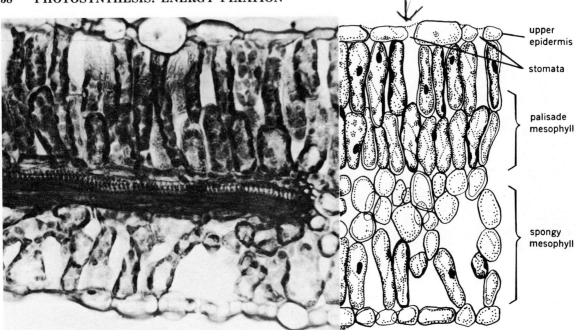

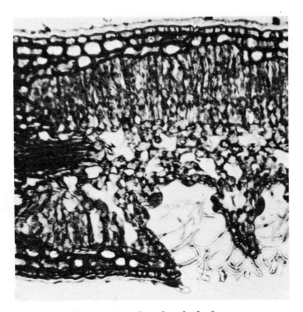

Figure 4.10. Cross section of an alfalfa leaf.

Figure 4.11. Cross section of an oleander leaf.

crease its efficiency in trapping light energy. Second, the palisade layer is more tightly packed than the spongy mesophyll. This tends to reduce air circulation around the cells and to trim water loss.

A dilemma becomes apparent when the interplay of sunlight and carbon dioxide is considered. Increased light intensities do not result in increased photosynthesis unless plenty of carbon dioxide is present (Figure 4.13). Free circulation of air between the cells is necessary to supply this carbon dioxide. However, an increase in the circulation of air along with absorption of heat heightens water loss.

If the plant is to succeed in any environment, it must have enough air circulation through the leaf to provide the necessary level of carbon dioxide for photosynthesis. The photosynthetic rate must be high enough to allow the plant to compete with other plants. On the other hand, the circulation of air cannot be so great that the loss of water becomes critical.

Photosynthesis is indispensable to the existence of life for two reasons. First, the release of oxygen serves to restore the atmospheric supply and to maintain it at a level consistent with the requirements of the organisms needing oxygen. Second, the production of all energy-containing molecules utilized by all organisms occurs originally through photosynthesis in green plants.

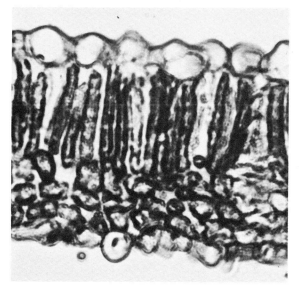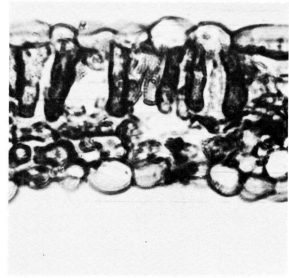

Figure 4.12. Leaves of a maple grown in the sun (left) and in the shade (right).

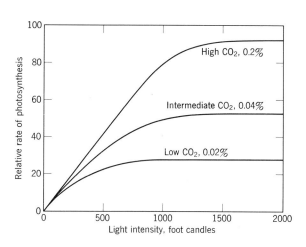

Figure 4.13. Both light intensity and carbon dioxide concentration influence the rate of photosynthesis. In weak light, the rate is directly proportional to intensity. In very bright light, the rate is not influenced by small changes in intensity but is dependent on the carbon dioxide concentration and temperature. (W. H. Johnson and W. C. Steere, This Is Life, Holt, Rinehart and Winston, 1962, New York.)

Principles

1. Photosynthesis is the method by which light energy, not usually utilizable by most organisms as an energy source, is transformed into a readily utilizable form in chemical bonds.

2. Photosynthesis is essentially reduction of carbon dioxide with hydrogen obtained by splitting water molecules.

3. The energy obtained from this, or any other source, is transferred to high-energy phosphate bonds in ATP before being used for cellular activity.

4. The various structural arrangements of leaves are adaptations to facilitate photosynthesis in their own environments.

Suggested Readings

Arnon, Daniel I., "The Role of Light in Photosynthesis," *Scientific American,* Vol. 203 (November, 1960). Offprint No. 75, W. H. Freeman and Co., San Francisco.

French, C. S., "Photosynthesis," in *This Is Life,* edited by W. H. Johnson and W. C. Steere. Holt, Rinehart and Winston, New York, 1962, pp. 3–38.

Lehninger, Albert L., "How Cells Transform Energy," *Scientific American,* Vol. 205 (September, 1961). Offprint No. 91, W. H. Freeman and Co., San Francisco.

Priestley, Joseph, "Observations on Different Kinds of Air," in *Great Experiments in Biology,* edited by M. L. Gabriel and S. Fogel. Prentice-Hall, Englewood Cliffs, N. J., 1955, pp. 155–157.

Rabinowitch, Eugene I., "Photosynthesis," *Scientific American,* Vol. 179 (August, 1948). Offprint No. 34, W. H. Freeman and Co., San Francisco.

Questions

1. What relationships, if any, existed between historical advances in the knowledge of photosynthesis and improvements in scientific techniques? Can you give a specific example?

2. Explain why it is necessary to use isotopes to prove that water is split during photosynthesis.

3. Summarize, in your own words, what occurs during the light reaction of photosynthesis. Do the same thing for the dark reaction. (The flow sheet diagram should help you do this.)

4. What major uses may be made of PGAL in cells?

5. What is the direct (immediate) source of energy for all cells? Does this mean that cells do not use PGAL or other organic compounds for energy directly? Explain.

6. Why is most of photosynthesis described as a *reduction reaction*?

7. Explain why the formula $6CO_2 + 6H_2O + Energy \xrightarrow{\text{Chlorophyll}} C_6H_{12}O_6 + 6O_2$ is adequate as a *summary* of photosynthesis, but is inadequate to describe the chemical reactions that take place.

8. What external features of leaf shapes and forms adapt them for photosynthesis?

9. Is the internal anatomy of a leaf adapted to facilitate photosynthesis? In what ways?

10. Tell what effect, if any, each of the following environmental factors have on photosynthesis: light intensity, air temperature, relative hours of daylight and darkness, humidity, amount of oxygen in the atmosphere, type of soil, amount of water in the soil.

Respiration: Energy Harvest

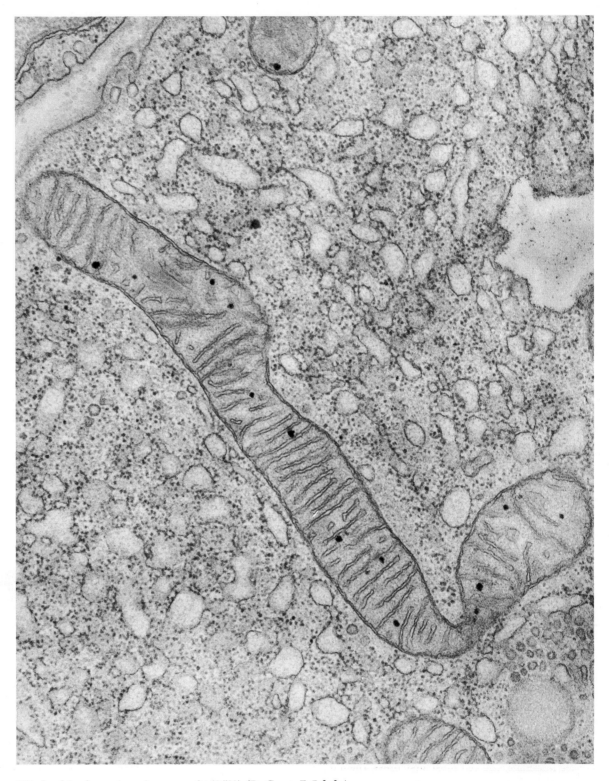

Mitochondrion from guinea pig pancreas (×41,500). (Dr. George E. Palade.)

Respiration: Energy Harvest

Photosynthesis is the mechanism that transforms the energy for most of the living world into bonds in carbon-containing compounds. However, many organisms have no ability to carry out photosynthesis and are dependent for energy upon the intake of complex carbon energy sources. The energy in these sources comes either directly or indirectly from green plants. Regardless of how the organisms get the energy-containing compounds to the cell, all of them must break down these compounds in a way that will allow the cell to harvest a maximum of utilizable energy. The sum of these energy-yielding processes is called *respiration*.

The term respiration is used in two ways. The processes we are referring to here occur within each cell and are called *cellular respiration*. The more familiar connotation of respiration refers to the exchange of respiratory gases (carbon dioxide and oxygen) between the organism and the environment. This is *external respiration*. (See pp. 73–75.)

Organisms generally store energy within the cell in the forms of either complex carbohydrates or fats. Proteins may also be used as a source of energy during periods of starvation but do not primarily serve an energy storage function. To obtain energy from any of these materials, the cell must first break them down into simpler molecules. This digestion always consists of hydrolytic reactions. As we have seen, most carbohydrates yield glucose or closely related six-carbon sugars; the fats yield fatty acids and glycerol, whereas the proteins yield amino acids. First let us look in detail at the reactions glucose undergoes. Later we shall see how the other types of molecules fit this scheme.

Reactions of Respiration

The release of the energy found in these smaller molecules is effected by their oxidation, that is, cell respiration. Dehydrogenation is important in this process because it results in energy changes in the hydrogen-donor molecule. Consequently, the steps where dehydrogenation occurs are important in the release of energy. Electron removal accompanies each of these dehydrogenations. By following the path of electron transport to oxygen, the final electron acceptor, we can gain insight into the methods of energy release in the cell.

The equation for respiration is usually given as

$$C_6H_{12}O_6 + 6O_2 \longrightarrow 6H_2O + 6CO_2 + \text{Energy}$$

Although this equation contains the reactants and the products of the over-all reactions, it neither describes anything about the processes nor tells what other substances are necessary. Rather than being a simple, one-step reaction as we might infer from the equation, respiration is an intricate series of reactions. Each reaction requires complex molecules, such as enzymes, for its operation.

For convenience, we may divide respiration into four stages (Figure 5.1). It is important to remember that in

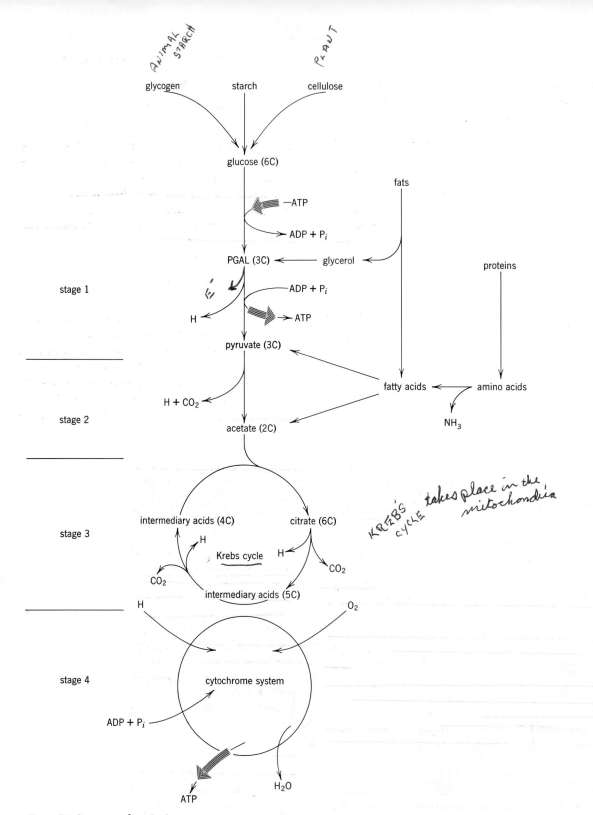

Figure 5.1. Summary of respiration.

[handwritten margin notes: "KNOW STAGES Test Tell every thing in EQUATION & what STAGE its IN."]

discussing these stages we are summarizing the reactions that occur and are not treating them in detail.

Stage 1: Glycolysis

2ADP + 2P$_i$ + glucose (6C, i.e., a six-carbon compound)

$$\longrightarrow 2 \text{ pyruvate (3C)} + 4H^+ + 4e^- {}^* + 2ATP$$

The major events are: (*a*) cleavage of a six-carbon molecule to two three-carbon molecules; (*b*) some oxidation (the removal of hydrogen ions and electrons); (*c*) some direct energy transfer to ADP and P$_i$ to form ATP.

Stage 2: Bridge between Glycolysis and the Krebs Cycle

Pyruvate (3C) $\longrightarrow$

$$\text{acetate (2C)} + CO_2 + 2H^+ + 2e^-$$

The major events are: (*a*) some oxidation; (*b*) decarboxylation (removal of CO_2) from a three-carbon to a two-carbon molecule.

*H^+ and e^- are the symbols for a hydrogen ion and an electron, respectively.

Stage 3: The Krebs Cycle

$$3H_2O + \text{acetate (2C)} \longrightarrow$$
$$2CO_2 + 8H^+ + 8e^-$$

The major events are: (*a*) removal of all remaining carbon as CO_2; (*b*) a great deal of oxidation by the removal of hydrogen ions and electrons.

In stages 1, 2, and 3, $H^+ + e^-$ have been released to carrier molecules. These must now pass to other molecules and finally to oxygen to form water. This occurs in the cytochrome system.

Stage 4: Cytochrome System

$$6ADP + 6P_i + 4H^+ + 4e^- + O_2 \longrightarrow$$
$$6ATP + 2H_2O$$

The major events are: (*a*) transfer of energy to ADP and P$_i$ to form ATP; (*b*) formation of water.

Of these four stages, only the first occurs through most of the cytoplasmic sap. The last three stages all occur in the mitochondria. The enzymes necessary for these latter reactions are found only in the mitochondria. In studying cell structure we noted that the inner

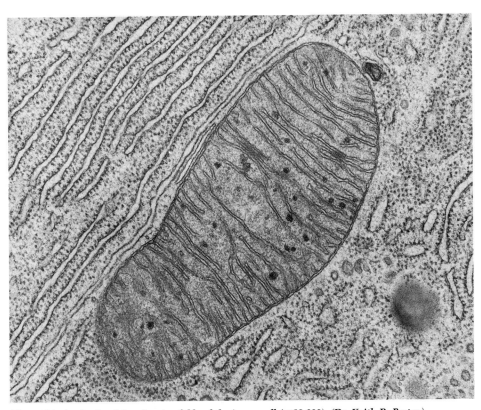

Figure 5.2. A mitochondrion showing folds of the inner wall ($\times 39{,}000$). (Dr. Keith R. Porter.)

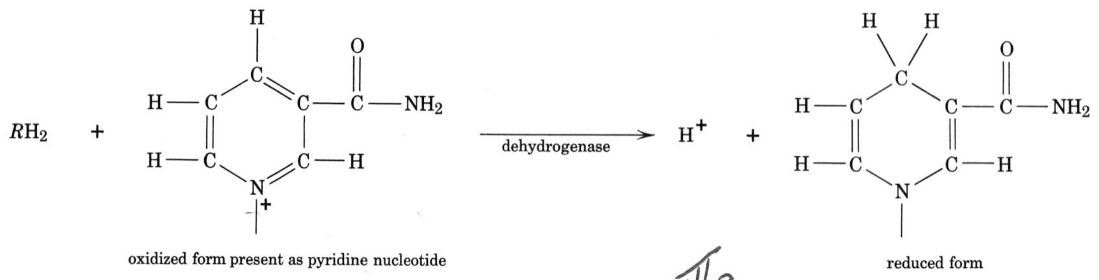

$$RH_2 \quad + \quad \text{[oxidized pyridine nucleotide structure]} \xrightarrow{\text{dehydrogenase}} H^+ \quad + \quad \text{[reduced form structure]}$$

oxidized form present as pyridine nucleotide

reduced form

Figure 5.3. The pyridine nucleotides serve as hydrogen and electron carriers.

wall of the mitochondrion was folded (see Figure 5.2). This folding enlarges the surface area on which the enzymes are located, thereby increasing the amount of the enzymes present and the speed at which respiration may occur. Let us consider each of these four stages in more detail.

Glycolysis. For glycolysis ("glucose splitting") to occur, the energy level of glucose must be increased. Activation energy is transferred from ATP to glucose by shifting a high-energy phosphate group. Notice that in order to obtain ATP from respiration we must first expend ATP (see Figure 5.1). The resulting molecule is then split into two three-carbon molecules, which we call PGAL. PGAL is an important crossroad in the metabolism of the cell because it is common to the pathways of photosynthesis, other syntheses, and respiration (see pp. 56–57).

Three types of reactions occur in the transformation of PGAL to pyruvate: the rearrangement of bonds in the molecule, the direct transfer of energy to ADP and P_i to form ATP, and the removal of hydrogen with electrons. The amount of ATP produced directly in glycolysis is twice as much as was used in supplying the activation energy. A net gain of energy is evident.

The hydrogen atoms released here and elsewhere in respiration do not appear in the form of free hydrogen. Rather, they are donated to molecules which serve as hydrogen and electron carriers. These carriers are complex organic molecules, called pyridine nucleotides (Figure 5.3), which are necessary for respiration. We cannot synthesize some portions of the molecules in human cells but must bring them in already made in the form of some of the B vitamins. After the electrons are transferred to the cytochrome system, the hydrogen is released into the cytoplasmic sap as H^+.

Bridge. The three-carbon molecule pyruvate now enters into the mitochondria from the cytoplasmic

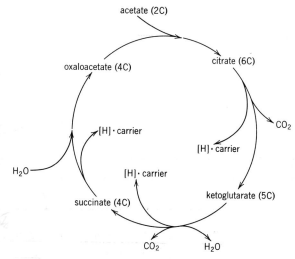

Figure 5.4. The Krebs cycle.

sap. Here one of its carbons is removed as carbon dioxide leaving a two-carbon molecule, acetate. In addition, more hydrogen atoms are transferred to a hydrogen carrier.

The Krebs Cycle. The acetate now enters a series of reactions called the Krebs cycle after its discoverer, and is illustrated in Figure 5.4. This two-carbon molecule is combined with a four-carbon molecule to form the six-carbon citrate from which the cycle gets another of its names, the *citric acid cycle*. By the successive removal of carbon dioxide the citrate is first changed to a five-carbon molecule and then to a four-carbon molecule. This *decarboxylation* along with other reactions, like the addition of water and the transfer of hydrogen atoms to a carrier, result in the original four-carbon molecule's being reconstituted. This completes the cycle. The four-carbon molecule may now combine with another acetate molecule and the series of reactions occur again.

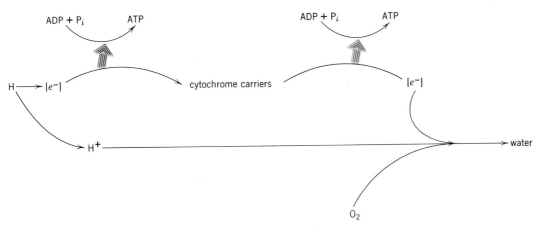

Figure 5.5. The cytochrome system.

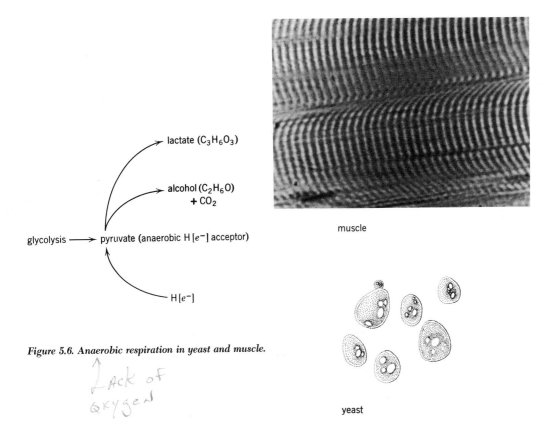

muscle

yeast

Figure 5.6. Anaerobic respiration in yeast and muscle.

Lack of oxygen

Cytochrome System. Thus far we have talked of several reactions in which carbon dioxide is produced or hydrogen atoms are transferred to a carrier. What happens to these substances? Carbon dioxide is an end product of respiration and simply diffuses from the cell as a waste product. In the cytochrome system, the electrons from the hydrogen atoms are transferred successively through a series of complex organic molecules (the cytochromes) to oxygen. At this time hydrogen ions from the cytoplasmic sap are also picked up by the oxygen, and water is formed (Figure 5.5). The energy that is released at three transfer points in moderate amounts is used to synthesize ATP from ADP and inorganic phosphate. Notice that the energy is not released all at once but in several small amounts. If energy were released in one large amount, as in many oxidations, most of it would be lost as heat. The cell, however, is able to harvest a high percentage of the available energy in the form of ATP. *Most of the energy available to the cell from respiration is obtained by the treatment of the electrons in the cytochrome system.*

Respiration of Fatty Acids. One further step is required for the fatty acids remaining from the digestion of proteins (via amino acids) and fats to enter the same general oxidative scheme suitable for carbohydrates. Most fatty acids are long chains of carbon atoms with some oxygen and a great number of hydrogen atoms attached. These chains are broken down by the successive removal of two-carbon fragments (acetate). The last fragment may contain either two or three carbon atoms (acetate or pyruvate), depending on the number of carbons in the fatty acid which is being broken down. Thus, the subsequent reactions by which fatty acids are oxidized become exactly the same as those involved in the oxidation of carbohydrates.

Glycerol is another product of the digestion of fats. It is a three-carbon compound similar to PGAL and may enter the glycolytic reactions at the same point.

So far we have assumed that all cells carry out oxidation in the same way under all conditions. This is not true. We find all kinds of variations from this basic route. We shall discuss three of these.

Some Variations in Respiration

Fermentation is a familiar variation. Yeast and many other micro-organisms follow the glycolytic pathway as far as pyruvate. Then in fermentation, pyruvate is changed into ethyl alcohol (a two-carbon molecule) and carbon dioxide. These reactions require the transfer of hydrogen atoms from the carrier to pyruvate to complete the transition to alcohol (Figure 5.6).

Two aspects of this pathway should be underlined. First, it requires no oxygen consumption. This makes it useful to many organisms that live in environments lacking oxygen (*anaerobic* environments). Second, the addition of hydrogen atoms to pyruvate provides a means of disposing of the hydrogen obtained during glycolysis. Pyruvate substitutes for oxygen as a final hydrogen and electron acceptor. If this did not occur, reduced carrier molecules would accumulate, no oxidized carrier molecules would be available to accept hydrogen atoms from PGAL, and all the reactions of glycolysis would cease.

Anaerobic Respiration in Muscle. Another variation in the pathway for respiration is found in muscle cells under anaerobic conditions. This variation of respiration is similar to fermentation in that it undergoes the same reactions from glucose to pyruvate. The pyruvate is now transformed, however, to lactate, another three-carbon molecule (Figure 5.6). During this transformation pyruvate substitutes for oxygen as in fermentation so that no oxygen is required.

Why is it that all respiration in muscle cells does not occur by this route? Two characteristics of the pathway make this undesirable. Only about 5 per cent of the energy obtained by the normal aerobic pathway is acquired by anaerobic glycolysis. Second, lactate tends to build up in the cell. If the concentration rises too high, muscular fatigue and soreness results. This pathway is used only when a need for energy arises during a shortage of oxygen as in extreme muscular exertion.

Sulfur Bacteria. Certain bacteria show a third respiratory variation. In sulfur bacteria wide variety exists in the patterns of respiration. One group of bacteria may use sulfur rather than oxygen as the final hydrogen acceptor.

$$4H_2 + H_2SO_4 \longrightarrow H_2S + 4H_2O$$
sulfuric acid

Students of chemistry know the similarity of the reactions of oxygen and sulfur. The final product, H_2S or hydrogen sulfide, is famous for its "rotten egg" odor because the bacteria that produce it are found in decaying eggs. The first hydrogen in this equation may come from several different sources. These bacteria use hydrogen gas if nearby bacteria are producing it. If not, they may use a number of organic molecules like pyruvate as a hydrogen source. A source is essential; which source does not matter.

Oxidation involving the removal of electrons is an important feature which all forms of respiration share. However, great diversity exists in the details of the processes of respiration found in different kinds of cells. Both this variation in detail and the similarity in the bases of phenomena are in themselves characteristic of living systems.

Principles

1. Respiration is the process by which useful energy is made available to cells by the breakdown of fuel (carbon-containing) molecules within each cell.

2. The three major events of respiration are:

   (a) Oxidation of the fuel molecules by dehydro-genation.

   (b) The energy is released in small quantities by the stepwise transfer of hydrogen to oxygen to form water.

   (c) This energy is utilized in the synthesis of ATP.

Suggested Readings

Green, David E., "The Mitochondrion," *Scientific American,* Vol. 210 (January, 1964). Offprint No. 175, W. H. Free-man and Co., San Francisco.

Lehninger, Albert L., "Energy Transformation in the Cell," *Scientific American,* Vol. 202 (May, 1960). Offprint No. 69, W. H. Freeman and Co., San Francisco.

Lehninger, Albert L., "How Cells Transform Energy," *Scientific American,* Vol. 205 (September, 1961). Offprint No. 91, W. H. Freeman and Co., San Francisco.

MITOCONDRIA

Questions

1. Follow a molecule of glucose through the events of cellular respiration, using the flow sheet as a guide.

2. What is erroneous about the common statement that cells burn foodstuffs for energy?

3. Explain the statement that the primary function of cellular respiration is to transfer energy into phosphate bonds.

4. Review the five general types of reactions which occur in cells (Chapter II), then see how many of them take place during cellular respiration.

5. During which stage of respiration would you expect to find the largest number of ATP molecules formed?

6. During the respiratory process, H^+ are released into the cell. What does this do to the pH of the cell? How does the cytochrome system eventually utilize these hydrogens?

7. Why is glycolysis an *anaerobic* reaction even in aerobic organisms?

8. Anaerobic respiration produces far less useful energy for a cell than does aerobic respiration. Why?

9. Yeasts can live in either oxygen-poor or oxygen-rich environments. Do you think they produce ethyl alcohol in the presence of oxygen? Why?

10. Muscles that are used regularly seldom become sore even with vigorous exercise. Can you think of some reasons why this should be true?

11. Sulfur bacteria illustrate what basic concept about respiration?

12. In what specific parts of cells does respiration take place? In what structural way might one cell be better adapted for respiration than another, e.g., an active cell compared to a relatively inactive one?

CHAPTER VI

Systems for Treatment and Transport of Materials

Barnacles feeding. (© *Walt Disney Productions.*)

Systems for Treatment and Transport of Materials

Living organisms consist of a wide variety of different substances. In order to maintain life and to grow, each organism must obtain a supply of these substances or the materials from which to synthesize them. In Chapter II we outlined the general types of materials found in living systems. The inorganic materials comprise small molecules, which, upon reaching the cells, pass readily through membranes. Animals generally obtain the complex organic materials in a form that must be digested before they can be transported through the cell membrane. In larger animals, the digested materials must be moved through the wall of the digestive tract, be carried to the cell, and then transported into the cell. Even though most plants manufacture their own organic materials, these materials must still be transported from the site of production to the site of utilization. This involves problems similar to those met in animals.

Three different processes are involved: intake of materials, digestion, and transport to cells. Transport through membranes, which plays an important part in these processes, was discussed in Chapter II.

Intake of Materials

In discussing intake we use as examples external respiratory structures. Generally, these structures are areas specialized for the exchange of oxygen and carbon dioxide with the surrounding environment. The examination of a series of the structures shows their adaptation to an organism's needs and environment.

General Body Surface. Some organisms do not have any specialized respiratory structure. They simply exchange gases through the general body surface. This is usually the case in small, less active organisms that live in moist environments. All single-celled organisms (Figure 6.1) and some multicellular organisms such as the rotifers and *Hydra* illustrate this group (Figure 6.2). For respiration to occur in these organisms, the surfaces must remain moist, because the gases must dissolve into water in order to diffuse through the membranes which are thin.

Larger animals like the earthworm, which live in moist environments, also exchange respiratory gases through the general body surface. In these animals blood is transported to the body surface where it exchanges respiratory gases with the environment. The blood then carries the gases throughout the body.

Gills. In other animals in moist environments gills serve as respiratory structures (Figure 6.3). These can be considered as outfoldings of the body surface. This system increases the amount of surface available for respiration and allows more rapid exchange. Although the gill systems are similar to the general body system in that they lose water rapidly in a dry environment,

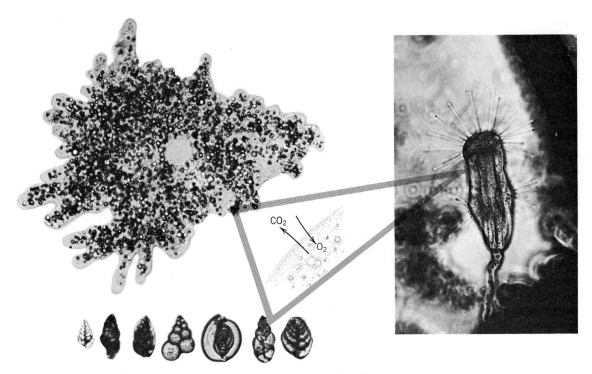

Figure 6.1. Protozoans that show respiratory gas exchange through the cell surface.

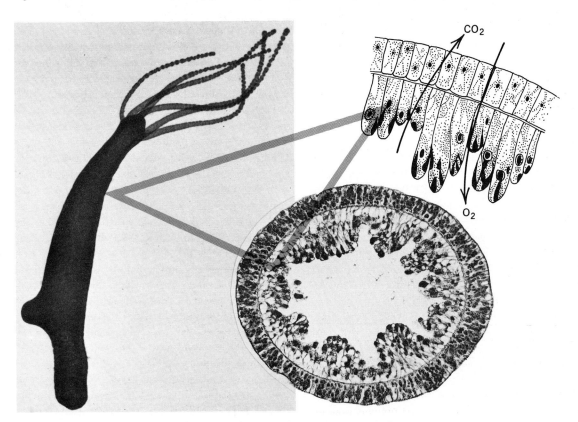

Figure 6.2. Hydra. *An example of multicellular animals that respire through the body surface. Notice that* Hydra *has only two cell layers.*

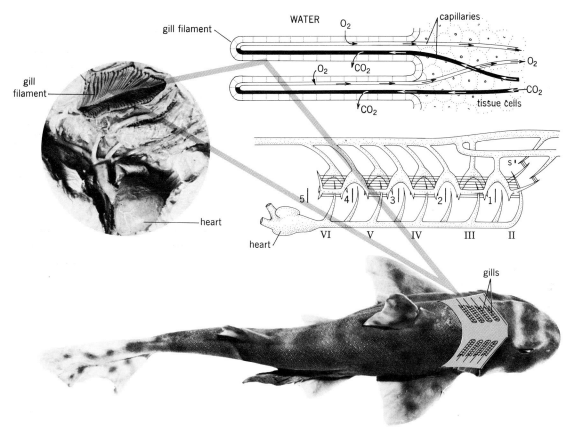

Figure 6.3. The respiratory structures of the dogfish shark showing the gills and associated blood vessels (photograph upper left and diagram middle right) and the detail in two gill filaments (upper diagram).

they often differ in having associated with them a structure that can close off the gills from a temporarily unfavorable environment and prevent water loss for a period of time.

⌒ *Lungs and Tracheae.*   Land-dwelling animals that are not restricted to moist environments generally have either lungs or tracheae. *Lungs* may be considered infoldings of the body surface (Figure 6.4). The infolding results in a larger area for gas exchange, but because the lungs are inside the animal the moist surface necessary for respiration is protected from a large water loss. By moving air in and out of the lungs rapid exchange of gases may occur.

Tracheae are a series of tubes extending throughout the body of insects (Figure 6.5). Air moves in and out of the tracheae and dissolves in the fluid which fills the ends of the tubes. Water loss is minimal and, incidentally, there is no need for respiratory gas transport by the blood because the tubes pass near every

cell in the body. An animal that possesses tracheae cannot be very large. The weight of such reinforced tubes would make a large animal too heavy.

Digestive Systems

Since respiratory gases are composed of small molecules, they always pass readily through the membranes. Food materials must be broken down, however, to molecules such as simple sugars, amino acids, fatty acids, and glycerol before they can cross membranes.

Digestive processes are found in all types of organisms. The reactions involved are called hydrolytic reactions. Hydrolysis is characteristic of digestion inside or outside cells.

Vacuoles.   Digestion that occurs inside cells (intracellular digestion) involves the breakdown of both molecules that have been synthesized within the same cell and those brought into the cell. Digestive enzymes are secreted into food vacuoles in the cytoplasm where

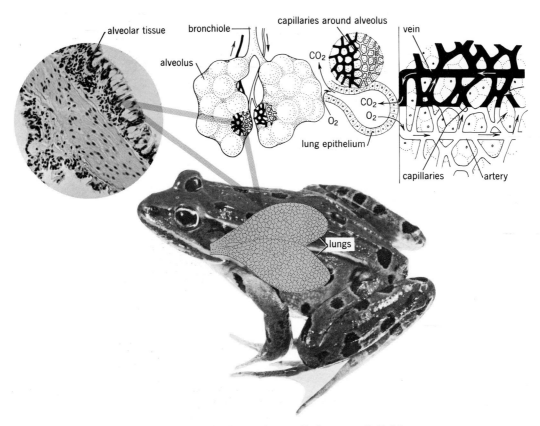

Figure 6.4. Frogs possess lungs as do most land animals. Usually lungs are divided into alveoli (upper left and center). The pattern of gas exchange is shown at the upper right. (Dr. John Moore.)

digestion to simple molecules occurs (Figure 6.6). This type of digestion generally occurs in less active animals. *Amoeba* is an example of an animal that carries on only intracellular digestion.

External Digestion. Although intracellular digestion might be considered the simplest form, many fungi (molds) actually secrete the enzymes onto the food outside their bodies and absorb materials that are already in the form of simple molecules (see Figure 6.7). Of course, many internal parasites absorb predigested food from the environment and lack digestive processes themselves.

Gastrovascular Cavity. Some animals like *Hydra* and planaria have incomplete digestive tracts (Figure 6.8). These tracts with only one opening are associated with either intracellular digestion or a combination of intracellular and *extracellular* digestion. Cells lining the digestive tract engulf particles of food. The tracts do not show specialization of areas for different functions. Since the digestive tract may also serve as a transport system, it is called a gastrovascular cavity.

Complete Digestive Tracts. More complex animals generally have complete digestive tracts (Figure 6.9). This allows food material to be moved in one direction and permits specialization of regions of the digestive tract. Food may be in different stages of the process of digestion in different areas at the same time.

Transport Systems

After food has been reduced to particles which can be moved through the membranes into the organism itself, the materials must be transported to the areas where they are needed. The mechanisms for this transport also generally remove waste materials and carry products from the cells. Some organisms need special transport systems while others do not. A consideration of the size of the organism illustrates some of the problems involved.

When all of an organism's cells are close to its surface, materials may move rapidly enough by simple

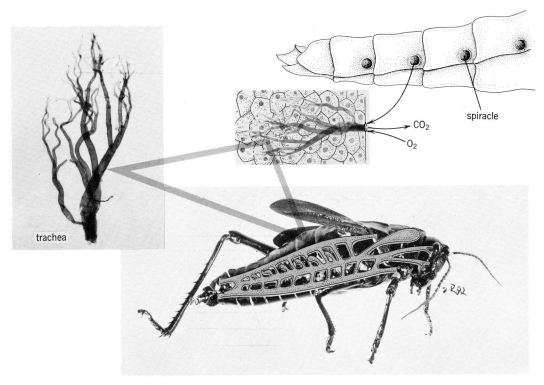

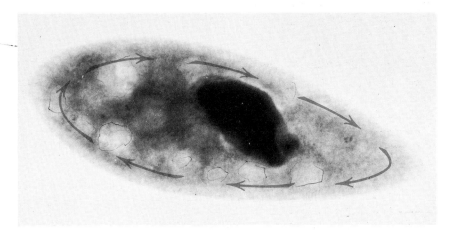

Figure 6.5. The respiratory system of insects consists of a series of tubules called tracheae. These open to the outside of the insect by small openings (upper right). Notice the relationship of the tubes to each cell (upper center).

Figure 6.6. The movement of food vacuoles in Paramecium follows a definite path.

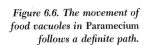

diffusion to supply its needs. In most such cases no transport system is present. Single-celled organisms and thin, flat organisms are examples. When there are cells that are more than a few cells removed from the surface, some means must be available to move materials to and from them or the cells will die.

Gastrovascular Cavity.   Some animals have a gastrovascular cavity which penetrates to within a short distance of every cell (Figure 6.10). This brings the source of materials close enough for diffusion to effect their transfer over the remaining distance to the cells. Movement of materials within this cavity is limited to "sloshing" of the fluid. Complete mixing of the contents results, and the efficiency of transport is low. The size, level of complexity, and rate of activity of the animals having this system are also low.

Xylem-Phloem. The transport system of higher plants is composed of two distinct sets of tubular elements (Figures 6.11 and 6.12). One of these, the xylem, is composed of only the walls of dead cells and carries mostly water and minerals. The cells of the other set, the phloem, are living and carry organic materials.

The water-bearing xylem is associated with the wood of the plant. This dead-cell system presents a relatively open set of tubes through which the water may pass but which is incapable of expending any energy to help move the water. Two forces from other sources move the water: *root pressure* and *transpiration pull.* The tips of the roots of plants have root hairs extending into the soil. Water molecules are usually found in higher concentration in the soil than in the root hairs. Therefore, water molecules move by osmosis from the soil into the root hair. The resulting increase in water concentration in the root hair causes water molecules to move into the next cell, and so on in sequential fashion to the xylem at the center of the root.

In addition, water is carried from the soil into the root by active transport. Therefore, root pressure is partly due to the concentration gradient from the soil to the cells in the center of the root and partly to the active transport of water by the living root cells.

Transpiration pull is brought about by the interplay of three factors: transpiration (evaporation of water from the leaves), osmosis, and the cohesion of water. Water is constantly being lost from the exposed cells of the leaves by transpiration. This lowers the concentration of water in the exposed cells. Water moves into these cells from the veins by osmosis, equalizing the concentrations. The whole column of water in the xylem of the veins is pulled upward because the water molecules cohere, that is, tend to cling to one another.

Minerals from the soil are brought to the xylem of the root by active transport and then moved with the water. This active movement of minerals helps to enhance the passage of water owing to osmosis. The motions described are all in one direction. The roots pick up the material from the supply in the soil and transport it to the rest of the plant, particularly the leaves where the materials are used or lost. Since the source is at one end and the site of utilization or loss is

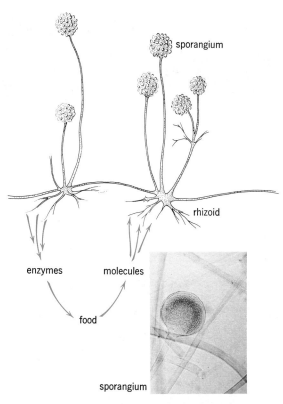

Figure 6.7. The bread mold exhibits extracellular digestion. The sporangia are reproductive structures.

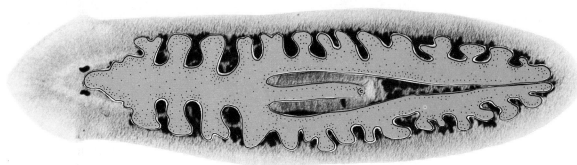

Figure 6.8. The extensive incomplete digestive tract of planaria is shown in blue. (Ward's Natural Science Establishment, Inc.)

Figure 6.9. The fish's digestive system is shown in blue. Specialized regions for digestion and absorption are present.

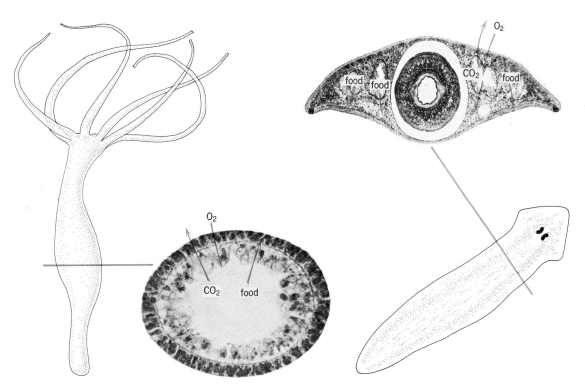

Figure 6.10. The gastrovascular cavity of Hydra *(left) and that of planaria (right) pass near each cell. (General Biological Supply House, Inc.)*

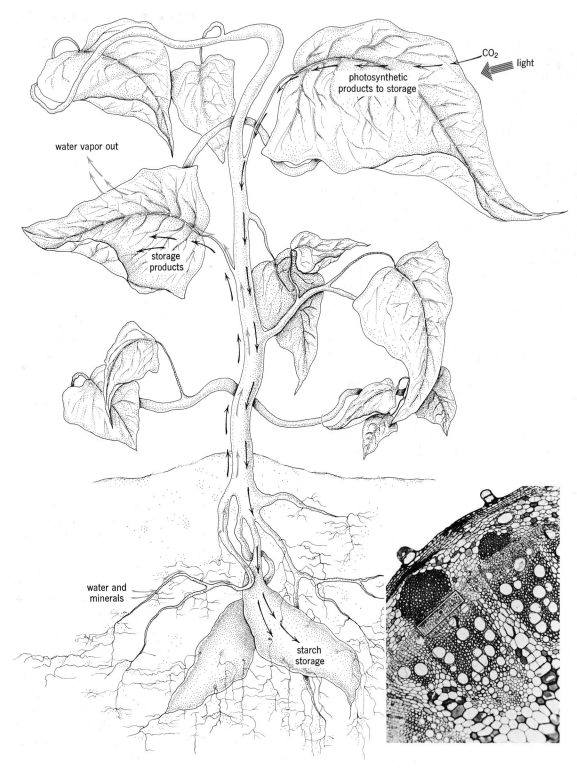

Figure 6.11. *The transport system of flowering plants. The xylem is indicated in blue and the phloem in black. The relationship of these is shown in the photograph at the lower right. (Ward's Natural Science Establishment, Inc.)*

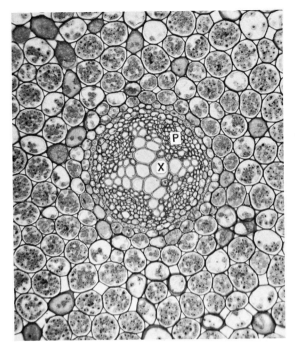

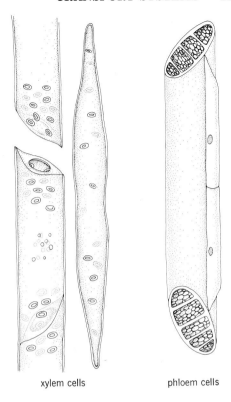

xylem cells   phloem cells

Figure 6.12. The detail of cells that make up xylem and phloem is shown schematically (right). The actual appearance of these cells in the cross section of a root is shown in the photomicrograph. (Xylem cell redrawn from Harry J. Fuller, The Plant World, *third ed., 1955, Holt, Rinehart and Winston, New York; photomicrograph of* Ranunculus *root, Ward's Natural Science Establishment, Inc.)*

at the other end, no return pathway is necessary. This is not a circulatory system.

The method by which the living cells of the phloem transport organic materials is not well understood. Diffusion and cytoplasmic flow probably play some part. Osmosis also may play a part in the transport of substances through the phloem. By active transport sugar molecules or other large molecules are moved into phloem cells at the site of their origin. This decreases the relative water concentration in these cells and additional water moves in by osmosis. Since a cell (particularly those with cell walls, as in plants) can only hold so much, the additional water drives the solution along the chain of tubelike cells of the phloem. At the point of the utilization of the organic materials, their removal will result in a lowering of the concentration of dissolved particles in the phloem cells and water will move out by osmosis.

The transport in phloem, unlike that in xylem, is in two directions. Since the organic material is originally produced in the leaves, most of the transport is away from the leaves to the rest of the plant. However, other organic substances are produced from carbohydrates in many parts of the plant, and these move from the site of origin to other regions.

Circulatory Systems. True circulatory systems occur in many animals. These generally have one or more specialized pumping vessels called hearts. The fluid base (blood) moves from the heart through the tissues and back to the heart in a circuit.

These systems are divided into two categories: open and closed systems. In an *open system* the blood is pumped a short distance from the heart in vessels and then into the spaces between cells (Figure 6.13a). It bathes the cells directly, exchanges materials with them by diffusion, and then returns to the heart. Open systems have a low blood pressure and rate of flow. In addition, the relative amounts of blood flowing to various structures are poorly controlled.

In a *closed system* the blood is always contained in vessels (Figure 6.13b). Consequently, the cells of the body are separated from the blood by the walls of the

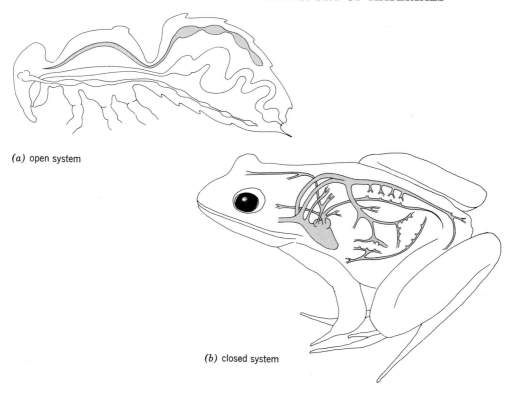

(a) open system

(b) closed system

Figure 6.13. Major vessels of circulatory systems. In the open system in insects (a) *blood is pumped by a large vessel into cavities in various parts of the body. The blood of a frog, which has a closed system* (b), *is contained within vessels.*

blood vessels and a space between the vessels and the cells. This space around the cells is filled with a fluid called *lymph*. Exchange of materials between the cells and the blood occurs through the lymph.

Blood pressure drives all constituents of the blood except the cells and the largest molecules (the proteins) through the walls of small vessels called *capillaries* into the lymph. By diffusion, each cell obtains from the lymph such substances as glucose, amino acids, and oxygen. Cellular waste products such as carbon dioxide and ammonia diffuse into the lymph.

For two reasons fluid must be constantly removed from the intercellular spaces. First, the concentration of cellular waste products in the lymph must be kept low. Second, more fluid is always being added to the lymph from the capillaries. If fluid were not removed, swelling would result. Part of this fluid exits by diffusion into the capillary ends near the veins.

The lymphatic system serves as the other fluid removal route. This system begins as small, blind vessels in the spaces between the cells. These vessels coalesce

to form a few large ones which empty the lymph into the blood near the heart. Fluid does not accumulate in the spaces around the cells but remains in circulation through the body. This allows adequate exchange of materials between the cells and the environment.

Since the blood is always in vessels, higher blood pressures are possible. By changing the relative sizes of the blood vessels, the blood flow to different portions of the body may be varied. Both factors mean that a greater supply of materials is regularly available to those cells that need it.

In mammals and birds a four-chambered heart is found in combination with a closed system. The freshly oxygenated blood from the lungs does not mix with venous blood but is repumped after passing through the lungs so that it reaches the tissues at higher pressures. When we consider that all these advantages are present, it is not surprising to find such constant high activity rates in many of these organisms.

The methods by which materials are treated and

transported depend on the following three character-istics of the organism: (1) its size and shape, (2) its activity rate, and (3) the habitat in which it lives. The structures an organism possesses are not distributed in random fashion but form a coordinated unit which allows the organism to succeed in its environment.

Principles

1. Transport systems are necessary when some of the organism's cells are too distant from the environment to obtain materials by diffusion.

2. The organism's activity, size, and habitat determine the nature of the digestive, respiratory, and transport systems.

Suggested Readings

Biddulph, Susann, and Orlin Biddulph, "The Circulatory System of Plants," *Scientific American,* Vol. 200 (February, 1959). Offprint No. 53, W. H. Freeman and Co., San Francisco.

Brooks, Steward M., *Basic Facts of Body Water and Ions.* Springer Publishing Co., New York, May, 1961.

Mayerson, H. S., "The Lymphatic System," *Scientific American,* Vol. 208 (June, 1963). Offprint No. 158, W. H. Freeman and Co., San Francisco.

Ray, Peter Martin, *The Living Plant,* Prentice-Hall, Englewood Cliffs, N. J., 1963, pp. 44–59, 70–77.

Schmidt-Nielsen, Knut, *Animal Physiology.* Second edition. Prentice-Hall, Englewood Cliffs, N. J., 1964, pp. 1–36.

Zimmermann, Martin H., "How Sap Moves in Trees," *Scientific American,* Vol. 208 (March, 1963). Offprint No. 154, W. H. Freeman and Co., San Francisco.

Zweifach, Benjamin W., "The Microcirculation of the Blood," *Scientific American,* Vol. 200 (January, 1959). Offprint No. 64, W. H. Freeman and Co., San Francisco.

Questions

1. Which lives in the richest oxygen environment, a water dweller or a land inhabitant? What is the major problem an organism faces as an air breather in contrast to one that obtains its oxygen from water?

2. Classify the devices used by organisms for extracting oxygen from the environment.

3. Do plants exhibit any specializations for the exchange of respiratory gases? Explain.

4. If an organism ingested a mixture of glycerol, amino acids, and glucose, would digestion be necessary? Why?

5. A tapeworm has neither a digestive tract nor a respiratory system. How does this multicellular organism respire and obtain food materials?

6. Do plants have digestive organs or digestive tracts? Do they carry out the process of digestion? Where?

7. Classify the kinds of digestive systems found in organisms.

8. What advantages may a complete digestive tract have for animals that show high activity rates? Why do large animals show this type of system?

9. Do plants have a transport system? If so, describe it.

10. If xylem consists of dead cells, how can it function?

11. Why should the xylem and phloem not be termed a circulatory system?

12. What functions are served by circulatory systems?

13. What advantages does a closed-type vascular system have over the open type? Which type is characteristic of higher animals, e.g., vertebrates?

CHAPTER VII

Control within Cells

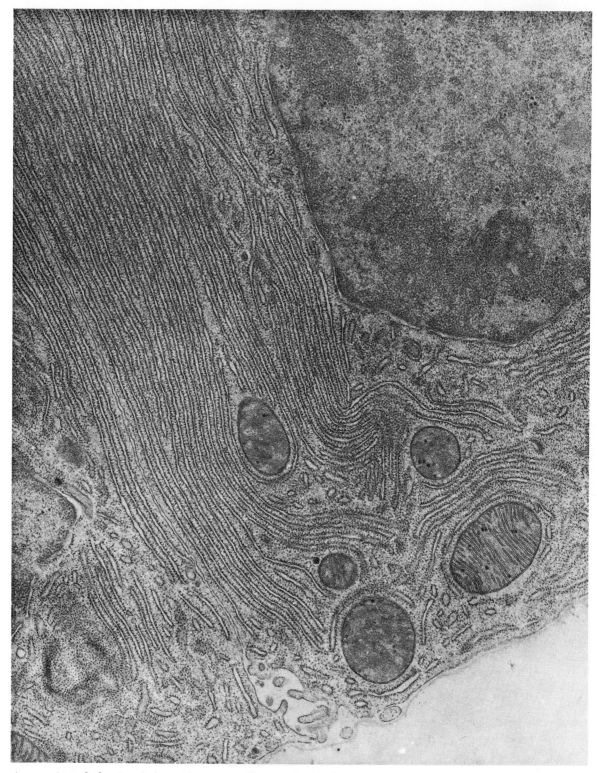

An extensive endoplasmic reticulum with numerous ribosomes. (Dr. Keith R. Porter.)

Control within Cells

The cell is the seat of many complex and varied reactions. Those reactions that are part of the basic mechanisms of energy transfer occur with few variations in every living cell. Other reactions result from the particular needs and activities of the cell that are related to its specialization. What mechanisms or processes control these reactions so that they are carried out in an orderly fashion? What mechanisms cause the available raw materials to follow one pathway on one occasion and another on some other occasion? What mechanisms account for differences in the activities of individual cells even though the basic energy transfer phenomena are the same? For answers to these questions we turn to some of the types of cellular control.

Source-Sink Phenomena

Let us first consider the control introduced by the susceptibility of the reactions to mass action or source-sink phenomena. The *law of mass action states that the rate of a reaction is proportional to the product of the concentrations of the reacting substances. An increase in the concentration of reactants increases the rate of reaction, while an increase in the concentration of the products decreases it.* An example from respiration helps to illustrate this law. If pyruvic acid were to accumulate in the cell, the accumulation should tend to slow down the reactions leading from PGAL to pyruvic acid because the concentration of

one of the products of these reactions has increased.

PGAL, however, is a reactant in many reactions in the cell. It is involved in respiration by way of pyruvic acid, transformed into glycerol and incorporated into fats, and synthesized into glucose and more complex carbohydrates. The law of mass action will affect each of these reactions. For example, when the pyruvic acid concentration increases, the reaction slows down and results in the higher concentration of PGAL. This increase in the concentration of PGAL causes an increase in the rates of the other reactions for which PGAL is a reactant.

In the cell this means that the accumulation of the end products of one reaction favors the occurrence of one or more other reactions. Conversely, the smaller the concentration of end products, the faster the reaction will be. This is a highly adaptive feature because the rate at which a substance will be produced is determined in part by the rate at which it is being used.

Why do the reactions leading from PGAL to products tend to move only in one direction, away from PGAL? There are two answers to this question. The name source-sink tells us that there is a source (photosynthesis in plants, material from outside the cell in animals) which is constantly introducing new PGAL into the cell and a sink (metabolic reactions) which is constantly changing the end products, or removing them from the cell. This activity tends to favor the reactions leading away from PGAL.

(a)

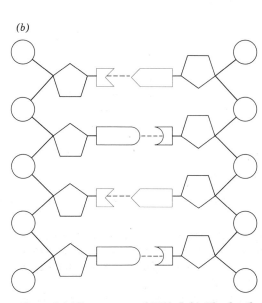

guanine

cytosine

adenine

thymine

(b)

Figure 7.1. The structure of DNA (left). The detail of a small segment is shown at the right. Each pentagon represents a sugar molecule and each circle indicates a phosphate.

molecules may be transformed into molecules of higher energy content.

Genetic Control

Not all cells show the same energy transfer reactions. Remember the differences between anaerobic respiration in yeast and muscle cells? Why do these differences occur? A simple way to answer this would be to say that not all cells have the same enzymes and therefore will not show the same reactions. This answer only begs the question. Why do not all cells have the same enzymes? This becomes apparent from examination of the interaction between the genetic material and the rest of the cell.

DNA Structure.   The genetic material of the cell constitutes the basic input of information that determines the activities of the cell. It is composed of very long DNA (*deoxyribonucleic acid*) molecules sur-

The amount of energy present in the molecules before and after the reaction also helps to determine the direction the reaction takes. Every reaction will tend to favor the production of the substance containing the smaller amount of energy unless some force supplies the energy to drive the reaction in the opposite direction. If energy is supplied from the outside, the

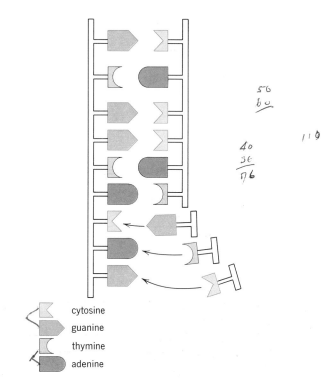

Figure 7.2. *Structural details of a nucleotide and the organic bases.*

nucleotide: deoxythymidine

bases

rounded by a protein coat. The information that controls the cell is included in the structure of the DNA. Some of the evidence for this statement will be given in Chapter XVII.

Every molecule of DNA is comprised of many nucleotides linked in a long chain (Figure 7.1). Each nucleotide contains a phosphate group, a five-carbon sugar (deoxyribose), and an organic base (see Figure 7.2). Bonds form between the phosphate group of one nucleotide and the sugar of the next nucleotide. The phosphate of this second nucleotide is bonded to the sugar of the third, and so forth—thus forming a long chain of nucleotide units each bonded from phosphate to sugar.

The bases of the nucleotides extend out from the phosphate-sugar chain. Four kinds of these bases are found in DNA: *adenine, cytosine, guanine,* and *thymine.* The four bases are all fairly similar and may occur in any order in the chain.

The DNA molecule is composed, however, of two of these chains of nucleotides spiraling around a common center to form a double helix. The bases of one chain are bonded by weak bonds (hydrogen bonds) to the bases of the other chain. These bonds form only between specific pairs of bases (see Figure 7.3). Adenine, in one chain, is always bonded to thymine in the other chain, and cytosine is always bonded to guanine.

cytosine

guanine

thymine

adenine

Figure 7.3. *Specific bonding of bases in DNA.*

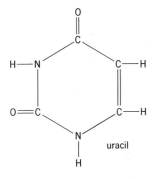

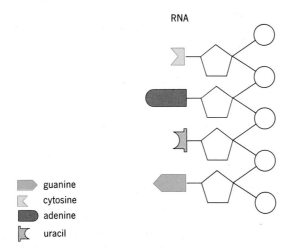

Figure 7.4. *The structure of uracil and of a segment of RNA.*

Because the bases will pair in only one way, the sequence of bases in one chain determines the sequence of bases in the other. Therefore we refer to the two chains as complements of each other. This theory for the structure of DNA was proposed by James Watson, a young American biologist, and Francis Crick, an English chemist. For this work they were awarded a Nobel Prize in 1962.

DNA Function.   DNA does not directly control cell activities. The directions contained in the DNA are translated into RNA molecules, which are similar to DNA. RNA (*ribonucleic acid*) is also composed of long chains of nucleotides connected by phosphate-to-sugar bonds. Similarly, we find four kinds of bases present in RNA. Three of them, adenine, cytosine, and guanine, are the same as those in DNA, but whereas thymine is found in DNA, a closely related base, *uracil,* takes its place in RNA (see Figure 7.4). The sugar present in RNA (ribose) is only slightly different from the one present in DNA (deoxyribose).

The DNA of the chromosomes serves as a pattern for the production of RNA. From the pool of free ribose-containing nucleotides in the cell, a complement to the DNA chain is built up by hydrogen bonds forming between the bases in the DNA and the free nucleotides. For most bases, this pairing occurs in the same way as in DNA: cytosine pairs with guanine and thymine with adenine, but because uracil replaces thymine in RNA, the DNA adenine becomes paired with uracil in the RNA.

After the phosphate-to-sugar bonds form, the new RNA molecule leaves the vicinity of the chromosomes and moves out into the cytoplasm. Thus far we have spoken simply of RNA. It now becomes necessary to distinguish between two different types, *transfer* RNA and *messenger* RNA, because they serve different functions in the cytoplasm.

(*i*) *Messenger RNA.*   Messenger RNA is a long, single-stranded molecule. Because the nucleotides line up in a specific order next to the DNA during messenger RNA production (Figure 7.5), messenger RNA will

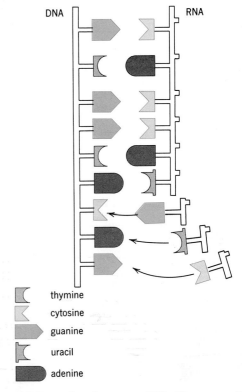

Figure 7.5. *Formation of messenger RNA. The pattern of bases in messenger RNA is controlled by the sequence of bases in the DNA molecule.*

contain in coded form the same information on cell activity as the DNA. Thus, the message from the DNA is carried to the cytoplasm by messenger RNA; hence its name. Since messenger RNA serves as a pattern by which proteins will be made, the resulting proteins will be those directed by the genetic information.

Recent experiments have clearly demonstrated the nature of the instructions carried by one specific type of messenger RNA. The experimenters worked with

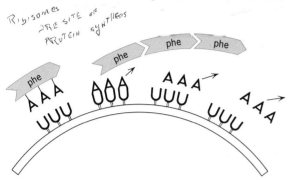

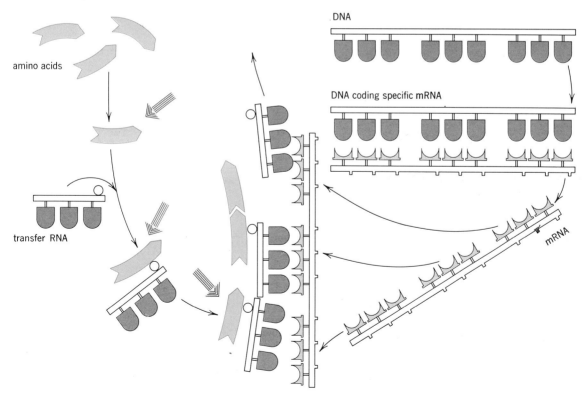

Figure 7.6. Results of an experiment using a messenger RNA containing only uracil. Only the amino acid phenylalanine will be incorporated into protein.

rabbits' immature red blood cells, which are mainly concerned with the production of hemoglobin. Using an ultracentrifuge they separated the messenger RNA and ribosomes from the other parts of the cells and placed them in an environment containing ATP, transfer RNA, and amino acids. The messenger RNA continued to synthesize hemoglobin from amino acids —but *only* hemoglobin and no other substances. This is evidence that a different messenger RNA controls the production of each kind of protein.

(2) *Transfer RNA.* Transfer RNA consists of much smaller molecules, which are also single-stranded but the strand is coiled about itself. It is said to exist in sixty-four different forms. Each kind of transfer RNA will combine with only one kind of amino acid. Since this RNA carries amino acids from any area in the cytoplasm to the messenger RNA, it is called transfer RNA.

Each transfer RNA has three bases on one end which serve to identify specific locations in the messenger RNA. This identification consists of hydrogen bonds between bases which pair in the pattern mentioned earlier: cytosine with guanine and adenine with uracil. For example, a transfer RNA having AAA

Figure 7.7. Summary of protein synthesis.

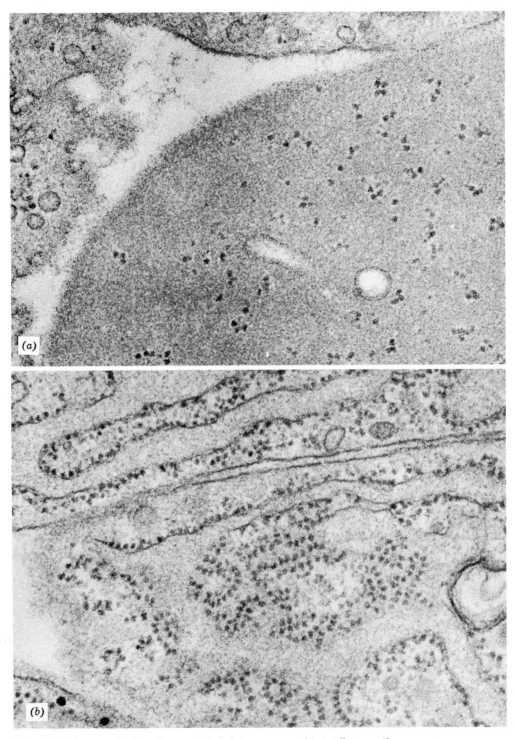

Figure 7.8. Ribosomes. (a) *The ribosomes, black dots, are arranged in small groups (from a cell of the rat heart,* ×79,000). (b) *In a young rat red blood cell, the association of ribosomes and endoplasmic reticulum is seen* (×79,000). (Dr. George E. Palade.)

(three consecutive adenines) at one end would combine only with a molecule of the amino acid phenylalanine, and line up with the messenger RNA only where UUU were present in the messenger RNA code (Figure 7.6). This coding of one amino acid by three nucleotides is called *triplet coding*. The specificity of this coding mechanism has been demonstrated by making synthetic messenger RNA from only uracil. The resulting protein contains only phenylalanine.

In order to understand the role these two types of RNA play in protein synthesis, let us follow their activities in the cell (Figure 7.7). A transfer RNA molecule picks up a specific type of amino acid molecule from the free amino acids in the cytoplasm. This acquisition expends the energy supplied by one ATP molecule. The transfer RNA now moves or transfers the amino acid to the locality of a messenger RNA. Because of the specific pairing of bases between these RNAs, a particular kind of amino acid will line up each time in the same places next to the messenger RNA. Each molecule of protein produced by this messenger RNA will have the same order of amino acids. After the amino acids have all been joined, the protein is released from the transfer RNA, which now moves away from the messenger RNA. This frees both kinds of RNA. Messenger RNA can now serve as the pattern for another molecule of protein, while transfer RNA can pick up another of the same kind of amino acid for incorporation into protein.

Two aspects of this process should be repeated for special emphasis. First, the location of each amino acid in the developing amino acid chain depends upon a sequence of three bases in the messenger RNA, and, therefore, indirectly on the sequence of bases in the DNA. Second, the sequence of amino acids in the chain determines what the protein will be. Any change in the sequence results in a different protein. Thus we see that the sequence of bases in DNA has been translated into specific kinds of protein.

Ribosomes have been known for some time to be the site of protein synthesis. How do they fit into this picture? Recently it has been discovered that ribosomes function in groups of three, five, seven, or more (Figure 7.8). It has been shown that a group of ribosomes attaches, one at a time, to a single messenger RNA molecule. Evidently as the ribosomes move along the messenger RNA they play a part in "zipping" the transfer RNAs to the messenger RNA.

It can now be seen that individual DNAs will produce different proteins. The questions asked at the outset of this chapter relate, however, not to control of protein production but to control of differing cell activities. We need only examine the roles that proteins play in the cell to complete this chain.

Proteins and Cell Activity

Let us consider three different classes of proteins: enzymatic proteins, structural proteins, and antibodies. In Chapter II we mentioned that all enzymes were at least partly protein. The protein portion of the enzyme is often responsible for determining whether the enzyme can affect a certain substrate. If we change the proteins being produced in a cell, we may change, in order, the enzymes being produced, the substances these enzymes can affect, the reactions that occur in that cell and the activity of the cell.

The role of structural proteins in affecting cell activity may not be as obvious. One example should point out their importance. Muscle cells contain a specific pair of proteins called *actin* and *myosin*. The activity of this pair is dependent upon their structural nature and interaction. If the cell is prevented from producing actin or myosin, it cannot contract. Similarly, modification of a protein that plays a role in any cell structure may modify cell activity. Think of the importance a change in one of the proteins involved in membrane structure might have for many of a cell's components.

Antigens and Antibodies. The presence of an *antigen,* a foreign protein, usually causes the formation of an antibody (see Figure 7.9). This response plays a major role in defense against disease. If antibodies capable of combating a disease-causing organism are present, they may completely inactivate the foreign organism and prevent the disease from developing. In one type of human leukemia, however, a change occurs in the genetic information of the cell which brings about two drastic changes in activity. One kind of white blood cell is no longer able to mature normally. This lowers the disease resistance in the body. In addition, these cells produce antibodies that react with the red blood cells of the body. This results in the mass destruction of red blood cells and the marked anemia characteristic of many leukemias.

Viral Effects. The changes in cell activity brought about by viral diseases can be understood in the context of the DNA-RNA-protein synthesis scheme of control. A virus is really only a DNA or RNA molecule with a protein coat (Figures 7.10 and 7.11). Since the protein contains sulfur but no phosphorus, and since

antibody production

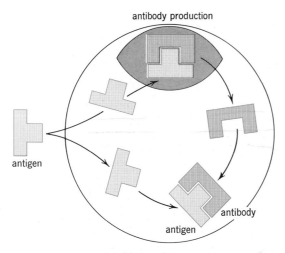

antigen

antibody

antigen

Figure 7.9. When an antigen enters the body it stimulates anti-
body production. The antibodies are then available to interact
with subsequent antigen molecules (below).

the nucleic acid contains phosphorus but no sulfur, it is possible to show that only the nucleic acid enters the cell. In order to demonstrate this, experimenters labeled some viruses with radioactive sulfur and others with radioactive phosphorus (Figure 7.12). Each group was allowed to infect a culture of bacteria. The bacteria were agitated to remove any external viruses, then washed and checked for radioactivity. Only those infected with the phosphorus-labeled viruses showed any radioactivity in the cell. Consequently, we know that the viral DNA but not its protein enters the cell.

The additional nucleic acid acts like new genetic information. It causes the production of new viruses (Figure 7.13). At the same time, the production of bacterial protein falls to almost nothing. The usual synthetic and energy-supply mechanisms are all diverted from maintenance and growth of the cell to production of viruses. After a large number of new viruses have been produced in the cell, the cell breaks open, releasing viral particles capable of invading other cells.

To exert this effect on the cell, the virus must cause the production of its own messenger RNA. This RNA must be able to carry out synthetic reactions at a higher rate than the cell's own RNA. Experiments with the messenger RNA from one particular virus show that this RNA does direct the incorporation of amino acids into protein much more rapidly than the RNA from the bacteria which the virus infects.

Cancer. A different effect on cell growth is found in cancer. The cells grow and divide without apparent

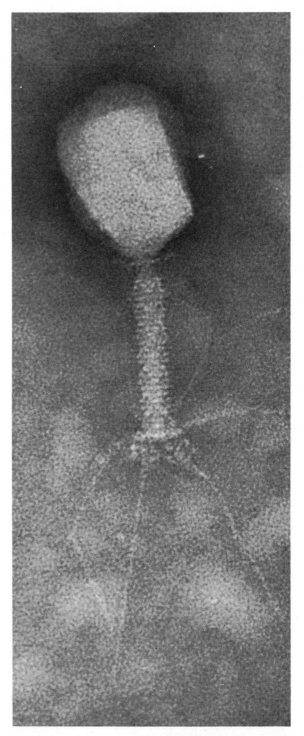

Figure 7.10. A virus that infects bacteria magnified 450,000
times by an electron microscope. (Dr. Thomas F. Anderson.)

Bacteria phage to heat

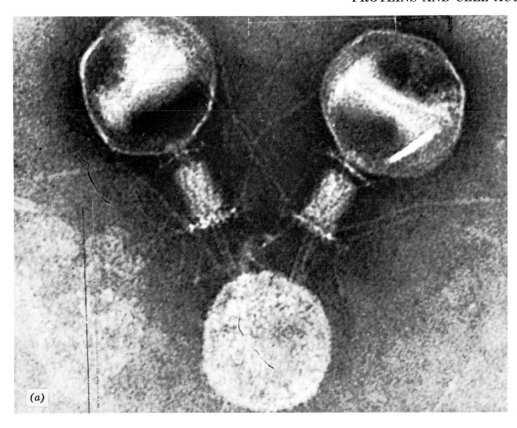

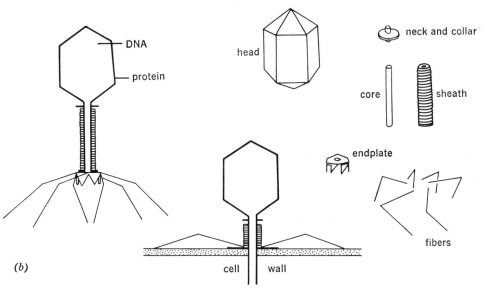

Figure 7.11. (a) In another bacterial virus the sheath is contracted (×365,000). (Dr. Thomas F. Anderson.) (b) A diagram illustrating the parts of the virus and its attachment to a bacterial wall (center). (Reprinted with permission, Copyright © 1965 by Scientific American, Inc. All rights reserved.)

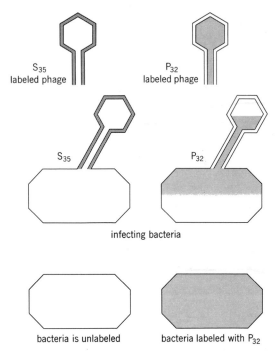

S_{35}
labeled phage

P_{32}
labeled phage

S_{35}

P_{32}

infecting bacteria

bacteria is unlabeled

bacteria labeled with P_{32}

Figure 7.12. An experiment showing that only the nucleic acid enters the bacterial cell.

control. This brings them into sharp conflict with the rest of the organism's cells, which are under normal control. Yet the cause of many sorts of cancers is known to be a virus. Even leukemia may fall into this category.

The same scheme of takeover by a new nucleic acid control system may be applied to viral cancers. It is interesting to trace a few of the effects of this system on cell activity. Familiar effects of cancer are increased protein synthesis resulting in more rapid cell growth and division, a higher metabolic rate, and lack of coordination with surrounding cells. However, certain structural changes may also be brought about. One of the most instructive examples of such change may be found in some forms of cancer cells. It was observed that nearly all respiration in these cells occurred anaerobically, regardless of the amount of oxygen available. Later work showed that there was a marked shift in the activity of the enzymes present. Here a change in the control of protein production resulted in a modification in enzyme activity and in an abnormal metabolism in the cell.

In summary, two very different types of control exist within cells. In one, genetic control determines *generally* what the cell will do within fairly narrow limits. The information contained in triplet code in DNA is translated into messenger RNA by the specific pairing of bases. The messenger RNA serves as a pattern which is translated into a specific kind of protein by the interaction of a triplet of bases in each transfer RNA with those in the messenger RNA.

In the other type of control, changes in the environment or changed conditions within the cell modify the cell's activity within these genetically imposed limits. Mass action phenomena present one example of the modifications by which the amount of a substance present in a cell helps determine how much of that substance is produced. In addition, the functions of other cells modify cell activity. Coordinated activity among many cells may result.

Principles

1. The relative concentrations of materials in a cell affect the rate and direction of metabolism.

2. DNA exercises the ultimate endogenous control over cell activities.

3. DNA's control is expressed by the synthesis of specific proteins. This control is mediated by messenger and transfer RNA and the ribosomes.

Suggested Readings

Beadle, George W., "Structure of the Genetic Material and the Concept of the Gene," in *This Is Life,* edited by W. H. Johnson and W. C. Steere. Holt, Rinehart and Winston, New York, 1962, pp. 185–211.

Crick, F. H. C., "The Structure of the Hereditary Material," *Scientific American,* Vol. 191 (October, 1954). Offprint No. 5, W. H. Freeman and Co., San Francisco.

Crick, F. H. C., "The Genetic Code," *Scientific American,* Vol. 207 (October, 1962). Offprint No. 123, W. H. Freeman and Co., San Francisco.

Ingram, Vernon M., "How Do Genes Act?" *Scientific American,* Vol. 198 (January, 1958). Offprint No. 104, W. H. Freeman and Co., San Francisco.

Nirenberg, Marshall W., "The Genetic Code: II," *Scientific American,* Vol. 208 (March, 1963). Offprint No. 153, W. H. Freeman and Co., San Francisco.

Rich, Alexander, "Polyribosomes," *Scientific American,* Vol. 209 (December, 1963). Offprint No. 171, W. H. Freeman and Co., San Francisco.

Spiegelman, S., "Hybrid Nucleic Acids," *Scientific American,* Vol. 210 (May, 1964). Offprint No. 183, W. H. Freeman and Co., San Francisco.

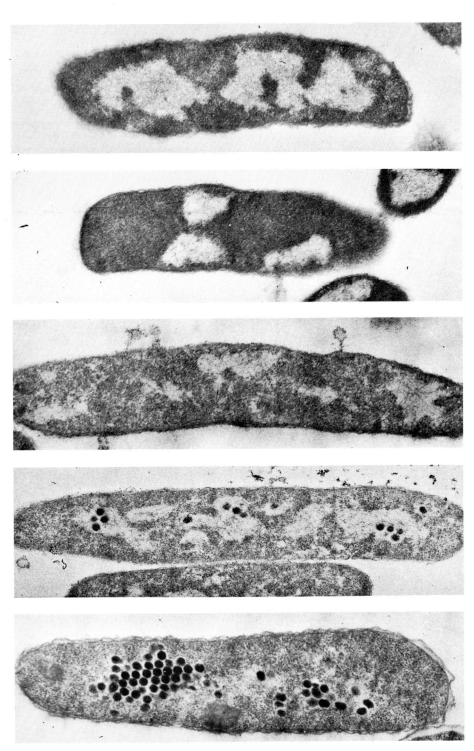

Figure 7.13. The changes a bacterium undergoes during viral infection (top to bottom). The third photograph shows the protein coats on the bacterial surface. In the bottom two photographs the black hexagons are new viruses produced in the cell. (Dr. Edouard Kellenberger, Université de Genève Institut de Biologie Moleculaire, Laboratoires de Biophysique et de Biochimie Genetique.)

Questions

1. Why is the analogy of source-sink an appropriate one for the law of mass action?

2. In what way is a DNA molecule analogous to a twisted ladder?

3. In what chemical sense is DNA a monotonous molecule? (Compare to protein.)

4. If you determined the amount of one of the bases, e.g., adenine, in a DNA sample, what would you know about the other bases?

5. The chapter specifies that there are sixty-four possible forms of transfer RNA. See if you can determine how this number was derived.

6. Trace the steps involved in the translation of a DNA code in the nucleus into an enzyme out in the cytoplasm.

7. Ribosomes are usually abundant in cells. Why is this necessary? Would you term this condition an adaptation?

8. What are three different sorts of proteins?

9. How does knowledge of the structure of DNA aid researchers in understanding the activity of viruses?

10. What is the consequence, in general terms, of altering a DNA or RNA "code" in a cell?

11. If DNA controls cellular activities, does the cellular environment play any role? Why?

Wed before Thanksgiving

7 8 9 10 11

Control by Chemical Agents

A mangrove crab. Hormonal control of molting has been studied in animals like this. (Jane Burton, Photo Researchers, Inc.)

Control by Chemical Agents

Observing the control of the cell's many activities, we learn a number of things about how its numerous reactions are kept in harmony. The scheme for controlling these cellular activities is called *coordination*. This regulation which involves DNA, RNA, protein synthesis, and control of source-sink phenomena, appears in every type of cell. Most of the coordination we see, however, concerns the activities of the many cells composing a multicellular organism. This coordination may be achieved in two ways: through chemical agents (hormones and related chemicals) and through nerve impulses.

Kinds of Hormones

Chemical agents that play a role in coordination show remarkable diversity in both their chemical nature and their mode of activity. In order to qualify as a hormone, a chemical agent must be produced by specialized cells (or cell) and participate in coordination elsewhere in the body. As we study examples of chemical coordination, however, we shall find many coordinators that do not fit this definition of a hormone. Some are clearly not hormones, whereas others are close to being so. All these agents demonstrate the great variety and wide distribution of chemical coordinating systems. As we know more about the hormones in mammals than in other groups, our general discussion will be based upon them.

The chemical structure of mammalian hormones

varies greatly (Figure 8.1 and Table 8.1). Three general groups are represented. The simplest hormones are composed of modified amino acids or small groups of amino acids. Examples of these are adrenalin and the hormones released by the posterior pituitary gland. Somewhat larger than the amino acid hormones are the steroid hormones. These are relatives of the fats. Cortisone, estrogen, and testosterone are all members of this group. The third and largest group of hormones are proteins. They range in size from smaller molecules, such as insulin, to very large molecules like gonad-stimulating hormones and growth hormones. All of the hormones from the anterior pituitary gland are proteins.

In mammals hormones coordinate a wide range of activities. Many of these coordinating roles, such as the part that insulin plays in carbohydrate metabolism, are well known. When the glucose concentration of the blood increases, more insulin is released by special cells in the pancreas. This release helps to move glucose from the blood into body cells, particularly the cells in the liver, and reduces the blood glucose concentration. Insulin is one of the few proteins whose structure we know in detail.

Some of the hormones produced by the adrenal cortex are important in the control of salt and water metabolism. One of their effects is the reduction of swelling in arthritic joints, which is accomplished medically by injection of cortisone. It is important to note

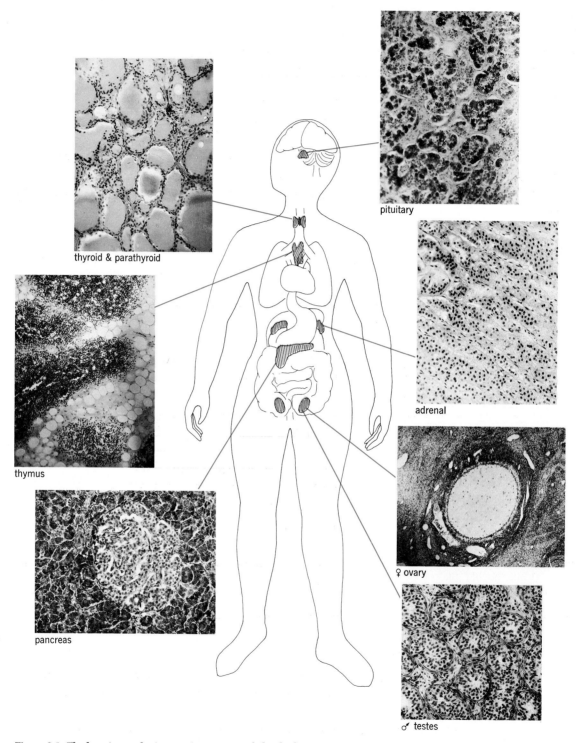

thyroid & parathyroid

pituitary

thymus

adrenal

pancreas

♀ ovary

♂ testes

Figure 8.1. The location and microscopic structure of glands that secrete some important hormones in man.

Table 8.1 Major Endocrine Tissues and Hormones of Man

Gland or Tissue	Hormone	Major Function of Hormone
Thyroid	Thyroxine	Stimulates rate of oxidative metabolism and regulates general growth and development.
Parathyroid	Parathormone	Regulates the levels of calcium and phosphorus in the blood.
Pancreas (Islets of Langerhans)	Insulin	Plays a central role in regulating the carbohydrate metabolism of the body; regulates fat storage.
Adrenal medulla	Epinephrine (adrenalin)	Various "emergency" effects on blood, muscle, temperature.
Adrenal cortex	Cortisone and related hormones	Controls carbohydrate, protein, mineral, salt, and water metabolism.
Anterior pituitary	1. Thyrotropic 2. Adrenocorticotropic 3. Growth hormone 4. Gonadotropic	1. Stimulates thyroid gland functions. 2. Stimulates development and secretion of adrenal cortex. 3. Stimulates body weight and rate of growth of skeleton. 4. Stimulates gonads.
Posterior pituitary	1. Oxytocin 2. Vasopressin	1. Causes contraction of some smooth muscle. 2. Inhibits excretion of water from the body by way of urine.
Ovary (follicle)	Estrogen	Influences development of sex organs and female characteristics.
Ovary (corpus luteum)	Progesterone	Influences menstrual cycle, prepares uterus for pregnancy; maintains pregnancy.
Uterus (placenta)	Estrogen and progesterone	Function in maintenance of pregnancy.
Testis	Androgens (testosterone)	Responsible for development and maintenance of sex organs and secondary male characteristics.
Digestive system	Several gastrointestinal	Integration of digestive processes.

After A. Nason, *Modern Biology,* 1965, John Wiley and Sons, New York.

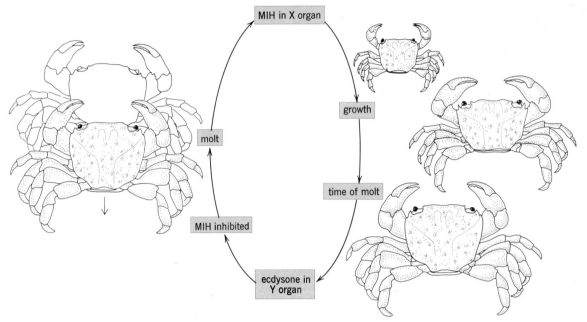

Figure 8.2. Hormonal control of molting in crabs.

that the result is only a relief of symptoms and not a cure for the disease.

Other types of activities coordinated by hormones involve many separate organs and mechanisms. One of these, reproduction, will be discussed later in the chapter.

Some Techniques of Study

Usually when we talk about chemical coordinating agents we think of examples which are truly hormonal. That is, they fulfill all the criteria of the definition. Both of the agents which control molting (ecdysis) in crabs are true hormones (Figure 8.2). One of these, *ecdysone,* causes the complex set of phenomena that accompanies actual molting. The other, *molt inhibiting hormone* (MIH), prevents the production of ecdysone. Under normal circumstances MIH is produced for a time as growth takes place. As the time of molt approaches the amount of MIH secreted falls, terminating the inhibition of ecdysone production. Ecdysone is released into the body fluid by the Y-organ, a small gland which produces it, and its increasing amount brings about the molt.

Experiments have been performed in which the X-organ, another small gland producing MIH, is removed. This removal eliminates the hormone that inhibits ecdysone production. The continuous production of ecdysone causes the crab to molt in rapid

succession without much growth. Death generally results.

If we grind up X-organs and inject their extract into a crab from which the X-organ has been removed, we find that we can prevent molt as long as we continue the injections. This set of experiments involving removal of the X-organ and replacement of the hormone by the injection of an extract demonstrates the classical method of determining whether a gland actually secretes a hormone.

In important additional control experiments called sham operations the same areas in the animal are cut as during removal of the gland. These experiments show that it is not the damage done to the animal by the surgery, but the actual removal of the gland that brings about the observed effects.

The action of MIH in the control of molting of crabs introduces one further fact about chemical coordinating systems. Many chemical coordinators prevent some activity from occurring, that is, they are inhibitors. Coordination can thus be achieved through inhibition as well as through stimulation. Notice that the definition of a hormone does *not* state whether the chemical agent has an inhibitory or stimulatory function.

The opposite effect on molt may be obtained by removing the Y-organ. Growth continues until the animal fills the external skeleton. MIH production de-

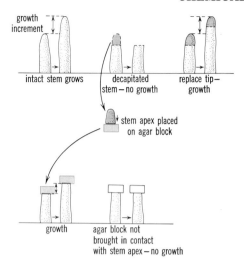

growth increment

intact stem grows

decapitated stem — no growth

replace tip — growth

stem apex placed on agar block

growth

agar block not brought in contact with stem apex — no growth

Figure 8.3. Effects of the removal of stem tips on growth in plants. (After Arthur W. Galston, The Life of The Green Plant, second ed., 1964, Prentice-Hall, Englewood Cliffs, N. J.)

creases but no molt is possible without ecdysone. Whenever we inject ecdysone into crabs, molt ensues. This shows that the Y-organ produced ecdysone, which stimulates molt, and that the MIH does not inhibit ecdysone's action but only its production.

Stimulating and inhibiting substances are also found in flowering plants. Of these, plant-growth hormones have been studied more than any others. Growth in the stem tips of plants results from the action of a hormone produced by the tip of the growing stem itself. Diffusing through the cells of the stem this hormone causes their elongation and then specialization into the various cell types found in a mature stem.

Removal of the stem tip halts growth. Replacement of the tip, or an agar block on which the tip has been allowed to stand, will cause growth to resume (Figure 8.3). An inverted stem tip has no stimulating effect, because the hormone only moves away from the original stem tip regardless of which way the stem is oriented. This is another method employed to discover whether a chemical agent is present.

When we look at the result of removal of the stem tip, we think of many possible explanations. The cessation of growth could be caused by:

(1) damage to the cells by cutting;

(2) loss of the contact between the cells in the tip and in the rest of the stem;

(3) removal of the source of a chemical which stimulates growth.

An experiment must be designed to test each possi-

bility. Since simple replacement of the cut tip results in the resumption of growth at a near normal rate, we can rule out the first explanation. As to the second possibility, we are able to achieve nearly normal growth from the stem again by inserting an agar block between the stem tip and the stump. Placing the stem tip on the agar block allows a chemical to diffuse into the block, which later moves into the stem to produce growth. Resumption of growth shows that contact between the stem and stem tip is unnecessary. Therefore, we are left with the third possibility: a chemical agent diffuses from the tip down the stem and stimulates growth.

The conclusive experiment involves placing agar blocks on two sets of stems. One group of blocks previously had stem tips resting on them, while the other group did not. Since growth resumes only in stems of the first set, we can eliminate the possibility that the pressure of the agar block against the stem is the stimulating agent. Clearly, some chemical must be involved. In the 1920s, F. W. Went obtained similar results from this type of experimental analysis involving the sheath that surrounds the growing stem in grass seedlings. Since then growth hormones called *auxins* have been isolated and many additional experiments carried out to clarify man's understanding of their action.

Synthetic auxins of many kinds are now available and are used commercially. Many weed killers belong to this group. The application of a large additional supply of hormones causes rapid growth and then death. The mechanism of this action is unknown.

Like many other hormones, auxins have different effects on different parts of the organism. A concentration of them which will stimulate stem growth will often inhibit the growth of roots.

Chemical Coordination and the Environment

Probably the most widely known and best understood examples of chemical coordination occur in the control of reproductive activity in the vertebrates. We find three different sites, the gonad, pituitary, and brain, all secreting hormones that are involved in this control.

Many of the things we associate with reproduction are due to the hormones that are produced by gonads. Examples of secondary sex characteristics (any characteristics of the sex, except gonads, are called secondary) are the differences between sexes in shape, color, or behavior. For example, in a male vertebrate

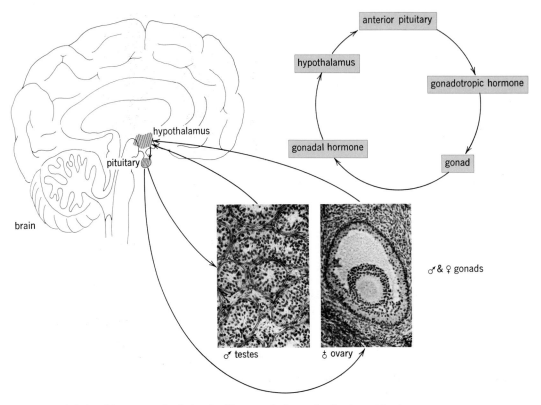

Figure 8.4. Relationships among glands involved in control of reproduction in vertebrates.

the testes produce *androgens,* male sex hormones, which are released into the blood stream. These hormones cause development of typical male structures, body form, and coloration as well as male behavior patterns for the species.

Androgens also affect some cells in the part of the base of the brain called the hypothalamus (Figure 8.4). These nerve cells produce a hormone (a neurosecretion) which is released into the blood. The only known activity of this neurosecretion is the stimulation of the cells in the anterior pituitary gland that produce gonadotropic (gonad stimulating) hormones. These hormones stimulate the testes to produce sperm and androgens, thus completing the cycle of action.

In this cycle hypothalamic cells stimulate the anterior pituitary cells, which then stimulate the cells of the gonads. These in turn inhibit the activity of the hypothalamic cells. All of this activity occurs by means of hormones. Throughout the cycle a nearly constant level of hormone production is maintained. If the amount of androgens rises above a certain level, the hypothalamic cells become inhibited and produce a smaller amount of hormone; there is less gonadotropic hormone from the pituitary and, consequently, less androgens. When the level of androgens drops, the inhibition of the hypothalamic cells is reduced, and they stimulate the pituitary to release a little more gonadotropic hormone. Balance is thus achieved. Such a mechanism—by which the controlling element is itself controlled by the element it controls—is called a *feedback* mechanism. This type of regulation is typical of hormonal systems.

We know, however, that the level of hormones involved in reproduction does not always remain the same. Rather, there is usually a distinct reproductive season and then a season during which the reproductive structures are inactive. How is the hypothalamic-anterior pituitary–gonad system of reproductive control stimulated into activity at some times and inhibited at other times?

Some excellent research into this problem has been done with the initiation of breeding in birds. W. Rowan's experiments in the 1920s showed that the gonad development and breeding behavior of birds

auxin Plant hormone

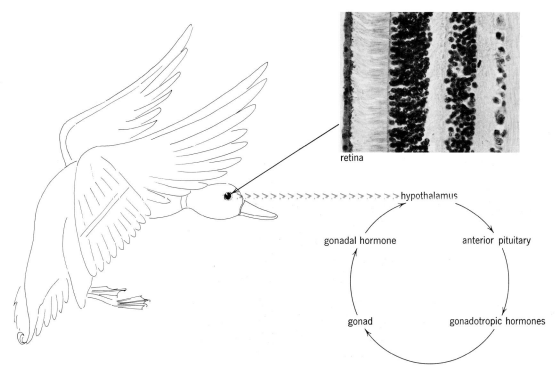

retina

gonadal hormone — hypothalamus — anterior pituitary — gonadotropic hormones — gonad

Figure 8.5. Light affects reproduction via the retina and hypothalamus.

was stimulated by exposure to an increase in the number of hours of light per day. Since then, through the experiments of many biologists, it has been shown that the increased day length is detected by receptors in the retina of the eye (Figure 8.5). The nerve impulses from the retina stimulate the activity of the neurosecretory cells in the hypothalamus through some unknown neural pathway. The hormones produced stimulate production of gonadotropic hormones. The factor that initiates the whole gamut of reproductive activities is the increase of day length.

We thus see that two mechanisms are responsible for control of the hormones that coordinate reproductive activity. The first we discussed in relation to feedback mechanism, which helps maintain, at a constant level, the hormones from the gonads, hypothalamus, and anterior pituitary. Initiation, modification, or termination of these hormonal processes are controlled by the second mechanism, the nervous system, through the secretion of hormones by certain nerve cells. Control exerted by the nervous system synchronizes the activity of chemical coordinating systems with environmental changes.

Interorganismic Control

Some chemicals produced by plants inhibit the growth of other plants. These phytotoxic materials are released into the soil and then diffuse from the plant. The concentration of these materials drops as the distance from the plant increases. Their secretion prevents the growth of other plants nearby. This action results in the spacing of plants and less rigorous competition for needed resources. A desert shrub found in the southwestern United States, brittlebrush, is a good example (Figure 8.6). Its leaves produce a toxic chemical which is carried into the soil by rain and by dropping leaves. This chemical prevents the growth of some species of plants around the brittlebrush, but unlike some other phytotoxic materials, it does not prohibit the growth of other brittlebrush individuals. This agent cannot be called a hormone, because it does not act within the body of the organism that produces it.

Other chemical agents similar to hormones that help to control activities of separate organisms are also found in animals. The sex that develops in slipper shells is influenced by the presence or absence of a mature female in the area in which the larvae settle.

Figure 8.6. Brittlebrush. Notice the bare area around the base of the plant. (Dr. Mildred Mathias.)

If a female is not already present, the larvae differentiate into about 50 per cent females and 50 per cent males. If a female is present, a chemical agent which she releases into the water influences the sex differentiation process so that about 95 per cent of the larvae settling in that area become males. This evidently increases the probability of matings occurring.

DNA and Chemical Control

In order to understand chemical control, we must discuss its relationship to the regulation of activity within the cell and to the production of chemical agents. This process is seen clearly in the unusual life cycle of one kind of slime mold (Figure 8.7). Single cells called *myxamoebae* are amoeboid and move about independently. These single cells then congregate, forming a sluglike mass (pseudoplasmodium) which moves and grows in a coordinated manner. Eventually the pseudoplasmodium stops, produces a stalk, and then a spore-bearing mass. The spores produce new myxamoebae if they land in a suitable environment.

What prompts the independent myxamoebae to aggregate? Some unknown factor causes an individual cell to produce a chemical agent called *acrasin*. This substance diffuses from the initiating cell and affects other cells by causing them to move toward the initiating cell and to produce more acrasin (Figure 8.8). Soon a large number of cells aggregate into a mass, forming the pseudoplasmodium.

Although the structure of acrasin is not known, it is obvious that the myxamoebae must have certain enzymes present in order to produce acrasin. The presence of these enzymes results from the activity of DNA through RNA and the synthesis of the enzymes. The activities of the myxamoebae are coordinated by chemicals produced under the control of DNA in other cells.

An interesting demonstration of a mechanism by

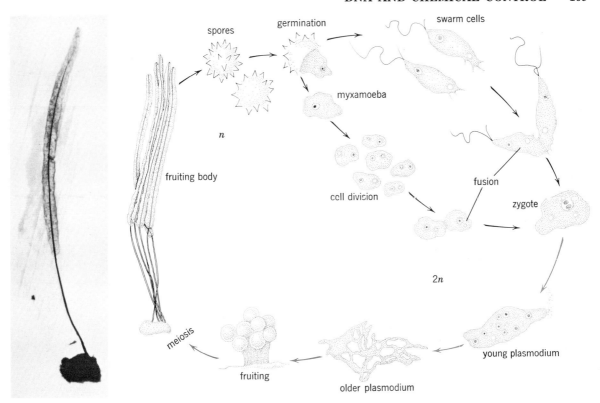

Figure 8.7. Life cycle of a slime mold.

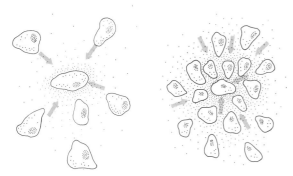

Figure 8.8. Initial stages in the aggregation of myxamoebae. Black dots indicate the concentration of acrasin and the arrows show the direction of cell movement.

which a hormone affects cells is found in female mammals. Phenomena similar to those found in male vertebrates control the ovary. The estrogens and progesterones (female sex hormones), which the ovary produces, cause growth of the mammary glands. The messenger RNA content of the cells in these glands increases with an increase in sex hormones. The pos-

sible relationships of larger amounts of messenger RNA to more rapid protein synthesis and to greater growth is obvious. This hypothesis, that hormones in general act by increasing messenger RNA production, is an attractive one.

Principles

1. Chemical coordinating mechanisms control activities at all levels from the cell to the population.

2. These chemical agents are either carried by fluids or move through the environment.

3. The amount of a chemical coordinating agent is usually controlled by some aspect of the process that it controls, that is, by a feedback mechanism.

Suggested Readings

Galston, Arthur H., *The Life of the Green Plant.* Second edition. Prentice-Hall, Englewood Cliffs, N. J., 1964, pp. 54–80.

Jacobson, Martin and Morton Beroza, "Insect Attractants," *Scientific American,* Vol. 211 (August, 1964).

Naylor, Aubrey W., "The Control of Flowering," *Scientific American,* Vol. 186 (May, 1952). Offprint No. 113, W. H. Freeman and Co., San Francisco.

Salisbury, Frank B., "Plant Growth Substances," *Scientific American,* Vol. 196 (April, 1957). Offprint No. 110, W. H. Freeman and Co., San Francisco.

Went, F. W., "Plant Growth and Plant Hormones," in *This Is Life,* edited by W. H. Johnson and W. C. Steere. Holt, Rinehart and Winston, New York, 1962, pp. 213–253.

Questions

1. At what level (cell, tissue, organ, etc.) do chemical coordinating substances operate? Support your answer with examples.

2. What is an example of a hormonelike chemical that travels through the environment rather than through body fluids?

3. Would you call this a mechanism for *coordination* or for *control?*

4. Why is it necessary for crabs to molt at intervals?

5. Are ecdysone and MIH antagonistic hormones? What causes each to be produced or to cease its action? Can you name other hormonal control mechanisms that function in this manner? Can you name any that do not?

6. What evidence indicates that plants also have hormonelike control mechanisms?

7. What advantage does a desert plant gain by releasing toxic chemicals into the soil?

8. Explain the role of feedback mechanisms in the control of reproduction.

9. Hormone production can be strongly influenced by the organism's environment. How do birds illustrate this?

10. Is acrasin a hormone? Does acrasin fulfill every part of the definition of a hormone? Would you call the independent cells part of the same body or not? Does acrasin travel by way of body fluids?

Control by Nervous Systems

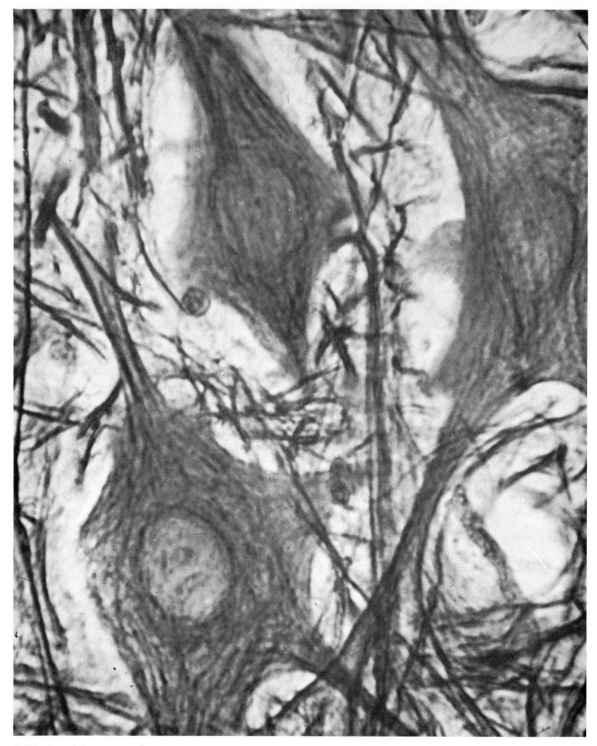

Cell bodies of three nerve cells.

CHAPTER IX

Control by Nervous Systems

Of the two types of coordinating systems, the nervous system is the more familiar to the general public. The operation of the nervous system and its relationship to the chemical coordinating systems are complex, but an understanding of both is essential for an insight into control phenomena in animals.

The specialized cells (neurons) that conduct nerve impulses in the nervous system are all somewhat similar in structure. Each neuron consists of a nerve cell body containing a nucleus, and of one or more cytoplasmic processes called fibers. These long fibers reflect the specialization of nerve cells for transmission of nerve impulses. The nerves found in higher animals are bundles of these fibers and their sheathing cells. The nerve cell bodies are found in or near the central nervous system.

The cells of the nervous system are not all alike, and they do not all have the same function (Figure 9.1). Certain ones have the task of picking up various changes in the environment (stimuli). These cells are called *receptors*. They change the energy of the stimulus into energy that is used to initiate nerve impulses. The first nerve cell receiving the impulse directly from the receptor is called the *sensory neuron*. Because receptors are in contact with only one end of the sensory neuron, this helps to insure the one-way transmission of the impulse through the nervous system. From the sensory neuron, the impulse may pass through a number of *association neurons*, the name applied to all nerve cells between the sensory neuron and the ultimate neuron. The final nerve cell that carries out the appropriate action in transmitting the

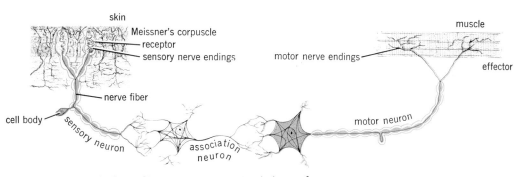

Figure 9.1. Structural relationships among sensory, association, and motor neurons.

113

impulse to the effector—usually a muscle—is called the *motor neuron.*

The Nerve Impulse

When a nerve fiber is at rest, that is, when it is not carrying an impulse, there is an unequal distribution of ions between the inside and outside of the cell mem-

brane (Figure 9.2). Sodium ions (Na^+) are found in high concentration outside the cell and in low concentration inside the cell. Conversely, potassium (K^+) shows a high concentration inside the cell and a low concentration outside the cell. The outside of the fiber is positively charged in contrast to the inside, which is negatively charged. The negative charges on the in-

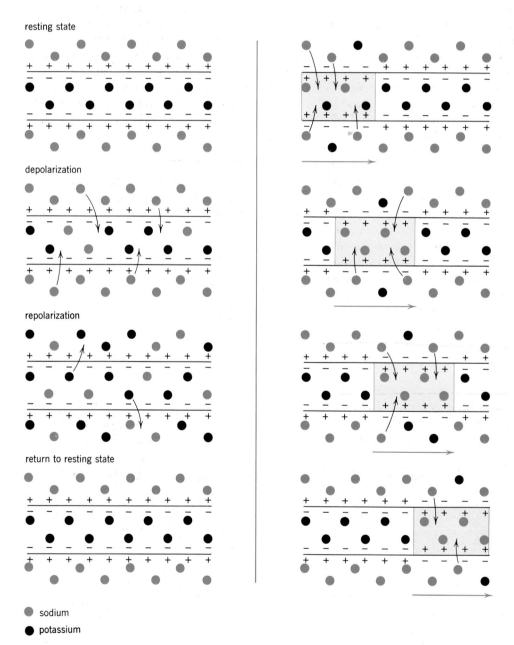

resting state

depolarization

repolarization

return to resting state

● sodium

● potassium

Figure 9.2. The events during conduction of a nervous impulse. The illustration on the left shows the movement of ions at a single point on the nerve fiber. Transmission along the fiber is indicated at the right.

side are associated mostly with chloride ions and large organic molecules. Since membranes characteristically maintain the separation of charged particles, the resulting difference in charge across the membrane is called the *membrane potential* or *resting potential*. The sodium ions outside the cell tend to move in by diffusion. Potassium ions tend to diffuse in the opposite direction. However, the cell actively extrudes the sodium ions and tends to accumulate potassium ions. This maintains the resting potential.

As the train of events that we call the nerve impulse starts at any one place on the fiber, a change in the cell membrane's permeability to sodium occurs. Prior to this time the membrane has let very little sodium through; suddenly the sodium is able to pass freely. Sodium ions rush into the cell. Since each sodium ion is positively charged, this movement of charged particles into the cell results in a positive charge on the inside of the cell as compared with the outside. This reversal of charge is called *depolarization*.

Potassium now begins to flow out faster than the sodium flows in. Since potassium ions are also positively charged, positive charges are again moved to the outside of the cell. This transfer initiates *repolarization* (the return of the resting state), and the inside of the cell again becomes negative. Return to a low level of the membrane's permeability to sodium hastens repolarization. The active transport of sodium out of the cell and the re-establishment of the potassium concentration inside it restores the cell to a resting state.

This describes only the events at one point on the nerve fiber. How does the impulse move along the fiber? As the sodium rushes into the fiber, the outside of the fiber briefly becomes negatively charged at that point. Adjacent to this point a part of the fiber remains positively charged. This difference in potential between the areas is the *action potential*. Since opposite charges attract one another, the positive charges move toward the negative charges on both sides of the membrane. The result is a partial neutralizing of the charge or a small decrease in the electrical potential (a depolarization) of the membrane adjoining the site of the impulse. This depolarization causes the membrane to become more permeable. Sodium rushes into the cell and the impulse continues. Bit by bit, the impulse moves down the fiber much more slowly than an electrical current and by a different means.

When an electrical current travels along a conductor, the conductor serves only as a passive carrier of the electrons which move in the same direction as the current because this movement of electrons *is* the current. During transmission of a nerve impulse, ions are the only particles that move. They move at right angles to the movement of the impulse, that is, they move in and out of the fiber. The nerve impulse is thus a self-propagating wave of depolarization followed by repolarization moving down the nerve fiber.

On any one nerve fiber, the impulse never varies in strength. If the change in environmental conditions (the stimulus) is barely great enough (threshold strength) to cause the nerve fiber to carry an impulse, the impulse will be of the same strength as one incited by a stronger stimulus. *The all-or-none law says that if the nerve carries any impulse, it will carry a full-strength impulse.*

Synaptic Transmission

As the impulse travels through the nervous system, it will soon reach the end of a fiber. Between the end of one fiber and the beginning of the next is a small

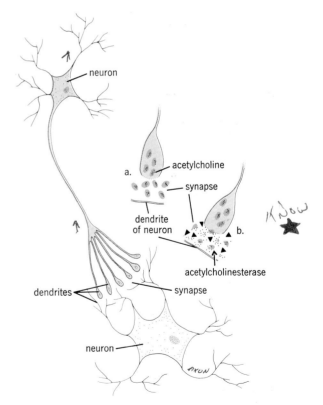

Figure 9.3. Synaptic transmission. Part (a) *shows the production of acetylcholine and part* (b) *depicts the breakdown of acetylcholine by acetylcholinesterase.*

gap, the *synapse* (Figure 9.3). The synapses are important parts of the nervous system because their properties determine many of the system's properties. Let us look at three of their characteristics: (1) the method of transmitting the impulse across the synapse; (2) the usual one-way transmission pattern; and (3) the modification of the transmission of nerve impulses by other nerve impulses.

Moving the nerve impulse across the gap requires a different transmitting means from the one that moves it along the fiber. When the impulse reaches the end of the fiber, it causes the tip to secrete a chemical. This agent diffuses across the synapse and depolarizes the membrane of the next nerve fiber causing it to become permeable to sodium and initiate an impulse.

Most of the synapses in our bodies have *acetylcholine* as the transmitter agent; the remaining synapses secrete other agents (Figure 9.3*a*). As nerve impulse after nerve impulse causes the secretion of acetylcholine into the synapse, we might expect that this chemical would become highly concentrated at the synapse and diffuse in all directions. Actually it does diffuse in all directions, but never gets very far or becomes very concentrated. An enzyme, *acetylcholinesterase,* which breaks down the transmitting agent, is present at all times in the vicinity of the synapses (Figure 9.3*b*). This process inactivates acetylcholine by splitting the molecule and thereby preventing continued depolarization of the next fiber or the inordinate spreading of the nerve impulse to other nerve fibers.

Under some conditions this enzyme is kept from functioning. If a person receives a dose of an organic phosphate insecticide, such as Malathion or Parathion, the activity of acetylcholinesterase will be blocked. What would be the effects of a dose of Malathion on synaptic transmission? What behavioral effects would result?

At a synapse only one of the two fibers is capable of secreting the chemical transmitter agent. Were a nerve impulse to be initiated somewhere in the middle of a nerve cell, it would proceed to both ends of the cell. But as only one end can produce acetylcholine, the impulse is able to cross the synapse to the next cell only at this point. At the other end of the cell, no chemical agent will be released and the impulse will be unable to proceed farther. This simple fact assures the one-way transmission of impulses through the system.

At some synapses the amount of chemical substance produced when an impulse reaches it may not be sufficient to transmit the impulse to the next neuron. In these cases many impulses must reach the synapse quickly if enough acetylcholine is to be released to initiate an impulse in the next cell. This phenomenon is called *summation,* because the effects of several nerve impulses or several fibers are added together to propagate the impulse in the next cell.

Differentiation of Stimuli

Even though each impulse a nerve fiber carries has the same strength, the nervous system is capable of perceiving both the kind and strength of a stimulus. Summation is only one of three mechanisms which permits differentiation of the strength of stimuli. The number of fibers carrying impulses and the number of impulses per second are the other two mechanisms.

Receptors. Various receptors respond to stimuli of different kinds and strengths. The retina of the eye is a good example. Under normal circumstances all retinal cells respond only to light. Some respond, however, to lower light intensities (have lower thresholds) than others. You may have noticed in a very dark room that by looking directly at an object you see less than by looking out of the corner of your eye. The receptors at the edges of the retina have lower thresholds than those near the center of the eye. As the strength of the stimulus increases, more and more receptors respond, and more and more nerve fibers carry impulses to the brain.

Under abnormal circumstances a receptor may respond to a different kind of stimulus, but this will be interpreted by the brain as the kind of stimulus usually picked up by the receptor. If you have ever been hit on the eye, you may remember having seen a flash of light. The retina was stimulated mechanically, but the nerve impulses were interpreted as light. Any stimulus to these receptors is always interpreted as light.

In addition to *different* receptors responding to various strengths of the same stimulus, the *same* receptor may cause more nerve impulses to be transmitted as the strength of the stimulus increases. Most likely, a single natural stimulus always causes each nerve fiber involved to carry more than one impulse. Most fibers carry a brief volley of impulses, the number per second increasing as the strength of the stimulus increases.

Summation and Differentiation. Differentiation of the strength of the stimulus by the nervous system depends on two factors, the number of fibers carrying impulses and the frequency of impulses each carries.

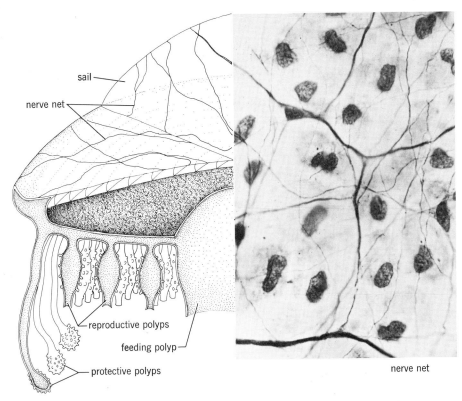

sail

nerve net

reproductive polyps

feeding polyp

protective polyps

nerve net

Figure 9.4. The nerve net of **Vellela.** *The left half diagrams the distribution of some of the nerve net in the animal. (Dr. G. O. Mackie.)*

A weak stimulus which causes a few fibers to carry few impulses may result in some of the impulses dying out at synapses. In such an instance, if more impulses had reached the synapse within the same period of time, the next cell might have carried one. Thus, summation also plays a part in differentiation.

The coordination of an animal's activities depends not only on the movements of impulses along nerve fibers, but also on the brain's interpretation of the information they contain and on their orderly transmission to the proper effectors. This is the function of an intact nervous system rather than of isolated parts.

Nervous Systems

Trends. The degree of control exerted over body activities depends on the complexity of the nervous system. Many organisms lack a highly specialized nervous system. In some, such as *Hydra* and *Vellela,* we find only a net of nerve cells (Figure 9.4). These are so unspecialized that impulses may travel in any direction. Because of this simple nervous system, *Hydra* are not able to show complex behavior. Only a few re-

sponses such as avoiding a stimulus by withdrawal or by bending away are possible.

As we look at other more intricate nervous systems, we find several general patterns of changes in their structure as they gain complexity (Figure 9.5). These are:

(1) Specialization of cells into receptors for particular stimuli, sensory neurons, etc., with transmission in only one direction along the nerve fibers.

(2) The development of many association neurons.

(3) The concentration of nerves into special structures such as nerve cords rather than a loose net.

(4) The concentration of association neurons near the head end of the animal. This concentration results in the formation of a brain, and is called cephalization. As more complex receptors are developed, these are also usually found near the head end.

Why are these changes important? The advantages brought about by the first two types of changes are evident if we compare a system containing association neurons with a simple system having only one nerve cell between receptor and effector. In the simple sys-

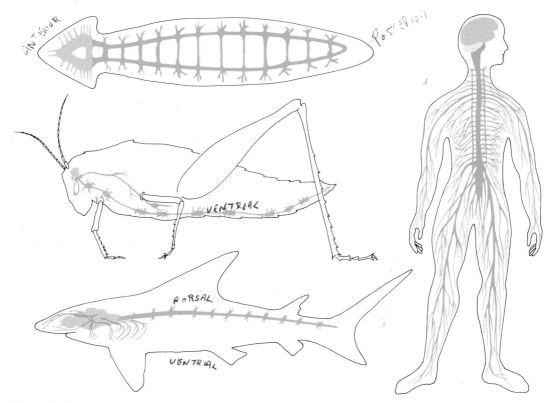

Figure 9.5. The nervous systems of several animals. These increase in complexity as one examines planaria (upper left), grasshopper, shark, and man.

tem, each time a neuron carries an impulse it must carry it to all effectors reached by this neuron, and the response is always the same. The presence of more neurons between receptor and effector introduces the possibility of many different pathways. The examples used represent extremes. However, the principle also operates at the intermediate stages: the more complex the nervous system, the more complex the behavior may become.

The third and fourth trends reflect the changes that accompany the development of movement in animals. One part of the animal is constantly coming into contact with new areas before the rest of the animal. It is important to have the sensory structures located here so that adverse conditions can be detected by the animal before it has reached them or before much of its body has made contact with them. It is advantageous for the nerve centers associated with these sense organs to be located near them. Consequently the nerve elements become concentrated at the leading end, and the structures that we call head and brain result.

Mammalian Nervous Systems.   As a result of these types of changes, highly specialized nervous systems have developed from simple ones. The nervous system possessed by mammals is the most familiar example of a complex nervous system. Broadly speaking, the mammalian nervous system has three different parts: the central nervous system, the peripheral nervous system, and the autonomic nervous system (Figure 9.6). Although these three parts are interdependent, each of them has different functions.

The central nervous system, which is composed of the brain and spinal cord, contains the majority of nerve cell bodies in the nervous system. Sensory neurons carry information from the receptors into the central nervous system. Here the various inputs are interpreted and integrated, and a coordinated set of impulses is sent along the motor nerves running from the central nervous system to the effectors. For simple responses this integration often occurs in the spinal cord (Figure 9.7). More complex activities result from the activities of one or more parts of the brain (Figure 9.8).

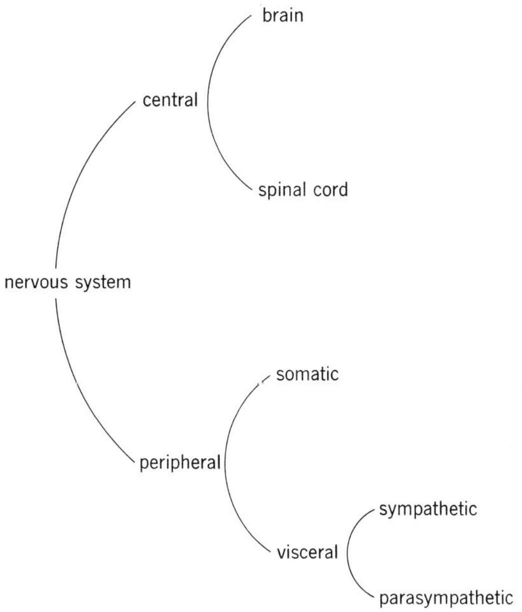

brain

central

spinal cord

nervous system

somatic

peripheral

sympathetic

visceral

parasympathetic

Figure 9.6. The divisions of the mammalian nervous system.

The peripheral nervous system consists of nerve fibers whose cell bodies lie near the spinal cord or within the central nervous system. Since this system has no synapses with association fibers within it, there can be no interpretation or integration. It functions solely to carry impulses to and from the central nervous system.

Although the autonomic nervous system is often considered a part of the peripheral nervous system (it is outside the central nervous system and, hence, peripheral) we shall treat it as a distinct system (Figure 9.9). This system actually comprises two antagonistic systems, the sympathetic and parasympathetic nervous systems, which provide the nerve supplies for the visceral organs such as the digestive tract, lungs, heart, and bladder, and a few other structures like the iris of the eye and some blood vessels. In controlling the activities of these organs, the autonomic nervous system is semi-independent of the central nervous system, since many of its activities are integrated within its bounds and, hence, are involuntary.

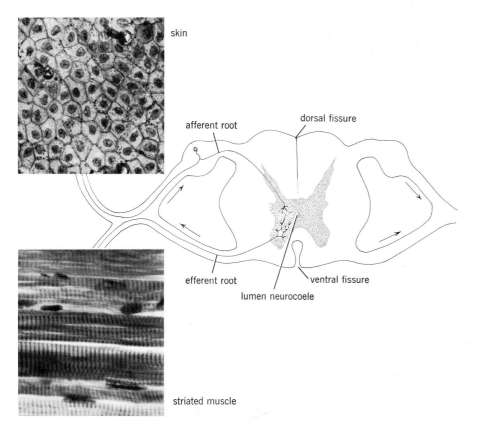

skin

afferent root

dorsal fissure

efferent root

ventral fissure

lumen neurocoele

striated muscle

Figure 9.7. A neural pathway for spinal integration (a spinal reflex). Each pathway consists of receptors (upper left), neurons, and effectors (lower left).

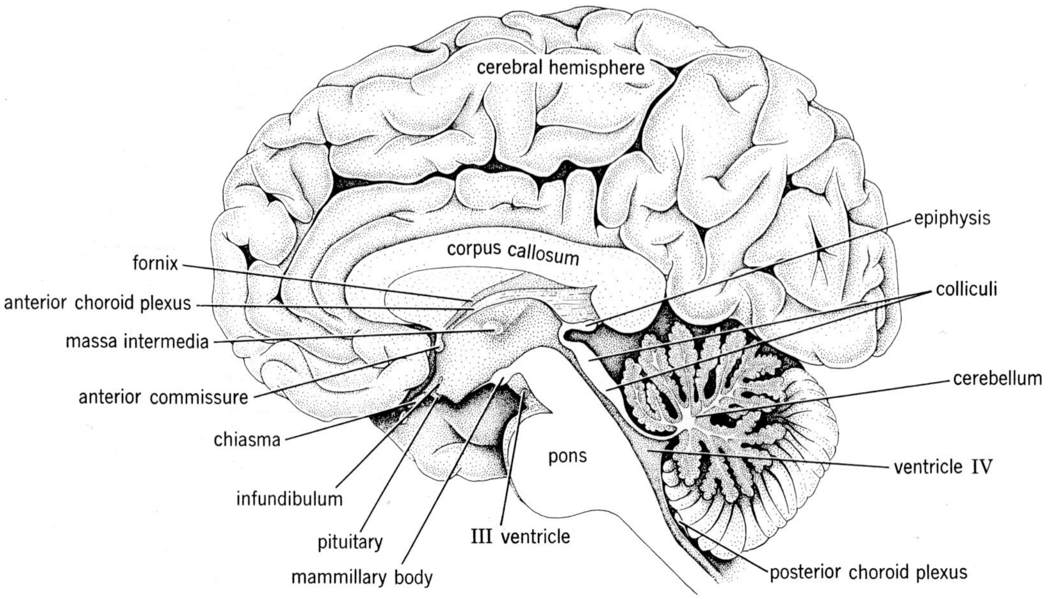

Figure 9.8. The structural complexity of the mammalian brain parallels its functional characteristics.

We may characterize the action of the sympathetic nervous system, which releases adrenalin as a transmitter agent at the nerve ends, as preparing the animal for "fight or flight." That is, the functions that are needed for immediate and extensive muscular activity, such as heart and respiration rate, are increased; those involved in longer-term energy needs, such as digestion, are decreased. The parasympathetic nervous system affects these organs in exactly the opposite way by releasing acetylcholine at its nerve endings.

If we judiciously choose an action controlled by these systems, we can achieve the same results either by blocking the activity of one system or by stimulating the activity of the other. For some years a drug called atropine was used in eye examinations because it caused dilation of the pupil by blocking the action of acetylcholine on the cell membranes. The long-lasting effects of this drug made its use somewhat undesirable. Now the same dilation of the pupil is accomplished by mimicking the action of the sympathetic nervous system with a synthetic adrenalin, called neosynepherine, which does not have such long-lasting effects.

In addition to the adrenalin secreted at the nerve endings, the stimulation of the entire sympathetic nervous system, as in fright or anger, releases into the blood stream large amounts of adrenalin from the interior of the adrenal gland. This adrenalin, a hormone, moves to all portions of the body reinforcing the activity of the adrenalin released at the nerve endings. The apparent overlap points out one area of relationship between the neural and hormonal systems. The two systems may bring about the same effects but differ in the time aspects of coordination. The nervous system acts quickly because the transmitter agents are released so close to the site of action but its action is of short duration; hormones take some time to reach the site of action through the blood stream but continue to be effective for a longer period of time (Figure 9.10).

Another area of overlap between the coordinating systems has been discovered recently. For some time we have known that nerves sometimes stimulate the release of a hormone (adrenalin from the adrenal gland), but it is now known that some nerves actually secrete hormones. The hormones produced by the hypothalamus, which help coordinate reproductive activity, are good examples of neurosecretions that control the production or release of other hormones by more typical glands (Chapter VIII). Some neurohormones act directly on effector organs to coordinate body functions.

This overlap and interaction of the nervous and

Cephalization - concentration of nervous tissue in the anterior end

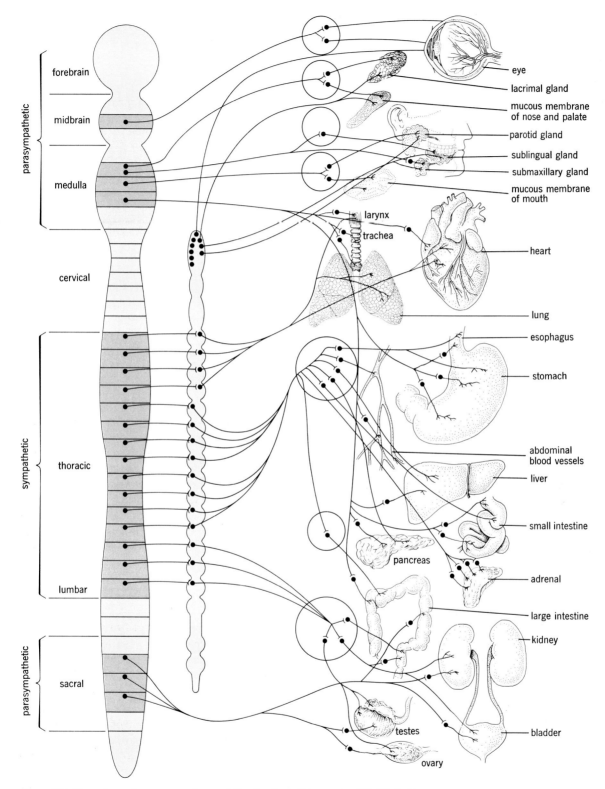

Figure 9.9. *The autonomic nervous system and the structures it innervates. (Modified after A. Nason,* Modern Biology, *1965, John Wiley and Sons, New York.)*

parasympathetic

forebrain

midbrain

medulla

cervical

sympathetic

thoracic

lumbar

parasympathetic

sacral

eye

lacrimal gland

mucous membrane of nose and palate

parotid gland

sublingual gland

submaxillary gland

mucous membrane of mouth

larynx

trachea

heart

lung

esophagus

stomach

abdominal blood vessels

liver

small intestine

adrenal

large intestine

kidney

pancreas

bladder

testes

ovary

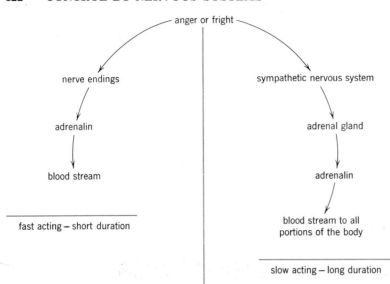

Figure 9.10. Pathways leading to adrenalin release during anger or fright.

endocrine systems help to achieve the proper coordination of body functions and the maintenance of a satisfactory level of materials necessary for continued existence.

Principles

1. Neural coordinating mechanisms are found in most multicellular animals and are characterized structurally by specialized cells: neurons and receptors.

2. A nerve impulse is a depolarization and repolarization of the neuron that occurs sequentially along the cell.

3. Chemicals produced by the ends of nerve cells facilitate the passage of the impulse between nerve fibers.

4. Neural and hormonal coordinating systems overlap functionally, but the neural coordination acts more rapidly and has a shorter duration.

Suggested Readings

Eccles, Sir John, "The Synapse," *Scientific American,* Vol. 212 (January, 1965).

Galambos, Robert, *Nerves and Muscles.* Doubleday and Co., Garden City, N. Y., 1962.

Keynes, Richard D., "The Nerve Impulse and the Squid," *Scientific American,* Vol. 199 (December, 1958). Offprint No. 58, W. H. Freeman and Co., San Francisco.

Questions

1. Can a neuron function as an *effector?* Why?

2. Describe the chain of events that constitutes the movement of an impulse along a nerve fiber.

3. Some texts maintain that no one really knows what a nerve impulse is. Explain why this statement is or is not accurate.

4. What aspect of nerve impulse transmission requires the expenditure of ATP?

5. Why do we not consider a nerve impulse just a type of slow electricity flowing along a fiber?

6. What aspect of neural function illustrates neural and chemical control systems operating together?

7. Does acetylcholine fit the definition of a hormone given in Chapter VIII? Why?

8. What is the basic function of a receptor?

9. Why, in general, do complex receptors occur only in relatively complex organisms?

10. Can you think of any organism that has receptors which humans lack?

11. Why is it convenient or necessary, from a structural standpoint, for animals to have an autonomic nervous system as well as a central nervous system?

CHAPTER X

The Interaction of
Control Systems: Homeostasis

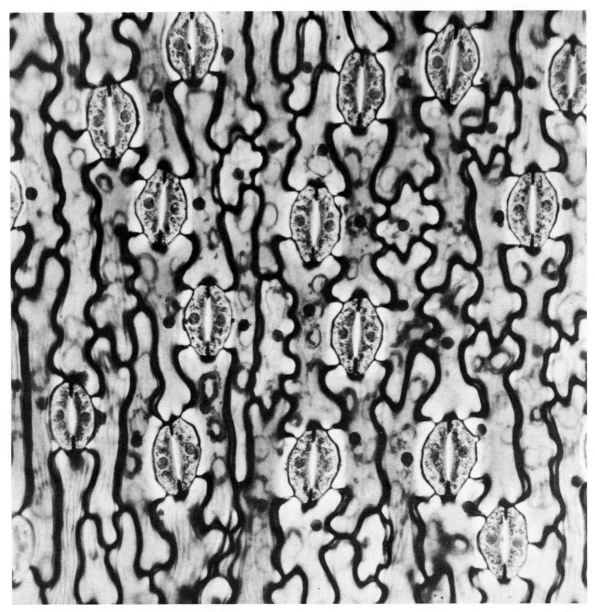

Stomata. (Ward's Natural Science Establishment.)

The Interaction of
Control Systems: Homeostasis

In the nineteenth century Claude Bernard, a French physiologist, observed that the internal environment of organisms was maintained within narrow limits. For example, he noted that the chemical composition of blood fluctuated only slightly regardless of dietary intake or other activities of the organism. Bernard termed this maintenance process *homeostasis*. The concept of homeostasis, or *steady-state* control, is now recognized as one of the fundamental principles of biology. A high percentage of the energy expended by any organism is utilized in the maintenance of the steady state. If the energy supply is cut off, disorder ensues.

Principles

Steady state does not refer to a static or unchanging condition. Rather it signifies a dynamic equilibrium. When we speak of a normal body temperature, blood-sugar level, or heartbeat rate, we allude to values which fluctuate slightly around a norm. These fluctuations occur because a functionally desirable level is maintained through equalization of the input and output of the materials. The regulation of these fluctuations involves various steady-state controls (homeostatic mechanisms), and these occur on all levels, from the concentration of molecules within the cell (remember the effects of mass action) to the numbers of each species in a community.

The study of homeostatic mechanisms impresses two principles upon us. First, the maintenance of a steady state generally necessitates the interactions of the chemical and neural coordinating systems. Second, a steady state is necessary to the maintenance of anything that resembles life.

Examples

1. *Lymph Volume.* Diseases in general may be regarded as alterations of homeostasis. Normally, human beings are capable of maintaining a nearly constant volume of fluid between the cells. A steady input adds material to the fluid as blood pressure drives materials out of the capillaries. There are two routes for the return of materials pushed in by blood pressure: capillaries and lymph vessels (Figure 10.1). If either route for fluid return is impeded in any way, the resulting accumulation of fluid in the intercellular spaces causes edema (swelling) of the tissues.

In a tropical disease caused by a small roundworm, the worms block the lymph vessels and prevent the return of fluid, which results in elephantiasis. The limbs swell to a grotesque extent. The normal homeostatic mechanism for removing intercellular fluid at the same rate at which new fluid enters the spaces from the capillaries has been upset.

2. *Stomata.* Although the relationships among the different control systems in homeostasis can be easily

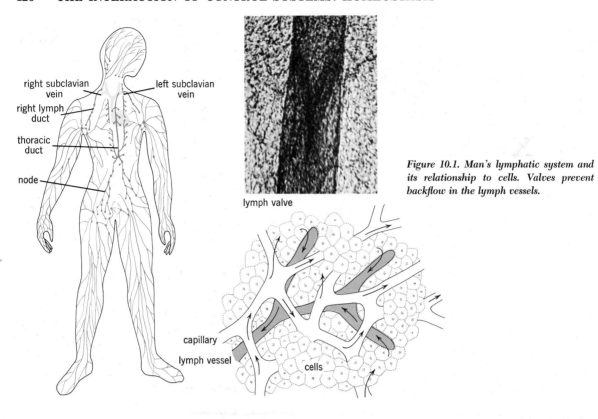

right subclavian vein

left subclavian vein

right lymph duct

thoracic duct

node

lymph valve

capillary

lymph vessel

cells

Figure 10.1. Man's lymphatic system and its relationship to cells. Valves prevent backflow in the lymph vessels.

illustrated with animal examples, comparable examples in plants are difficult to find. The absence in plants of complex coordinating systems, such as nervous systems, necessitates simpler mechanisms. The actions of the guard cells around the openings (stomata) in the leaf surface, for example, show some characteristics of a homeostatic mechanism in maintaining an ample supply of carbon dioxide when it is needed for photosynthesis (Figure 10.2). When light falls on the leaf, the concentration of carbon dioxide molecules near the stomata decreases owing to utilization of carbon dioxide for photosynthesis. The decrease in carbon dioxide concentration causes water to move into the guard cells by osmosis. When the cells become turgid, their shape and structural relationships result in the opening of the stomata. Thus, the stomata are usually open during photosynthesis. This allows the necessary exchange of carbon dioxide and oxygen with the air. It also increases evaporation of water from the cells in the interior of the leaf. Excess water loss must be prevented.

As long as it is light the stomata usually remain at least partly open and allow free exchanges of carbon dioxide and oxygen. The absence of light causes an in-

crease in the concentration of carbon dioxide molecules in the leaf. This brings about a loss of water from the guard cells. The stomata then close, thus reducing water loss.

This theory of control of stomatal opening seems to explain the experimental evidence available. However, because we do not know the mechanism by which changes in carbon dioxide concentration affect the movement of water in the guard cells, we must emphasize that this is a tentative explanation and that we do not know why stomata open and close.

Excessively high water loss from the leaves during the day activates another water-conservation mechanism. As the water available in the leaves decreases, the cells become relatively limp and the leaf wilts. This wilting helps prevent water loss by reducing the surface exposed to the air.

Thus a balance is found between two opposing needs of the plant, the maintenance of carbon dioxide concentrations for photosynthesis and the maintenance of a suitable concentration of water. Notice that no definite system is involved in this homeostatic mechanism. Although it relies on relatively simple physical phenomena, life continues through the maintenance

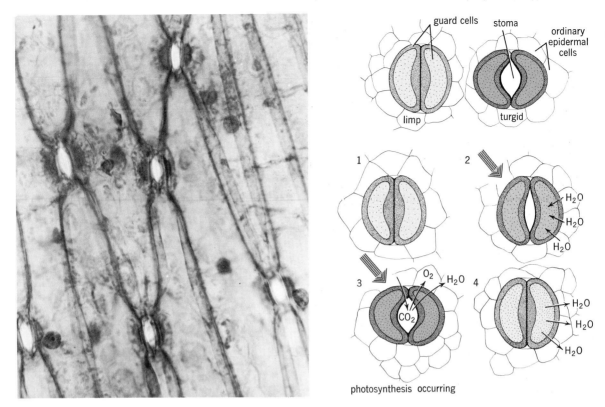

Figure 10.2. The structure and function of stomata. The photomicrograph shows open stomata. The upper diagrams depict closed and open stomata. Parts 1-4 illustrate a normal cycle of stomatal activity during photosynthesis.

within narrow limits of the internal environment in the leaf.

Blood Gases. The control of carbon dioxide and oxygen in the blood stream is an example of homeostasis in which some sense receptors outside the central nervous system and others in the brain itself affect coordinating centers in two different parts of the brain (Figure 10.3). These centers in turn stimulate action in two different effectors to accomplish one goal, maintenance of the proper amount of oxygen in the blood. We also see a principle present in most homeostatic mechanisms: the fluctuations of a material around its proper level maintain that level.

The basic metabolic relationship between oxygen and carbon dioxide makes it possible for mammals to control indirectly the oxygen content of the blood stream. Remember that if the cell's utilization of oxygen increases, the cell will generally produce a greater amount of carbon dioxide. Conversely, in the lungs the loss of carbon dioxide from the blood stream reflects an increase in oxygen intake.

The rates of respiration and heartbeat influence the carbon dioxide and oxygen content of the blood. The more frequently the air in the lungs is expelled and a fresh supply rich in oxygen is inhaled, the more oxygen is available to the blood. In addition, the fresh supply of air will contain less carbon dioxide, resulting in a more rapid diffusion of carbon dioxide from the blood stream. A more rapid heartbeat propels more blood through the lungs, and this also increases the rate of exchange of the respiratory gases.

Most of the mechanisms involved in the control of these gases are initiated by the changes in the carbon dioxide content of the blood. When the oxygen content of the blood stream falls, the carbon dioxide concentration usually rises. An increase in carbon dioxide concentration produces both a faster heart rate and a higher respiratory rate. A small body on the carotid

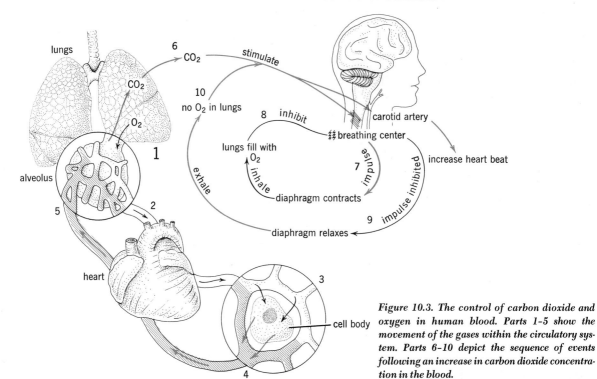

Figure 10.3. The control of carbon dioxide and oxygen in human blood. Parts 1-5 show the movement of the gases within the circulatory system. Parts 6-10 depict the sequence of events following an increase in carbon dioxide concentration in the blood.

artery (main artery to the head) senses the increased carbon dioxide concentration and sends impulses to the brain which result in other impulses being sent to the heart to step up its rate of beat. Furthermore, the increased carbon dioxide concentration has a direct effect on a nerve center in the brain stem, which also causes the respiratory rate to increase through nerve impulses to the diaphragm and other muscles of the rib cage.

Osmoregulation. Many homeostatic mechanisms involve still more complex interactions of coordinating systems. To understand the complexities and the variations in accomplishing the same end in different organisms, we must examine the same homeostatic mechanism in several organisms.

Many organisms are capable of controlling the concentration of water and salts in the cells, that is, osmoregulation. Control of these materials is essential if the organism is to live in freshwater or dry land environments. Although the level of complexity varies in different organisms, the same general processes occur in the osmoregulatory organs of most larger animals. First, the organ receives a massive input of useful and waste products from the body fluids. This is followed by a massive return of most materials, including waste

products, to the body fluids and then by a selective adjustment of the waste products determined by the conditions existing in the organism at that time.

The kidney found in crayfish clearly shows these basic processes (Figure 10.4). The low blood pressure is sufficient to drive fluid from the body cavity into the tube of each kidney. This fluid contains both useful and waste products. In the first part of the tube, called the labyrinth, most of the materials are reabsorbed into the blood stream by active transport and diffusion. This, of course, requires the expenditure of energy by the cells of the kidney. In the next portion of the tube some materials which are conserved by the crayfish are reabsorbed from the remaining fluid. Other materials are transported from the blood to the fluid inside the tube. Now the fluid can be called urine and is simply stored and then released to the outside of the organism.

Although the basic unit of the vertebrate kidney, the nephron, differs from the crayfish kidney in external appearance, the general processes are parallel in both (Figures 10.5 and 10.6). We find an area of massive input of fluid (*glomerulus* and *Bowman's capsule*), an area of relatively nonselective reabsorption *(proximal convoluted tubule)*, an area for selective reabsorp-

contractile vacuole - amoeba

nephridia

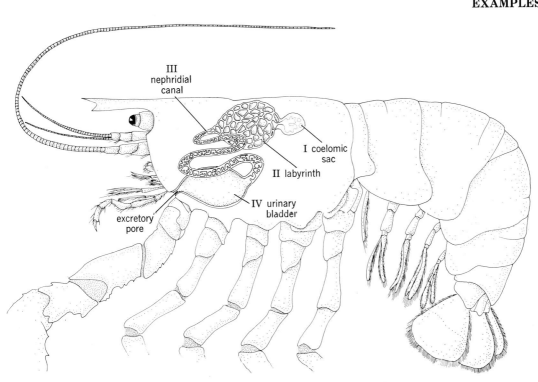

III
nephridial
canal

I coelomic
sac

II labyrinth

IV urinary
bladder

excretory
pore

Figure 10.4. Crayfish kidney. I–IV indicate areas for intake, massive return, selective adjustment, and storage, respectively. (Modified from C. L. Prosser and F. A. Brown, Jr. (after A. Krogh and H. Peters), **Comparative Animal Physiology,** *second ed., 1961, W. B. Saunders Co., Philadelphia.)*

tion (*Henle's loop* and *distal convoluted tubule*) and an area (*collecting duct*) for the final water uptake and for removal of the remaining materials, the urine, from the nephron. The only marked functional difference between the nephron and the crayfish kidney is the presence of the area of final water uptake in the former.

The filtration of fluid into the tubule through the glomerulus and Bowman's capsule is due to blood pressure. Most of the materials in the blood are composed of molecules small enough to pass through the capillary wall. Only large molecules, like proteins, and blood cells fail to pass into the kidney tubule. Unless some disease or injury modifies or breaks the capillary walls, neither proteins nor blood cells ever appear in the urine. The remaining materials consist of waste products, such as a nitrogenous waste product(urea),which is less toxic than ammonia, and useful substances such as water, glucose, salts, and amino acids.

About two-thirds of the volume of blood and intercellular fluid passes into the kidney tubules each hour. Because the amount of fluid passing into the tubule is so large it is essential that most of this fluid be reabsorbed. The reabsorption occurs in the proximal convoluted tubule. Here, under normal conditions, all the glucose and amino acids are reabsorbed by active transport into the capillaries surrounding the tubule. In addition, active transport removes about 99 per cent of the salts. Water and urea diffuse from the kidney tubule as the other materials are transported out.

In addition, a few other minor modifications occur in this convoluted tubule. Some molecules too large to filter through the capillary wall are carried by active transport from the blood into the tubule. Most of these molecules, like penicillin, do not normally appear in the animal.

The reabsorption of water in the proximal convoluted tubule occurs without regard for the shortage or excess of water in the animal. In contrast, the sections of the tubule from Henle's loop through the collecting duct carry out processes which result in the selective reabsorption of water. The exact amount reabsorbed depends on the concentration of the blood stream.

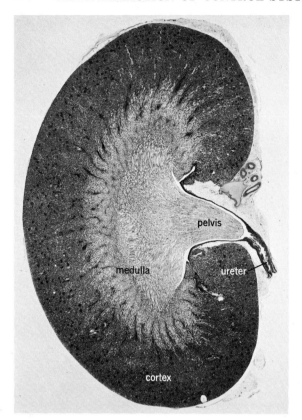
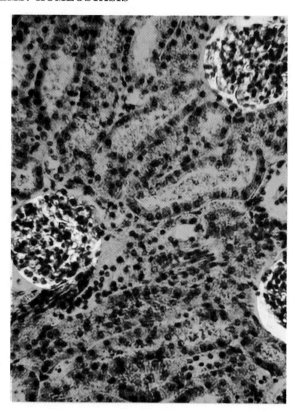

Figure 10.5. The general structure of the rat kidney (left). (General Biological Supply House.) Tubule cells (blue) and glomeruli are shown at the right.

If the blood has a low amount of water, cells in the hypothalamus sense this shortage (Figure 10.7). They cause the release of a hormone from the posterior pituitary gland into the blood stream. This hormone increases the permeability of the distal convoluted tubule to water. Water leaves the tubule more freely and consequently a greater amount is reabsorbed here.

Once the osmotic concentration in the blood reaches a normal level, or lower, the same cells in the hypothalamus no longer cause the release of as much of the hormone from the posterior pituitary gland, and the permeability of the distal convoluted tubule to water drops to its normal level, or below. Less water is reabsorbed, thus causing a tendency to maintain a constant amount of water in the body.

Another example of the hormonal control of reabsorption in the distal convoluted tubule concerns the reabsorption of salts. Some of the steroid hormones

from the adrenal gland tend to increase both reabsorption of sodium and excretion of potassium in the tubule. When potassium increases in the body, more of the hormones are released from the adrenal gland. A return to normal salt concentrations results in a reduction in the amount of adrenal hormones released. Although the control of the amount of water involves neural and hormonal elements, the mechanisms for reabsorbing salt are apparently partially controlled by purely hormonal coordination. The kidney is therefore a good example of the interplay of several parts of different coordinating systems to bring about homeostasis or steady state of the body fluids.

The examples presented here all emphasize the single universal characteristic of homeostatic mechanisms: their tendency to preserve life. After these examples, one may be tempted to call life itself a steady state. Most biologists would agree.

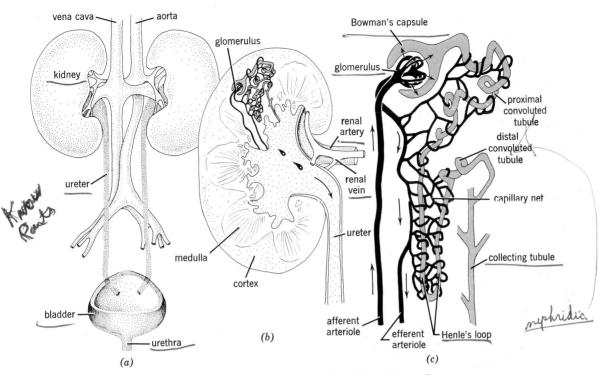

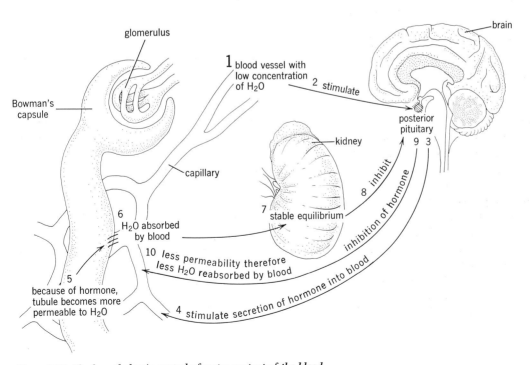

Figure 10.6. (a) *The excretory system.* (b) *A longitudinal section of the kidney showing the position of a nephron.* (c) *Detailed structure of the nephron.*

Figure 10.7. *The hypothalamic control of water content of the blood.*

131

Principles

1. Organisms maintain their internal environment within narrow limits by regulating intake and loss of necessary materials.

2. Most of the regulatory mechanisms involved in homeostasis comprise neural and hormonal processes.

Suggested Readings

Benzinger, T. H., "The Human Thermostat," *Scientific American,* Vol. 204 (January, 1961). Offprint No. 129, W. H. Freeman and Co., San Francisco.

Langley, L. L., *Homeostasis.* Reinhold Publishing Co., New York, 1965.

Merrill, John P., "The Artificial Kidney," *Scientific American,* Vol. 205 (July, 1961).

Schmidt-Nielson, Knut, *Animal Physiology.* Second edition, Prentice-Hall, Englewood Cliffs, N. J., 1964, pp. 47–67.

Smith, Homer W., "The Kidney," *Scientific American,* Vol. 188 (January, 1953). Offprint No. 37, W. H. Freeman and Co., San Francisco.

Questions

1. What is health from a biological viewpoint? Is it a homeostatic state?

2. Why is it difficult to find examples of steady-state systems in plants?

3. Do you think that the plant growth substances described in Chapter VIII function as a homeostatic system? Explain.

4. Explain how the amount of carbon dioxide in the blood regulates the rate of heartbeat and breathing.

5. How does this mechanism affect the length of time that a person can hold his breath?

6. Explain why the kidney is often used as an example of a homeostatic organ.

7. Which of the following seems to play the most important function in steady-state systems: nervous system, hormonal system, or a combination of the two?

Communication: The Basis for Interorganismic Coordination

A honeybee returning to the nest. (© Walt Disney Productions.)

Communication: The Basis for Interorganismic Coordination

The maintenance of life requires more than the maintenance of a constant environment within an organism. The activity of various organisms must be coordinated. In animals, for example, communication of information plays a part in this coordination. If the communication does not occur, the life of the individual and of the species will be endangered. This communication may be accomplished by four different types of signals: auditory, visual, chemical, and tactile. Although these are nearly self-explanatory terms, examples help to indicate the kinds of signals in each category. We must keep in mind that the degree of communication possible between organisms is dependent on the degree of their complexity. We shall mention three kinds of structures, all of which must be present in sufficiently complex form to handle the signal involved.

In each example some specific color or movement, sound, smell, or touch serves as the vehicle for transferring information from one organism to another. First, if these signals are not to be confused with others, there must be effectors available which can produce exactly the same signal each time. Second, the organism that receives the signal must have receptors capable of distinguishing it from other similar signals. Third, a system must be present which can interpret and coordinate the information received.

As a rule, more complex behavior results from the greater number of distinctive behavior patterns available to an animal with a more advanced nervous system. Since these animals can make different responses to slightly different stimuli, they generally employ more intricate sets of signals for communication.

Types of Signals

Auditory. Bird songs are familiar auditory signals. By singing, a male bird may inform other birds as to his species, the fact that he is a male, and that he is in breeding condition on a territory (any defended area). All of this information is important to other birds. It helps females to find males of the same species who are ready to mate. It helps prevent unnecessary fighting between males by notifying other males of the presence of the resident bird in the territory. Singing is also an important factor in bringing the female of some species into breeding condition. These activities help to maintain the species by furthering reproduction and reducing losses from competition. (See Figure 11.1.)

Visual. Birds also communicate by color or pattern of plumage (visual signals). The male flicker has a black "whisker" mark on his face which is lacking in the female. Otherwise the plumage appears to be

135

signals must have same meaning all the time
must interpret them the same way
perceive it the same way

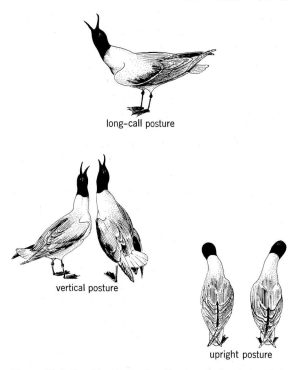

long-call posture

vertical posture

upright posture

Figure 11.1. Combinations of auditory and visual signals in gulls. (Adapted from an illustration by Louis Darling for TIME-LIFE BOOKS, 1963, Time Inc.)

identical in the two sexes. Normally males court females and try to drive other males from their territories. If a male is caught and the black whisker marks painted out, he will be treated by the rest of the population as a female. Other males will allow him on their territories and will attempt to court him. Females will ignore him. Here one small difference in coloration is obviously very important to the species.

Lizards often use visual signs for courtship or threat. The male green anole (frequently mistaken for chameleons) extends a red-orange flap of skin from the throat. This simple signal identifies the species, sex, and breeding condition of the individual. Again this attracts females and helps prevent unnecessary fighting.

Chemical.   A famous example of the use of a chemical signal is found in the gypsy moth. Females produce a special chemical called gyplure, which the wind carries great distances. Males perceive the odor and follow the "trail" to the female. This enables the sexes to find each other at night and reduces the exposure of the moths to predators. Man has learned to lure the male gypsy moths to traps by releasing gyplure at trap sites.

In ants the laying down of a chemical to mark the pathway to a new food source is another example of

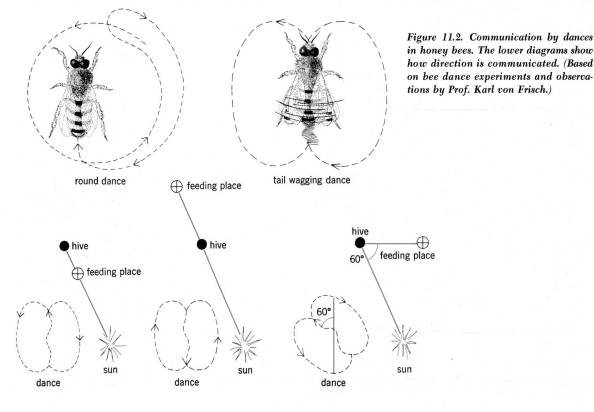

round dance

tail wagging dance

feeding place

hive

hive

feeding place

hive

60°

feeding place

sun

dance

sun

dance

60°

60°

sun

dance

Figure 11.2. Communication by dances in honey bees. The lower diagrams show how direction is communicated. (Based on bee dance experiments and observations by Prof. Karl von Frisch.)

the communication of exact information in animals. This chemical is secreted by a special gland and applied to the ground by means of a stinger. Other ants following the first ant may reinforce the trail. This enables ants to move to and from the food along a well-marked pathway rather than to wander about searching for food. Since the trail disappears as the chemical evaporates, only relatively new trails will be followed.

Combinations of Signals. Honey bees manifest a combination of methods of communication. Many people are acquainted with the "dance" by which a bee may indicate to other bees the distance and direction to a source of food or a suitable nest site (Figure 11.2). If the food is near the hive, the bee that discovers the source performs a round dance. This gives no information on the direction to the food but simply says that it may be found within a short distance of the hive. When the food is located farther from the hive, the bee performs a wagging dance. This follows a modified figure-eight pattern. Two variations in the dance occur—one giving the direction to the source, the other the distance.

The direction is always given in terms of the angle from the sun. If the central portion of the figure eight is vertical on the comb in the hive, the food lies in the direction of the sun. The angle from the vertical axis indicates the angle from the sun at which the food is located. The central portion of the dance is the only part during which the bee waggles, that is, moves its abdomen from side to side. The number of times this waggling occurs per unit of time indicates the distance to the source. The closer the source is, the more rapid the waggling. The precision of the information concerning the location of the food is demonstrated by man's ability to record the frequency and direction of the dance, and then find the food source on the basis of these data.

As other bees fly out, gather food, and return to the hive, they also dance. As the food source becomes depleted, the dancing for that source diminishes and the attention of bees is drawn to some other food source. Taking into account the fact that bees are attracted to the dancing that has the greatest activity, what kind of food source would draw the most bees if dances for two sources were being carried out at one time?

The emphasis has been on the visual elements of the dance. When we remember that the dance is usually performed in the hive, which may be nearly dark, the importance of tactile and auditory elements of communication is apparent. Recent experiments show that the frequency of a sound produced during the dance alters with a change in distance to the food source. In addition, the presence of the food on the dancing bees communicates the type of food available.

Studies on different varieties of honey bees have shown some interesting variations of the dances. The most unusual is the variation in the coding of the distance to the food in different varieties of bees. All varieties use the same basic code but differ in the distance at which they change from the round dance to waggle dance (10–275 feet) and also in the distances coded by various rates of waggling. Four waggle dances in 15 seconds may range in meaning from 1,000 feet in one variety to well over 2,000 feet in another. Hives with a mixture of varieties of bees show interesting results in the misinterpretation of the dances.

Under some circumstances the communication does not benefit the individual but does benefit the rest of the population. Many schooling species of fish release a specific chemical signal when seized by a predator. It is too late to help the individual but it warns other members of the species in the area of danger. The benefit to the species rather than the individual will be an important concept in the discussion of selection and adaptation (Chapter XIX).

Deception in Communication

In the examples discussed so far, information was passed from one individual to another of the same species. Communication is also found between individuals of different species. Many species of insects, such as the monarch butterfly, which are impalatable or capable of hurting the predator advertise their presence by distinctive coloration. Once a predator discovers the bad taste or the sting, it will avoid other individuals that look similar. Occasionally other species look very much like the noxious species but do not have the sting or the bad taste. This similarity in appearance is called _mimicry_ (Figure 11.3). Individuals of these mimic species are also avoided by predators and are protected in this way. Notice that the information communicated to the predator in this case is false.

Coloration may serve to communicate false information in another way. Many organisms are protectively colored, that is, they match their normal background. Here the predator seems to see only the background but no prey. (See Figures 11.4 and 11.5.)

Scent also is a means of communication between species. Many prey are found by predators through

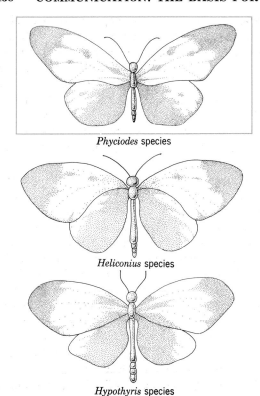

Phyciodes species

Heliconius species

Hypothyris species

Figure 11.3. Mimicry. The lower two species of butterflies are inedible. The third species is not eaten by predators even though it is edible. (Adapted from an illustration by Margaret L. Estey for TIME-LIFE BOOKS, 1964, Time Inc.)

Figure 11.4. A leaflike insect. (Dr. Edward S. Ross.)

Figure 11.5. Arctic hare. This mammal closely matches its snowy background. (© Walt Disney Productions.)

their odor. The skunk presents the opposite picture (Figure 11.6). We know the effect that the smell of skunk has on our own behavior. Many other animals react in similar fashion.

Most bird calls or songs are very specific, relaying information only to other members of that species. However, some types of warning notes affect individuals of many species. If a hawk appears, a single warning note may silence the activity of nearly all the birds in the area. The same nonspecific warning note may be given by many species and recognized as a warning note by many small birds.

Sound may also serve as a carrier of false information. The hognosed snake, or "puffing adder," when threatened will spread its neck and hiss (Figure 11.7). It also makes false striking motions. This fierce act seems to be relatively successful in misleading other animals. Even people think the puffing adder is dangerous. Those who have kept hognosed snakes in captivity have discovered that they are really docile.

Behavior and the Nervous System

In Chapter IX we stated that complex behavior required a complex nervous system. Since plants do not have nervous systems, their behavior offers a good example by contrast. Higher plants react to light by bending toward it (Figure 11.8). Not all of the plant is involved in this reaction; only cells near the growing tip are affected. Because the plant growth hormone (*auxin*) tends to accumulate on the side of the stem opposite the light, the cells on that side elongate more than the other cells of the stem. This causes the stem to bend toward the light. This type of movement, in response to a difference in stimulation of the two sides of the organism, is called a *tropism*.

Figure 11.6. A skunk displaying its distinctive coloration. (Dr. Lloyd Ingles.)

Many simple organisms like *Euglena* show a similar response to light by moving toward it (Figure 11.9). If the light becomes too strong, many organisms move away from it to a zone of lesser light intensity. Even a few multicellular animals may be included in the group showing simple responses to light. The pill bug will turn toward the side that has the highest light intensity until the light reaching the two eyes is of equal strength. Thus the bug will move toward the light.

Most multicellular animals show much more complex reactions to light. The ability to distinguish colors, shapes, and other characteristics of the light enables the animals to respond more specifically to the light. An earthworm may be trained to turn toward the light in a simple T maze. The worm is placed at the end of the upright of the T and crawls toward the crossbar. When it reaches the center of the crossbar, it can turn toward either the lighted side or the dark side. If it turns toward the dark side, it receives a shock. After a large number of trials the worm almost always turns toward the light. This modification of behavior by experience is called learning.

The amount of learning possible is dependent upon the complexity of the nervous system present. Like

Figure 11.7. Hognosed snake. Many people see a similarity to rattlesnakes. (General Biological Supply House, Inc.)

Figure 11.8. A bean seedling bending toward the light.

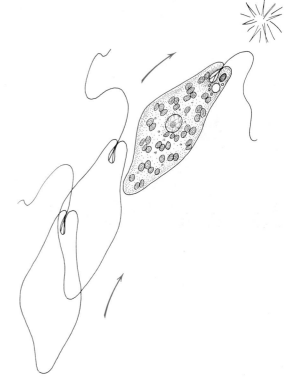

Figure 11.9. A Euglena moving toward light.

communication, its value lies in protecting the individual and in increasing his chances of surviving long enough to reproduce. Only in this way may learning contribute to the survival of the species and the maintenance of life.

Principles

1. Auditory, visual, chemical, and tactile signals are the means by which organisms communicate information to one another to coordinate their activity.

2. The intricacy of the signals used and the variety of behavioral responses that may result depend upon the complexity of the nervous system.

Suggested Readings

Bonner, John Tyler, "How Slime Molds Communicate," *Scientific American,* Vol. 209 (August, 1963). Offprint No. 164, W. H. Freeman and Co., San Francisco.

Frings, Hubert and Mable, "The Language of Crows," *Scientific American,* Vol. 201 (November, 1959).

Frings, Hubert and Mable, *Animal Communication.* Blaisdell Publishing Co., Boston, 1964.

Krogh, August, "The Language of the Bees," *Scientific American,* Vol. 179 (August, 1948). Offprint No. 21, W. H. Freeman and Co., San Francisco.

Tinbergen, T., "The Curious Behavior of the Stickleback," *Scientific American,* Vol. 187 (December, 1952). Offprint No. 414, W. H. Freeman and Co., San Francisco.

Von Frisch, Karl, "Dialects in the Language of the Bees," *Scientific American,* Vol. 207 (August, 1962). Offprint No. 130, W. H. Freeman and Co., San Francisco.

Wenner, Adrian M., "Sound Communication in Honeybees," *Scientific American,* Vol. 210 (April, 1964). Offprint No. 181, W. H. Freeman and Co., San Francisco.

Wilson, Edward O., "Pheromones," *Scientific American,* Vol. 208 (May, 1963). Offprint No. 157, W. H. Freeman and Co., San Francisco.

Questions

1. Name the types of signals used by animals for communication. Which of these are used by humans? Are any used by plants?

2. Do you see a relationship between the kinds of receptors an animal has and the types of communication it utilizes?

3. Can you provide some examples of visual communication not described in the chapter?

4. How do you suppose that male and female mockingbirds, which are identical in appearance, communicate their sex differences to each other?

5. What functions are served by communication among organisms that belong to different species?

Asexual Reproduction

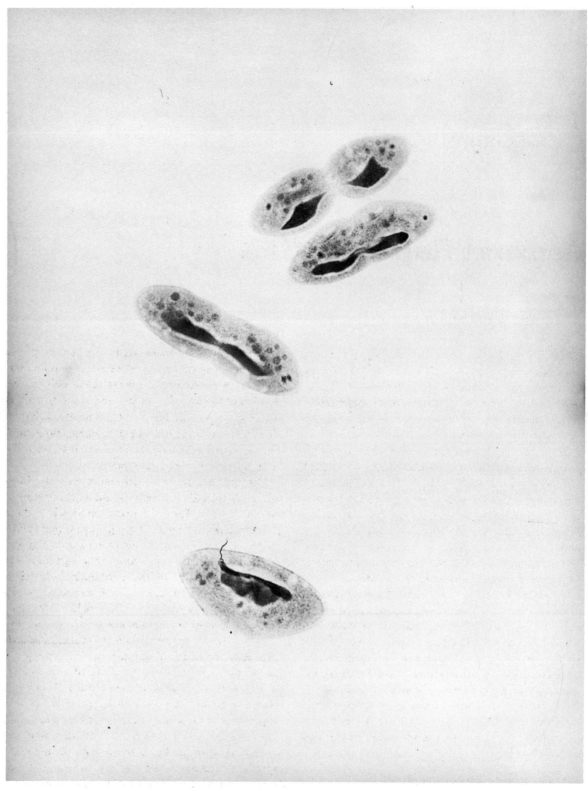

Paramecium undergoing binary fission. (Ward's Natural Science Establishment.)

CHAPTER XII

Asexual Reproduction

asexual
sexual

Up to this point we have covered topics pertaining to the maintenance of the individual, such as energy utilization, coordination, and communication. Important as these are they require another major factor of life, namely reproduction, in order to bridge the gap between generations.

In simple terms, reproduction is the biological process that provides new individuals. In the context of Chapter X, reproduction may also be considered a means of species steady state, that is, a means of maintaining population levels and genetic continuity. Whenever natural populations are studied over a period of time, their numbers are observed to fluctuate around a mean value, a phenomenon which usually suggests a homeostatic mechanism at work.

When one individual, one "parent," gives rise to one or more offspring without the participation of special sex cells, the process is known as *asexual reproduction*. There is an additional process, taken up in the next chapter, which involves the fusion of two specialized nuclei to produce a fertilized egg. This is termed sexual reproduction. Reproduction is first and fundamentally a cellular process. Thus to understand the mechanics by which new individuals are produced we must start at the cellular level and examine the way in which new cells are produced.

Cellular Reproduction: Mitosis

Reproduction, as a cellular activity, comprises a series of orderly events in the nucleus termed *mitosis*.

As a consequence of these events, the nucleus divides into two nuclei containing identical hereditary messages. Strictly speaking, mitosis refers only to the division of the nucleus; the division of the cytoplasm is called *cytokinesis*. Figure 12.1 illustrates cell division as a series of stages called prophase, metaphase, anaphase, and telophase. Each of these stages is described in the following paragraphs.

One of the first observable indications of mitosis occurs as threadlike structures, called chromosomes, become visible. These "threads" gradually become shortened, distinct bodies. Careful observation reveals that each chromosome at this time consists of a *pair* of threads known as *chromatids;* the significance of this does not become evident until later. As the chromosomes take form, partly by a coiling up of the threads, other events occur. The nuclear membrane gradually disappears and simultaneously a new structure, the *spindle,* appears. It consists of slender strands extending the length of the nucleus and expanded in its middle region like two cones placed base to base. The spindle is composed of long protein fibers which derive from the cytoplasm. In animal cells the centrioles appear to control formation of the spindle with one centriole located at each pole. Cells of most plants do not have centrioles, and the control device for spindle formation in these is not known. After the spindle forms, the chromosomes begin to orient themselves to it. All these events are grouped under the term, *prophase.*

143

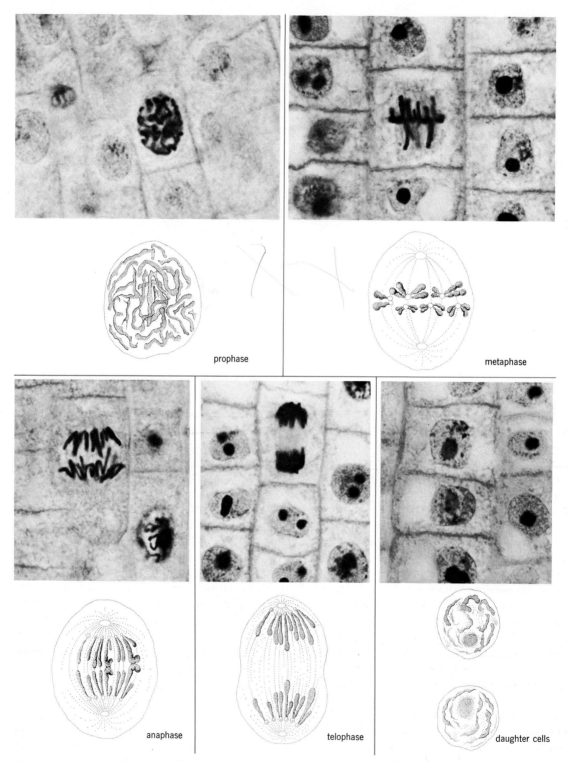

prophase

metaphase

anaphase

telophase

daughter cells

Figure 12.1. Mitosis in onion root cells.

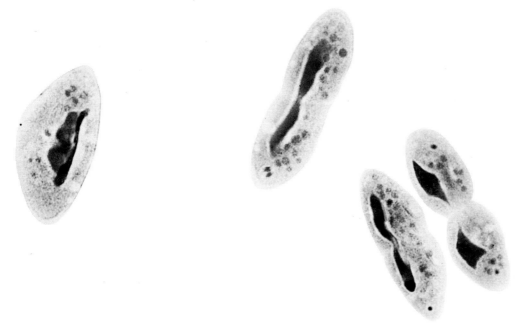

Figure 12.2. Fission in Paramecium. *(Ward's Natural Science Establishment.)*

Following this, the chromsomes gather toward the equator (middle) of the spindle. Each chromosome then attaches to a spindle fiber at a special region on the chromosome called the *centromere.* This stage, with the chromosomes lined up across the middle of the spindle, is termed *metaphase.* This is a particularly useful stage for the cytologist, since chromosomes are in their most distinct form and can be seen and counted more easily than in other stages. About 1935 it was found that the drug colchicine interfered with spindle formation and thus stopped mitosis at metaphase. The drug is a useful tool which is still widely applied when cytologists wish to study chromosome shapes and numbers in an organism.

After metaphase one of the most important stages of mitosis takes place: *anaphase.* The centromere of each chromosome divides, and each chromosome is pulled apart lengthwise (recall the earlier statement that each of the chromosomes consisted of a pair of chromatids). One chromatid of each chromosome moves toward one pole of the spindle, and the other chromatid toward the other pole. Since all chromosomes do this at the same time, identical amounts *and kinds* of chromosomal material (including DNA) move to opposite ends of the spindle. It has been suggested that the spindle contracts and pulls the chromosomal threads apart, and it has also been suggested

that some force repels the threads. The contractile idea seems more reasonable in view of the protein structure of the spindle fibers.

Anaphase ends when the chromosomal material reaches the ends of the spindle. In *telophase,* the last stage of mitosis, the chromosomes begin to return to the threadlike stage. They uncoil and eventually become as indistinct as they were at the beginning of prophase. The spindle gradually disintegrates, and a nuclear membrane reforms about each of the two masses of nuclear material, which are then spoken of as *daughter nuclei.* Cell division is not completed, however, since we have yet to deal with the cytoplasmic portion of the cell (cytokinesis). In animal cells, during telophase, the cytoplasm begins to constrict through the equator of the spindle until two daughter cells are formed. In plant cells a *cell plate* starts to form in the middle of the spindle and then appears to work out to the outside of the cell until two daughter cells form. In both plants and animals the end result is the same: two daughter cells are formed, genetically identical (identical DNAs) to each other and to the mother cell from which they arose. These daughter cells undergo a period of growth and assume their role with other cells in their environment. The duration of mitosis varies from thirty minutes to several hours with prophase taking the longest time.

Figure 12.3. Budding in Hydra. (General Biological Supply House, Inc.)

Figure 12.4. Budding in the jellyfish Aurelia.

The stage during which a cell is not visibly reproducing is called *interphase*. This stage plays a significant role in relation to mitosis because during it the DNA is duplicated. The duplication is necessary prior to anaphase for two threads to separate during anaphase into daughter cells and for these cells to be genetically identical. The primary function of mitosis is the quantitative separation of DNA molecules into two equal masses; however, we describe it in terms of what chromosomes do since they can be observed under the microscope, whereas DNA cannot.

Mitosis is a universal biological phenomenon and one of the most fundamental life processes. Not only does it produce new individuals but in addition replaces dead cells, heals wounds, and regenerates lost or injured parts of the body in some cases. Sometimes cell division appears to get out of control, resulting in abnormal growths like cancers and tumors. The controlling mechanisms that initiate and regulate mitosis remain unknown despite numerous research efforts.

Advantages and Disadvantages of Asexual Reproduction

Reproduction of the nonsexual type (Figures 12.2–12.6) is common among lower plants and animals and is advantageous in various ways. It is a relatively simple process involving only mitosis, in contrast to the complexities of egg and sperm formation found in sexual reproduction. Only one individual or parent is involved, and hence there is no necessity for complex mating procedures. Large numbers of offspring can be simultaneously produced. For example, one sporangium of a bread mold can release thousands of spores. Asexual reproduction often seems to be an adaptation for dispersal as illustrated by spores. These are frequently microscopic bodies which are light enough to be blown about in the air.

Offspring produced by asexual means are nearly exact copies of the parent and consequently exhibit virtually no variablility. This is not a disadvantage

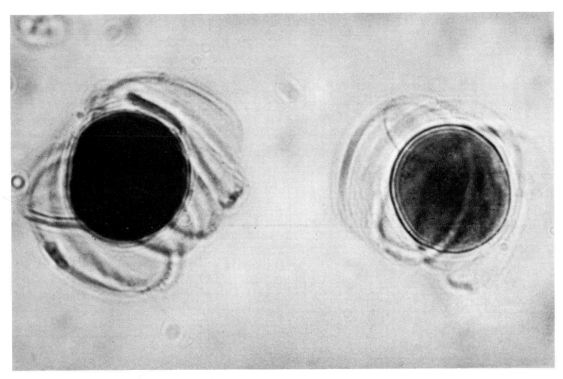

Figure 12.5. Spores from the horsetail plant (Equisetum).

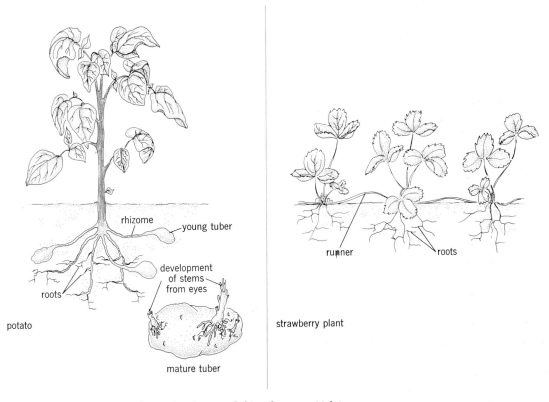

rhizome

young tuber

development
of stems
from eyes

roots

potato

mature tuber

runner

roots

strawberry plant

Figure 12.6. Vegetative reproduction by rhizomes (left) and runners (right).

147

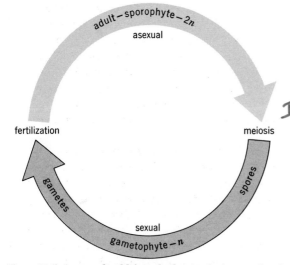

Figure 12.7. A generalized life cycle showing both asexual and sexual reproduction. 2n indicates the presence of a full complement of chromosomes.

provided the environment is fairly uniform and remains this way for long periods of time. On the other hand, a form which showed only asexual reproduction would have a limited range of adaptability and could not adjust rapidly to changing environmental situations. This is the major disadvantage of the process.

Major Categories of Asexual Reproduction

As we have emphasized, asexual reproduction starts at the cellular level with mitosis. In considering the modification of this kind of reproduction in relation to organisms we have chosen to subdivide it into categories of fission, budding, sporulation, and vegetative reproduction.

It could be argued that *all* cell divisions constitute reproduction including the growth of embryos or tissues. We shall restrict our discussion to the four categories named.

Fission. In fission the nucleus divides mitotically

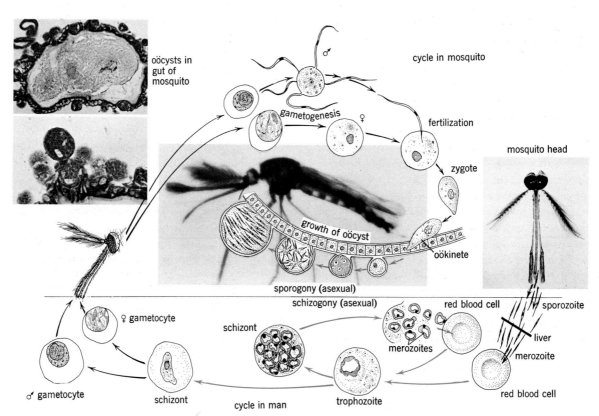

Figure 12.8. Life cycle of a malaria-causing parasite. The blue arrows represent the asexual phase and the black arrows indicate the sexual phase.

and then the entire organism divides to form two. This is a common means of reproducing among many of the unicellular organisms such as protozoans, bacteria, yeasts, and numerous algae (Figure 12.2). Few multicellular organisms reproduce by fission, partly because of their complexity. Some forms like flatworms show a modified form of fission in which their bodies constrict into two or more pieces, but this does not involve mitosis.

Budding. In budding, a portion of the parent's body grows through mitosis to form an appendage or region which will eventually become another organism. There are many variations of this type of reproduction. Yeast cells, for example, form new members in this way. In the small freshwater animal called *Hydra,* a portion of the body of an adult grows out and develops a mouth and tentacles (Figure 12.3). This offspring now resembles the adult and eventually breaks free to pursue its own fate. The small liverwort plant *Marchantia* grows small cellular masses (buds) in cups on its surface. These buds float away in films of dew or rainwater to start new liverwort plants in another location. Some of the jellyfish have a stage in their life cycles which utilizes a specialization of the budding process. Here a stalklike body, attached to the bottom, buds tiny disklike jellyfish (Figure 12.4). Budding also occurs in a number of other forms such as in some of the protozoans and sponges.

Sporulation. Sporulation, the formation of spores, is common in the plant world. The basic idea is the formation of cells which can develop into new plants under favorable conditions. Spores are often surrounded by a tough, protective coat which enables them to withstand adverse conditions (Figure 12.5). Fungi are singularly proficient at this since many of them, like the mushroom, can release tens of thousands of tiny airborne spores. This ancient and successful way of reproducing has even persisted as an important portion of the life cycle of flowering plants.

Vegetative Reproduction in Plants. Higher plants possess various means of asexual reproduction, or vegetative reproduction as it is sometimes termed. Many have underground stems (rhizomes) which grow horizontally in the soil and send up aerial leaves at intervals. Any piece of the rhizome can become a new plant. The common potato represents a short portion of a rhizome filled with food material (Figure 12.6). This is not primarily a reproductive device, but man discovered long ago that the "eyes" of the potato, which are actually buds, could be removed and planted to produce more potato plants. In potatoes, at least, this is a better way of insuring uniformity in the next generation than planting seeds. Each eye produces a replica of its parent, whereas plants grown from seeds are variable.

The runners of many grass plants are special horizontal branches which function as reproductive devices (Figure 12.6). Pieces of the stems of many plants (cuttings) and even their leaves are capable in some cases of growing roots and forming new plants. A widespread application of the versatility of plant reproduction is to bud or graft a portion of one plant onto a different, but related, plant. In this way a plant that bears desirable fruit can be grafted to a rootstock that is resistant to soil diseases. Most citrus is grown this way. It is even possible to have a citrus tree that simultaneously bears lemons, oranges, and grapefruit!

An additional aspect of asexual reproduction is what might be termed reproduction by *regeneration.* Here a portion of an organism, removed accidentally, is capable of growing into adult form. The arms of a starfish, segments of an earthworm, as well as the plants already mentioned exemplify this phenomenon.

Finally, it is noteworthy that a considerable number of organisms, including nearly all plants, reproduce both asexually and sexually during their life cycles (Figure 12.7). Many internal parasites such as malarial organisms (Figure 12.8), tapeworms, and flukes (Figure 12.9) reproduce asexually during certain parts of their life cycles as a means of increasing their numbers significantly. This improves their chances of dispersal to other hosts and frequently insures their own survival.

Thus we find that asexual reproduction is widespread among members of the plant and animal kingdoms, even persisting among forms which also reproduce sexually. This is another way of stating that the adaptive advantages of asexual reproduction outweigh the disadvantage of reduced variability. In Chapter XIII we consider the significance of sexual reproduction and see how some organisms utilize both means of reproduction during their life cycles.

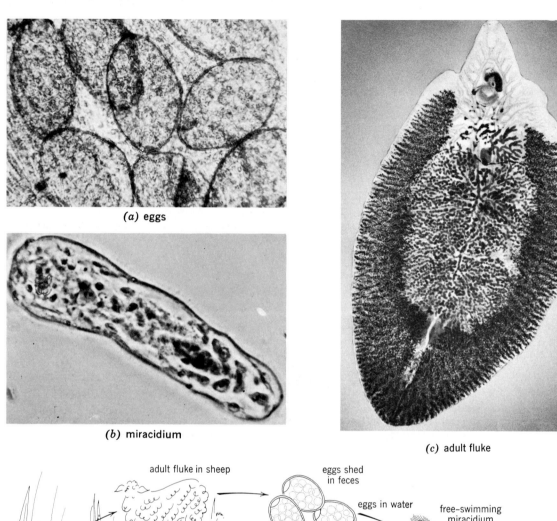

(a) eggs

(b) miracidium

(c) adult fluke

adult fluke in sheep

eggs shed
in feces

eggs in water

free-swimming
miracidium
in water

pasture

marsh or pond

snail on grass
in water

cysts on grass

cercaria

redia

free-swimming
cercaria in
water

redia in snail

sporocyst in snail

Figure 12.9. Life cycle of a sheep liver fluke.

Principles

1. Asexual reproduction derives its characteristics from mitosis.

2. Mitosis produces identical daughter cells because each receives identical hereditary material.

3. The similarity of asexually produced offspring is advantageous in stable environments, but disadvantageous in changing ones.

Suggested Readings

Mazia, Daniel, "Cell Division," *Scientific American,* Vol. 189 (August, 1953). Offprint No. 27, W. H. Freeman and Co., San Francisco.

Mazia, Daniel, "How Cells Divide," *Scientific American,* Vol. 205 (September, 1961). Offprint No. 93, W. H. Freeman and Co., San Francisco.

Singer, Marcus, "The Regeneration of Body Parts," *Scientific American,* Vol. 199 (October, 1958). Offprint No. 105, W. H. Freeman and Co., San Francisco.

Swanson, Carl P., *The Cell.* Second edition. Prentice-Hall, Englewood Cliffs, N. J., 1964, pp. 62–77.

Questions

1. What is the basic difference between asexual and sexual reproduction?

2. Reproduction is fundamentally a cellular event. Can you defend this statement?

3. What is the literal meaning of the term *mitosis?* How does this relate to the process of mitosis?

4. Describe in your own words the events which occur during cell division.

5. What is the most important end result of mitosis?

6. What advantages does asexual reproduction provide for an organism?

7. What is the major disadvantage of asexual reproduction? Is this always a disadvantage?

8. List the major types of asexual reproduction and provide an example for each one from your local area.

Sexual Reproduction

Queen bee tended by workers. (© *Walt Disney Productions.*)

OUT LINE
HAND IN = 10

CHAPTER

XIII

Sexual Reproduction

Sexual reproduction, as mentioned in Chapter XII, is the uniting of two specialized cells or nuclei known as *gametes* to form a fertilized egg or *zygote*. Although sexual reproduction is a complex biological activity, it occurs among nearly all groups of living organisms. We might conclude from this that there must be a marked adaptive advantage to reproducing in this manner.

Advantages and Disadvantages of Sexual Reproduction

Probably the greatest biological advantage of sexual reproduction accrues from the increased variability which results from uniting the hereditary material of two organisms. This creates a truly *new* organism, similar but never identical to either parent. Such variability is of tremendous evolutionary importance since it provides species with means of adapting over a long period of time to new environmental challenges. Even on a short-term basis this variability is advantageous since a population may encounter changes in its surroundings within relatively few generations. In this sense it gives a population a necessary plasticity.

There are three ways in which sexual reproduction seems to be a disadvantage: two parents are usually required, various courtship procedures are involved (in many animals) and the gametes must be brought together in nonmotile organisms such as plants. Despite these complexities, sexual reproduction prevails

at all levels of life. In fact, a large share of the anatomical and physiological adaptations found in organisms is related to this process.

Meiosis

The Necessity for Chromosome Reduction. Recall that sexual reproduction is defined as the fusion of two specialized nuclei (usually in sex cells). A moment's thought will suggest a paradox concerning the amount of nuclear (hereditary) material in the zygote. It appears that this material should double each time two gametes unite. However, it does not double, because of a special type of nuclear division called *meiosis*. This division precedes the formation of the gametes so that they contain only half as much hereditary material as the parent cells from which they derive. Thus when two gametes unite, the resulting zygote has the full or normal complement of hereditary substance. For example, human body cells contain 46 chromosomes (23 pairs): human eggs and sperm contain 23 chromosomes each (one member of each pair) as a consequence of meiosis. We refer to this reduced number as the *haploid* number and to the full complement of chromosomes as the *diploid* number.

Since meiosis is so important in sexual reproduction, we need to examine it in greater detail. Meiosis starts with a cell containing the full number of chromosomes characteristic of the organism (two haploid sets). The cell undergoes two mitosislike divisions but the chro-

155

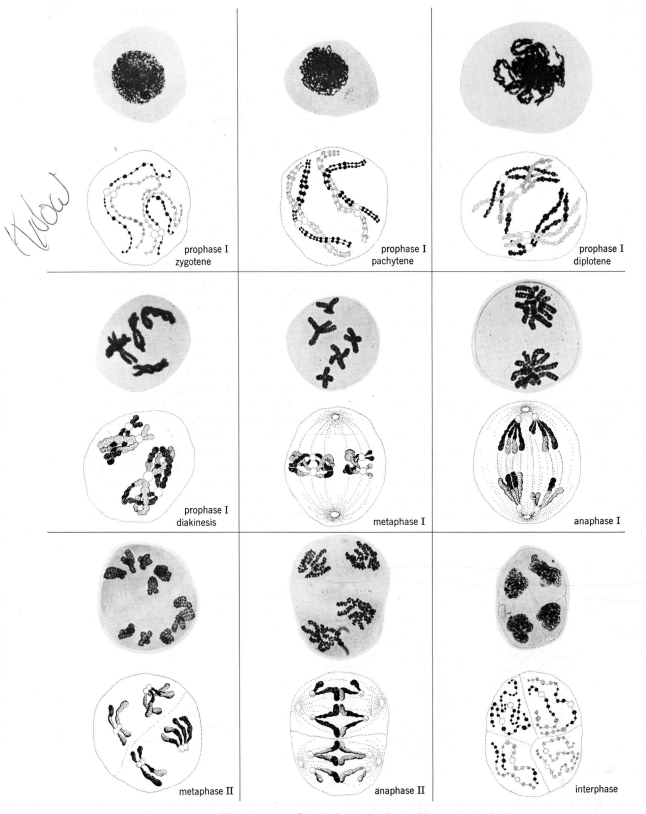

prophase I
zygotene

prophase I
pachytene

prophase I
diplotene

prophase I
diakinesis

metaphase I

anaphase I

metaphase II

anaphase II

interphase

Figure 13.1. Meiosis. (Dr. Arnold H. Sparrow and Mr. Robert F. Smith, Brookhaven National Laboratory.)

mosomes are duplicated only once. This process results in four daughter cells, each containing one-half the number of chromosomes in the original cell. The daughter cells specialize into gametes or gamete-bearing individuals.

Stages of Meiosis. In the prophase portion of the first division stage (*Prophase I*), the diffuse chromosomal network in the nucleus becomes a discrete network of threadlike bodies (Figure 13.1). The nuclear membrane gradually disappears and the spindle forms. As the chromosomes take shape, each one lines up with its homologue, that is, with another one like itself, and the two become closely entwined. This event is unique to meiosis; it does not occur in mitosis. An analogy to this pairing process can be made by pressing the palms of one's hands together. If you consider your fingers as chromosomes, then you have pairs of "homologous chromosomes."

The paired chromosomes are termed *bivalents*. Each chromosome in a bivalent contains two strands of hereditary material (two *chromatids*); thus a bivalent consists of four chromatids. Superficially, a bivalent appears as two chromosomes closely associated with each other. The chromosomes then move slightly apart as though the pairing process were ending. As this happens, the chromatids in some of the bivalents adhere to each other at one or more sites rather than separate. These sites represent places where the chromatids have exchanged parts with each other. This activity, known as *crossing over*, has considerable hereditary importance as we shall see in Chapter XVI.

As Prophase I terminates, the chromosomes in their bivalent arrangement begin to orient themselves on the spindle. Each bivalent has two centromeres, one for each homologous chromosome.

At *Metaphase I* the bivalents are arranged on the middle of the spindle in such a way that the homologues of each one can eventually move to opposite poles. In this process each bivalent acts independently of the others, a highly significant event because it results in random shuffling of the chromosomes into the daughter cells. For this reason it is termed *independent assortment*.

During *Anaphase I* the homologues separate to opposite ends of the spindle, one member of each pair going to each end of the cell. Again this is unique to meiosis because it results in the *segregation* of homologous chromosomes. *Telophase I* may follow in the conventional manner with two daughter nuclei or cells forming. Or, the two sets of chromosomes may enter directly into the second division.

In the second division of meiosis we follow two daughter cells or nuclei. In each a spindle forms and the chromosomes orient in the usual position at metaphase. The centromere of each chromosome splits so that at *Anaphase II* the two chromatids making up each chromosome pull apart and move to opposite ends of the spindle. At *Telophase II,* a nuclear membrane forms about each mass of chromosomal material, the spindle disappears, and finally, daughter cells (four in all) represent the end product of meiosis. Each of these cells has as many *kinds* of chromosomes as its parent cell but only *one* of each kind or half the total number in the parent.

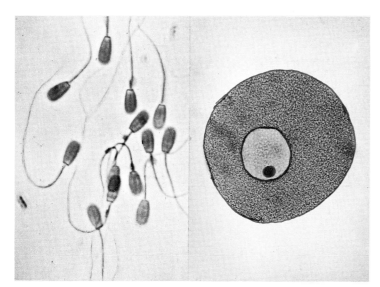

Figure 13.2. Mature sperm (left) and egg (right).

These meiotic daughter cells are not mature gametes. In animals further specialization of the daughter cells results in either sperm or egg cells. Sperm cells are generally small and motile, eggs are larger and nonmotile (Figure 13.2). In animals this specialization usually occurs in the ovaries and testes. In higher plants the production of gametes occurs in the flower. In lower plants we cannot make a generalization about the site of gamete production because it occurs in different types of structures in various groups.

Like mitosis, meiosis is virtually a universal process in the world of living things. The student of biology must understand the mechanisms and significance of both processes to develop an adequate appreciation of other fundamental biological events such as genetics.

Reproduction in the Animal Kingdom

Most animals conform to the basic life cycle plan shown in Fig. 13.3. Here a haploid egg and sperm nucleus form a zygote. The zygote matures into another gamete-forming generation and so the life cycle continues. Variations in this plan are almost endless as we can demonstrate by examining the reproductive cycles of several types of plants and animals.

Paramecium illustrates the basic tenet of sexual reproduction, the fusion of nuclei. Under certain physiological conditions, two paramecia unite side by side (Figure 13.4). A series of nuclear activities occurs within each animal, but eventually each exchanges a portion of its nuclear material with the other. Then they separate and undergo two fissions. This exchange of nuclear, and presumably hereditary, material satisfies the general definition of sexual reproduction even though no gametes are formed and the different sexes are not recognizable.

Hydra, the small many-celled freshwater animal mentioned in Chapter XII, exemplifies several aspects of reproduction. Some species are *hermaphroditic* in that ovaries and testes form on the same animal (Figure 13.5). Sperm are liberated into the water around the animal and swim about until they encounter a mature egg. Even in this relatively primitive form we find the gametes specialized into two types. This method of liberating gametes into the surroundings, which we call external fertilization, is common among water dwellers. Jellyfish, for example, do the same thing although they are not hermaphroditic. In the

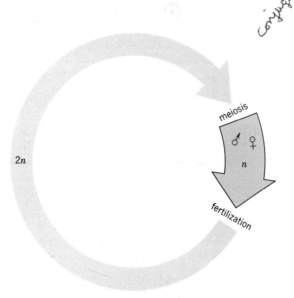

meiosis

♂ ♀

n

2n

fertilization

Figure 13.3. Generalized life cycle for animals.

Figure 13.4. Conjugating Paramecium. (General Biological Supply House, Inc.)

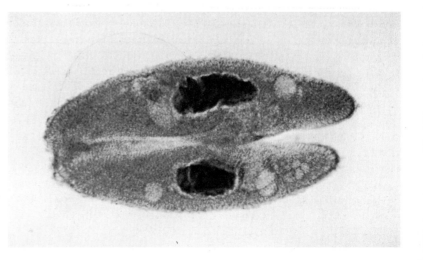

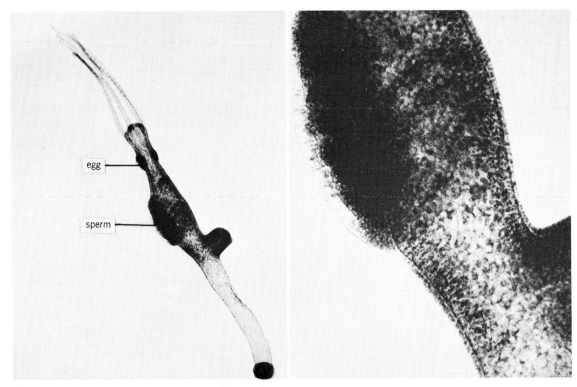

Figure 13.5. A hermaphroditic Hydra *(left). A more highly magnified view of the testis (right).*

life cycle of jellyfish both the asexual and sexual phases are diploid but involve two different forms (Figure 13.6).

Earthworms contain both ovaries and testes but must mate in order to bring the gametes together. During the mating process each worm emits sperm which flow down special grooves to be stored by the other worm in a special sperm receptacle. After the worms separate, each produces eggs which are fertilized with the sperm obtained earlier from the other worm. Crossfertilization, and hence, a mixing of hereditary material from two individuals is thus achieved.

Hermaphroditism is common but not universal among invertebrates. Some groups like the arthropods seldom have hermaphroditic members, whereas others like the mollusks have many. Generally it seems to be found among organisms that have limited means of locomotion or that may seldom encounter one another (like earthworms). In all of these groups it is not unusual for the female, or each member of a hermaphroditic pair, to store sperm cells for long periods of time and use them on successive batches of eggs. Most hermaphroditic forms also have adaptations which encourage crossfertilization, although a few animals (for example, tapeworms) and a large number of plants are known to fertilize themselves.

Another adaptation frequently found in invertebrates and plants is the ability of unfertilized eggs to develop into adults. This is called *parthenogenesis* and constitutes part of the normal reproductive cycle of many insects such as aphids and honey bees. In some species of aphids the females lay eggs throughout the spring and summer which develop parthenogenetically into more females. In the fall, some of the eggs hatch into males which mature and then mate with the females. They in turn begin laying diploid eggs. These eggs survive through the winter to start up new generations of aphids the following spring. In other species of aphids, the males have never been found and may not even exist.

Parthenogenesis in plants may be seen in certain species of hawkweed. In these species the production of egg cells does not involve meiosis, and the unfertilized eggs develop into diploid plants.

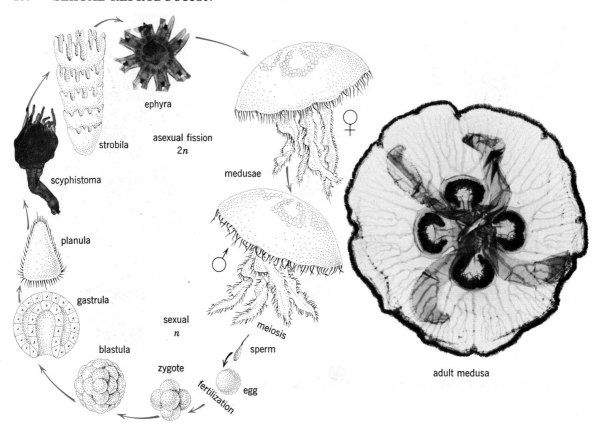

ephyra

asexual fission
2n

strobila

medusae

scyphistoma

planula

gastrula

sexual
n

meiosis

sperm

blastula

zygote

egg

fertilization

adult medusa

Figure 13.6. Life cycle of the jellyfish, Aurelia.

In honey bees, the queen mates only once and stores the sperm from this mating for use during the remainder of her lifetime. As she lays eggs in the cells of the honeycomb, some are fertilized and others are not. The fertilized eggs develop into females, mostly workers, and the haploid eggs become males (drones). (See Figure 13.7.) Here we have a rather extreme case of parthenogenesis as well as sex determination by chromosome number.

Parthenogenesis is nonsexual in that only one cell is involved. Nevertheless, it involves a special structure, the egg, which normally takes part in sexual reproduction. Hence some authors term it an asexual event and others treat it as a variation of sexual reproduction.

If we look at the reproductive patterns in groups of vertebrates, we continue to find considerable diversity. The bulk of fishes and amphibians have external fertilization with little or no parental care of the eggs and young. On rainy spring evenings every roadside ditch seems to be full of singing frogs. The males are making

this noise, in a sense advertising their presence to the females. As the females join the singing males the mating activity takes place. A male clasps a female from behind, and this behavior in turn stimulates the female to lay eggs. The male sheds sperm cells over the eggs as they emerge. The fertilized eggs remain in large masses in the water to develop with no further attention from the parents.

Most vertebrates, except mammals, are hatched from eggs and even here we encounter variations from the gelatinous coated eggs typical of amphibians to the shelled eggs of birds. In mammals, in contrast, the sperm cells are always deposited into the reproductive tract of the female, and there is a long period of parental care of the young. In addition, behavior, as related to reproduction, such as courtship between mates, becomes quite elaborate in birds and mammals.

Reproduction in the Plant Kingdom

The plant kingdom presents some other variations of the sexual reproduction theme. Figure 13.8 illus-

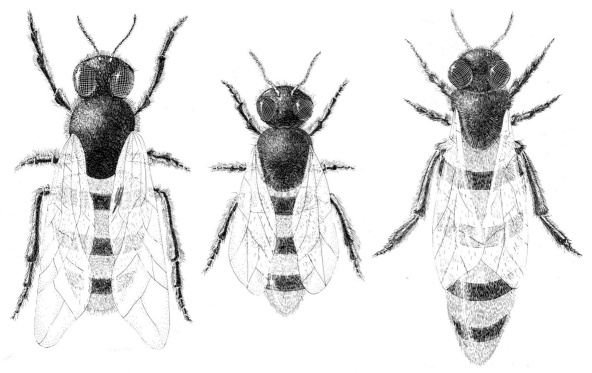

Figure 13.7. Three kinds of honey bees: the drone (left), worker (center), and queen (right).

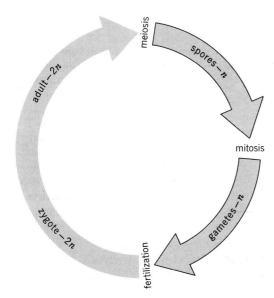

Figure 13.8. A generalized life cycle for plants. Many of the more primitive plants have a multicellular stage that develops from the haploid spores.

trates a generalized life-cycle scheme for plants. As in the animal life-cycle plan, a haploid egg and sperm unite to form a zygote. The zygote matures but takes a radical departure from the animal life cycle. This diploid member forms haploid spores, rather than gametes, by meiosis. For this reason it is called the *sporophyte generation*. The spores eventually become a gamete-forming generation, the *gametophyte generation*. Since the spores are already haploid, the gametes they produce by mitosis are haploid. This cycle bridges two generations, one haploid and one diploid, a plan basic to all plants above the bacteria. Meiosis occurs in the sporophyte generation but *not,* as in animals, in the gamete-producing organism. This is a situation peculiar to plants; it is often present as an adaptation for dispersal.

An Alga. *Chlamydomonas* is a motile, single-celled alga which is a common freshwater inhabitant. It reproduces asexually by a form of fission (Figure 13.9). In addition, two cells may fuse to form a zygote, sometimes termed a *zygospore* since it is surrounded by a protective coat and can resist unfavorable conditions like drying. A zygospore undergoes meiosis to produce

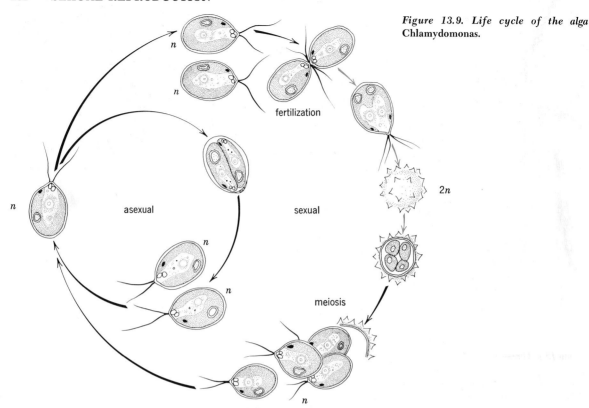

Figure 13.9. Life cycle of the alga Chlamydomonas.

four haploid cells. These cells enlarge slightly to become the adult form of *Chlamydomonas*.

Two points are notable here. First, the organism spends most of its life cycle in the haploid state; second, the two cells that perform the function of gametes are identical at least in size and appearance. The presence of like gametes (*isogametes*) is common among algae and fungi, but not among members of the remainder of the plant kingdom. As with animals, specialization of the sex cells into eggs or sperm (*heterogametes*) is the rule. Some biologists have speculated that the evolution of sexual reproduction could have begun with the fusion of similar cells (isogametes) during the life cycle of some primitive organism. Once this was successfully established further specialization of the gametes into motile cells (sperm) and cells containing a store of food materials (eggs) would make the process even more efficient.

Moss.   If we examine the life cycle of a much more advanced plant, a moss, we find still further adaptations of the reproductive process (Figure 13.10). The microscopic, haploid spores of the moss plant are transported by wind or water until they are deposited in a suitable environment, such as moist soil. A spore

then germinates into a small branching filament which later becomes a moss plant. The plants thus formed will bear either male or female reproductive cells although some species of mosses bear both. These moss plants compose the gametophyte generation of the moss life cycle. Note that each plant grows from a haploid spore; hence it is haploid and its sexual products (gametes) are automatically haploid. The male reproductive tissue consists of a stalklike body near the tip of the plant in which numerous sperm cells are formed. The female reproductive organ consists of an egg surrounded by a thick jacket drawn out into a long, hollow neck. Fertilization is effected by the motile sperm cells swimming to the female organs in a film of water, entering the neck, and eventually uniting with the egg cells.

The zygote is consequently diploid. It grows to become first an embryo, and then the embryo develops into a long stalk with a capsule at the end. This structure grows out of the end of the female gametophyte. This new diploid structure is termed a sporophyte because a mass of cells inside the capsule forms haploid spores by meiosis. When mature, the capsule opens so that the spores are dispersed. And this is where we

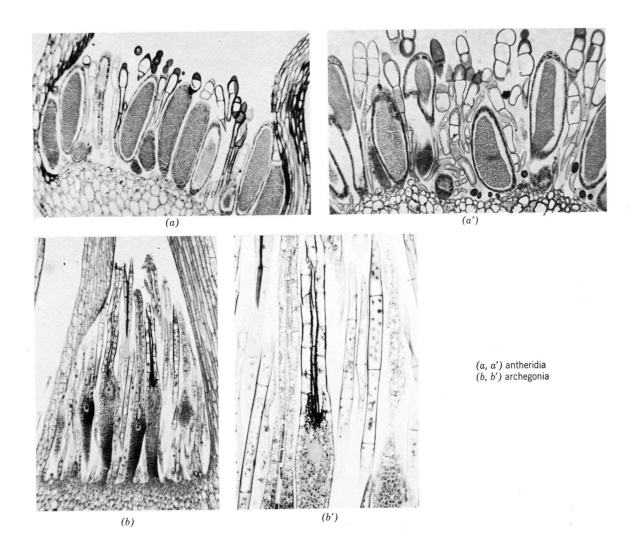

(a)   (a')

(b)   (b')

(a, a') antheridia
(b, b') archegonia

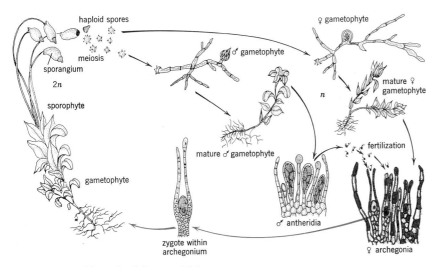

Figure 13.10. Life cycle of the moss Mnium.

163

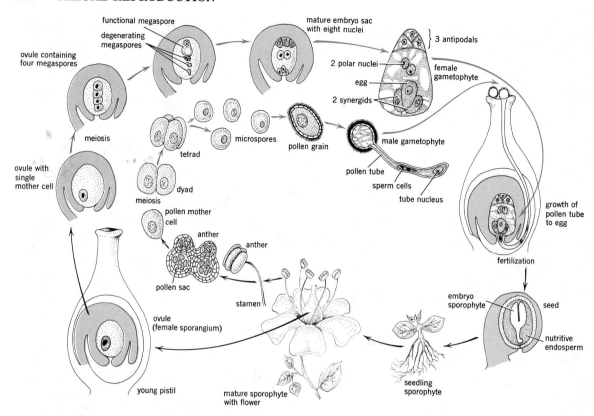

Figure 13.11. Life cycle of a flowering plant.

began our description of the reproductive cycle in mosses. In mosses the two generations, sporophyte and gametophyte, are about equally prominent in the life cycle. Among higher plants, the sporophyte is the most dominant part of the cycle, while the gametophyte is reduced to a brief, often microscopic, part. This reduction was evidently a major trend in the evolution of the plant kingdom.

Flowering Plants. The cycle of a flowering plant nicely illustrates this last comment (Figure 13.11). Our common herbs, shrubs, and trees consist almost entirely of the spore-producing generation. The *stamens* in the flower contain spore-forming bodies called anthers. Meiosis inside the anthers gives rise to haploid spores. Each spore undergoes a certain amount of differentiation (the nucleus divides once or twice) to become a male gametophyte or *pollen grain*.

The other type of spore-forming organ, also in the flower, is located in the base (ovary) of a structure called the *pistil*. Here cells again enter meiotic divisions to form haploid spores. Some of these, after a series of additional mitotic divisions and specializa-

tion, form female gametophytes called embryo sacs, each containing an egg (Figure 13.12).

If a pollen grain is transported to the stigma of the pistil, it grows a pollen tube down through the pistil to the embryo sac in the ovary. The contents of the pollen grain, usually two sperm nuclei, pass down the pollen tube into the sac where one sperm nucleus fertilizes an egg nucleus. The second sperm nucleus unites with another nucleus or other nuclei in the sac to form a tissue known as endosperm which nourishes the developing zygote and embryo. A plant embryo, surrounded by layers of food material and a tough outer coat, is termed a *seed*. This structure can exist and survive independently of the parent plant for considerable periods of time. It has all the capabilities of forming a new sporophyte when the environment permits it to germinate.

In most instances, seeds are not simply liberated from the plant as such, but are encased in various modified parts of the flower or plant as a *fruit*. These enclosing layers of material, juicy or dry, function in various ways to aid in dispersal of the seeds. For ex-

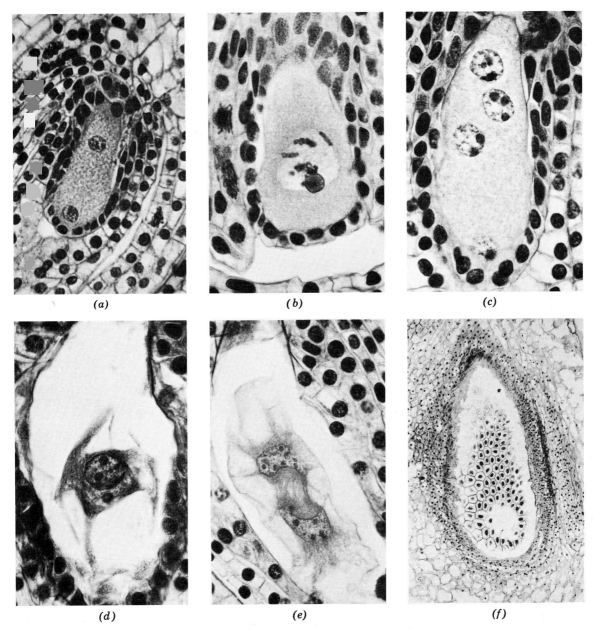

Figure 13.12. Photomicrographs of meiosis, fertilization, and early development in the ovary of a flowering plant, Fritillaria. (a) Ovule. (b) Megaspore mother cell. (c) Four-nucleate embryo sac. (d) Triple fusion. (e) Division of endosperm nucleus following fertilization. (f) Several-celled endosperm.

ample, mammals or birds may eat the fruit and then deposit the seeds undamaged in their droppings in some other location. Many additional adaptations exist for dispersing these nonmotile elements.

The examples of plant and animal life cycles presented here should give some idea of the many variations that exist. It is worth emphasizing that the basic plan of egg + sperm = zygote is nearly universal. Even those forms with isogametes foreshadow this idea. The many variations of this plan are adaptations to make the reproductive process more workable within the limitations of a particular kind of organism in a particular kind of environment. That is, a considerable number of the behavioral, anatomical, and physiological adaptations found in all organisms are built around their reproductive processes.

Principles

1. Sexual reproduction derives its characteristics from meiosis and fertilization.

2. Meiosis produces cells that vary in genetic makeup through a reduction in chromosome number.

3. The variation found among sexually produced offspring is advantageous in changing environments but less advantageous in stable ones.

Suggested Readings

Allen, R. D., "The Moment of Fertilization," *Scientific American,* Vol. 201 (July, 1959).

Loomis, W. F., "The Sex Gas of Hydra," *Scientific American,* Vol. 200 (April, 1959).

Monroy, A., "Fertilization of the Egg," *Scientific American,* Vol. 183 (December, 1950).

Pincus, G., "Fertilization in Mammals," *Scientific American,* Vol. 184 (March, 1951).

Rothschild, Lord, "Unorthodox Methods of Sperm Transfer," *Scientific American,* Vol. 195 (November, 1956).

Smith, C. Lavett, "Hermaphroditism in Bahama Groupers," *Natural History,* Vol. LXXVIII (June-July, 1964).

Swanson, Carl P., *The Cell.* Second edition. Prentice-Hall, Englewood Cliffs, N. J., 1964, pp. 78–93.

Questions

1. What major advantage does sexual reproduction provide for a population?

2. In what ways is it a drawback?

3. Why is it important that reduction in chromosome number accompany sexual reproduction?

4. Describe in your own words the events that constitute meiosis.

5. What is the difference between independent assortment and segregation?

6. In what respect does a sperm cell illustrate the concept from Chapter III that specialization in form takes place primarily in the cytoplasm? How does this apply to an egg cell?

7. An organism originating by parthenogenesis must be identical to which parent? Why?

8. In what major aspect do the reproductive cycles of plants differ from those of animals? Is this an adaptation? For what?

9. Compare the reproductive cycle of a moss to that of a flowering plant, noting the basic similarities and differences.

10. The size, color, and scent of flowers are adaptations for what?

11. What important adaptive advantage do seed-forming plants have over those that form spores only?

12. Consider several types of fruit familiar to you and make an "educated guess" as to their means of dispersal in nature.

13. Is man an important dispersal agent? Why?

Development

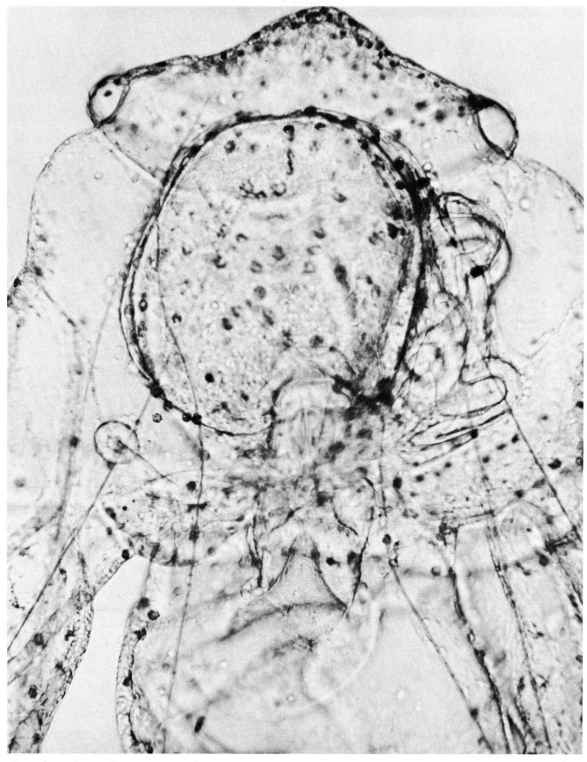

Pluteus larva of sea urchin.

Development

Stages of Development

In most organisms reproduction involves more than the production of gametes and fertilization. Because it is small and single celled, the undifferentiated zygote resulting from fertilization usually bears little resemblance to the adult organism. For the reproductive process to be complete, three types of events must occur: an increase in the number of cells (*cleavage*), the laying down of the outline of the structures of the organism (*morphogenesis*), and the specialization of cells and structures to perform their specific duties (*differentiation*). These events, taken together, constitute development.

Cleavage. Cleavage consists of the first divisions of the zygote, which are carried out with little intervening time. The number of cells greatly increases but the total amount of protoplasm remains the same as it was in the zygote. In animals, this process ends with the formation of the *blastula,* a hollow ball of cells (Figure 14.1). To this point no morphogenesis or differentiation occurs and there is little growth. After blastulation cell division continues at a generally lower rate, with an accompanying growth of cells and in concurrence, morphogenesis and differentiation.

Morphogenesis. Morphogenesis begins in animals with the laying down of the general pattern of the digestive tract. This activity produces the next stage, the *gastrula* (Figure 14.1). During the later phase of gastrulation (formation of the gastrula) other cell groups are separated from the primitive gut and from the cells that will form the outer layers of the skin and the nervous system. These groups eventually form such structures as muscle, gonads, circulatory system, and excretory system. The determination of which group of cells affects the formation of each animal structure is an arduous task. One method that has uncovered considerable information on this topic is the marking of areas in the blastula with dyes unharmful to the cells (vital dyes). (See Figure 14.2.) The cells colored with these dyes may then be followed so that their movements and the structures they affect can be discerned.

Differentiation. Differentiation is a more difficult subject to pursue because the changes in the cell are largely physiological and biochemical, and are morphological only to a limited degree. Later in this chapter we cite one example of this kind of study.

Variations in the Stages. Organisms carry out cleavage, morphogenesis, and differentiation in various ways. Even among the multicellular animals the processes are diverse. If we compare cleavage in molluscs and in the vertebrates we see some fundamental differences between them. In the vertebrates the new cells produced after the four-cell stage lie directly above the old cells, whereas in the molluscs the new cells lie in the furrows between them. Moreover, in molluscs, prior to each of the early cleavages a bulge,

169

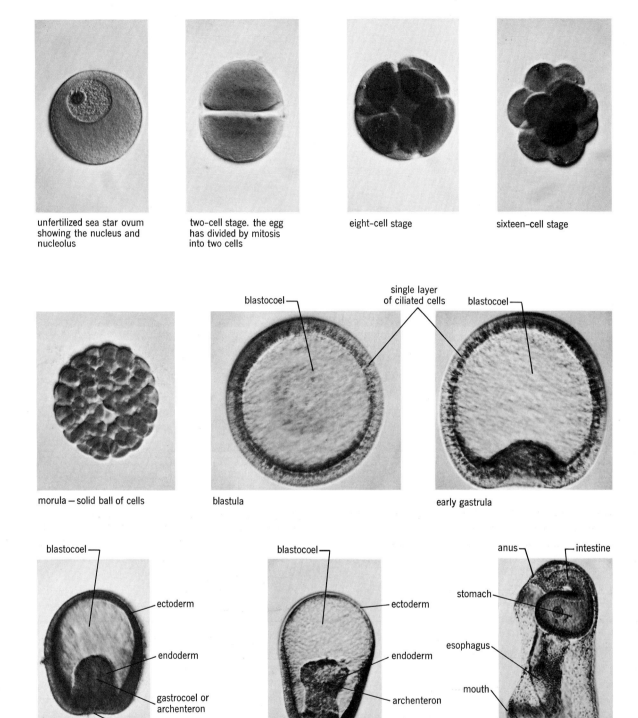

unfigured sea star ovum showing the nucleus and nucleolus

two-cell stage. the egg has divided by mitosis into two cells

eight–cell stage

sixteen–cell stage

morula — solid ball of cells

blastocoel

single layer of ciliated cells

blastocoel

blastula

early gastrula

blastocoel

ectoderm

endoderm

gastrocoel or archenteron

blastopore

gastrula showing blastopore and beginning of gastrocoel cavity

blastocoel

ectoderm

endoderm

archenteron

blastopore

late gastrula

anus

intestine

stomach

esophagus

mouth

preoral lobe

swimming dipleurula larva

Figure 14.1. Early development in a sea star. (General Biological Supply House, Inc.)

170

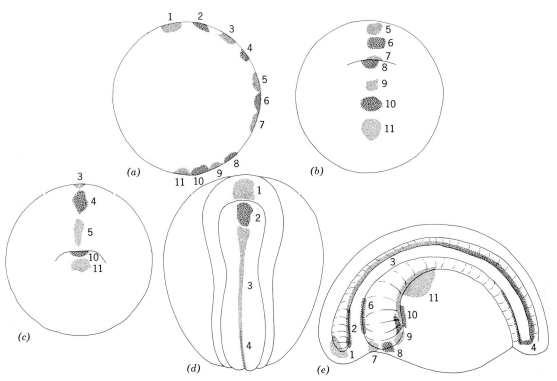

Figure 14.2. Tracing of cell movements using vital dyes. Each numbered area was dyed a distinct color (a). Parts (b) and (c) show that some of the areas have moved into the interior of the embryo. Parts (d) and (e) show the positions of these areas later in development as viewed from the top and side. (From Vogt, 1929; Balinsky, An Introduction to Embryology, *second ed., W. B. Saunders Co., Philadelphia, 1965.)*

the polar lobe, forms at the end of the cell farthest from the nucleus (Figure 14.3). This fuses with one of the resulting cells. No such structure exists in the vertebrates.

In many cases a free-living, larval stage forms following the gastrula. This is a developmental stage which differs markedly in appearance from the adult. Some animals have no larval stage because of the plentiful supply of food available to the developing embryo. This supply may come from the mother either by way of a placenta, as in mammals, or by stored yolk deposited in the egg. A large deposit of yolk affects development in still another way. It retards the rate of cleavage in the portion of the egg containing the yolk. In embryos developing from eggs with moderate amounts of yolk, the upper cells may be considerably smaller than the lower cells (Figure 14.4). If large amounts of yolk are present as in bird or shark eggs, only the upper portion of the egg cleaves and the early embryo develops as a disc on the upper surface of the yolk.

Like the green alga *Acetabularia,* the adults of many organisms are single celled. Obviously no cleavage occurs in development but morphogenesis and differentiation do. In *Acetabularia* the zygote becomes attached to the bottom, and produces a group of rootlike structures or rhizoids (Figure 14.5). A slender stalk grows upward and an umbrella-shaped cap forms at the top. The nucleus is found at the base of the stalk. Morphogenesis and differentiation have both occurred.

Morphogenesis is easy to identify in the formation of the three areas of the plant. Differentiation is difficult to see. Various areas *within* the single cell are specialized for particular roles partly by their shape and location and partly by their functional differences. Many single-celled plants and animals show rather similar patterns.

All multicellular organisms have developmental patterns which involve cleavage. In plants it is often difficult to distinguish cleavage, morphogenesis, and differentiation because all three occur at the same time

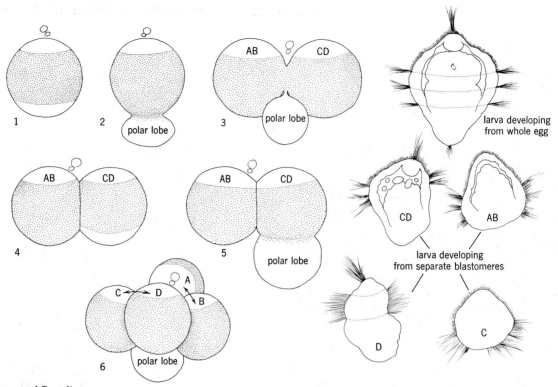

cleavage of *Dentalium*

Figure 14.3. Early development in the mollusc Dentalium showing cleavage (left) and the embryos that develop from separated cells (right). (From Fig. 1, Wilson, J. Exp. Zoology, Vol. 1, 1904.)

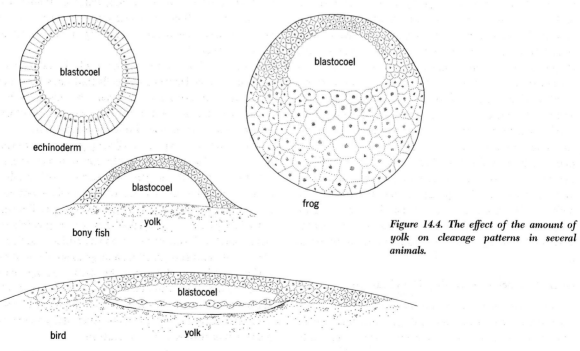

Figure 14.4. The effect of the amount of yolk on cleavage patterns in several animals.

172

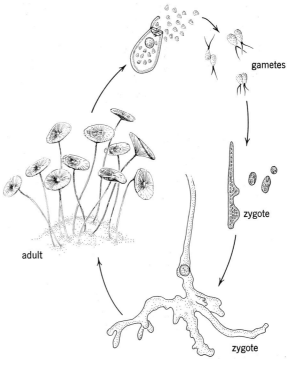

Figure 14.5. Life cycle of Acetabularia. *(Photograph from General Biological Supply House, Inc.)*

in separate parts of the same organism. In the production of the embryo in flowering plants, however, we find that the first cell divisions occur without morphogenesis. Then the cotyledons (food-storing, leaflike structures) and the root and stem structures form (Figure 14.6). In appearance the cells show no specialization from one structure to another. Later development produces the early stages of leaves on the stem and the first signs of the differentiation of cells.

After the seed germinates, cleavage, morphogenesis, and differentiation continue throughout the life of the plant mainly at the tip of the stem and root. Thus mature and embryonic tissues are present at all times in a mature, growing plant. Development in most multicellular animals does not continue throughout the life of the individual. Instead developmental changes cease by the time the organism becomes mature.

Some Factors Controlling Development

The patterns of development we have discussed show that within the same embryo, cells that appear similar move in various ways and differentiate into distinct forms. If we look at several types of organisms we find an even more confusing range of events. We learned earlier that most organisms have the same types of basic metabolic machinery. What accounts for the diversity?

We can find our answer more easily if we ask two other questions. How can two cells that have the same hereditary information differentiate dissimilarly? How much impact will a different set of hereditary information have on the development of a cell?

Three kinds of experiments supply answers to the first of the subsidiary questions. Important factors are: (1) the position of the cell in relation to other cells; (2) the changes in the nucleus during development; (3) the way in which the cytoplasm of the egg is divided.

Cell Position.   With certain plants it is possible to take a single cell and culture it on an artificial medium. The cell divides and produces a large mass of undifferentiated cells. At this time the cells look approximately alike. With the increase in the size of the cell mass we find near its center the development of specialized cells of the root and stem. Eventually an entire plant will be formed from the culture.

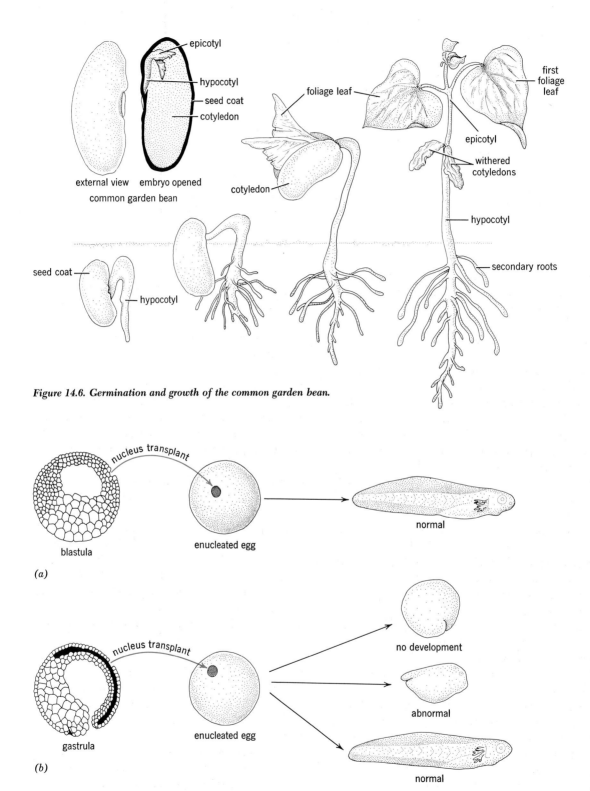

Figure 14.6. Germination and growth of the common garden bean.

Figure 14.7. Nuclear transplant experiment. Nuclei from a blastula transplanted into an enucleated egg yield normal larvae (a). Nuclei transplanted from a gastrula yield varied developmental forms (b).

174

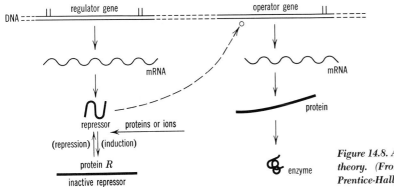

Figure 14.8. *A diagrammatic representation of the operon theory. (From Hartman and Suskind,* Gene Action, *Prentice-Hall, Englewood Cliffs, N. J., 1965.)*

If cells are prevented from accumulating into a mass by the experimenter's continued separating of the cells, no differentiation will occur. The relative position of cells causes differentiation of some of them when they are allowed to remain in contact with one another.

Nuclear Changes. Work with the embryos of frogs has shown that the nuclei change with the age of the embryo. If the nuclei are removed from unfertilized eggs and replaced with nuclei from embryos (blastula or younger), nearly all the resulting cells will produce normal embryos (Figure 14.7). If the nuclei transplanted into enucleated eggs come from older embryos, the resulting embryos vary widely; some do not develop at all, some develop normally, and some develop into abnormal embryos.

Even though the transplanted nuclei always contain the same hereditary information, their activity changes with age. The aging of the nuclei is not simply a matter of time but of time and interaction with the cytoplasm. Nuclei may be transplanted from blastulae to enucleated eggs. By repeating this mechanism the nuclei may be prevented from losing their "youthful" characteristic (ability to control the normal development of an enucleated egg).

Cytoplasmic Variations. Unequal separation of various components of the cytoplasm occurs naturally in molluscs by the formation of the polar lobe and its fusing with one of the cells resulting from the cleavage. Since this lobe is so distinct from the rest of the embryo, it may be easily removed. This will remove any substances peculiar to this part of the cytoplasm. Such experiments should give some indication of the role of these substances in development and of the importance of the manner in which cytoplasmic mate-

rials are distributed to the cells. A similar technique involves the separation of the cells at the two-cell stage. Each cell will now develop separately, one with the substances found in the polar lobe, one without.

Some variation in the details of the development of these embryos exists depending on the species used in the experiment. In general, the cells containing the polar lobe substances develop into nearly normal larvae. Those cells that do not contain polar lobe material develop into abnormal partial larvae which are missing major organ structures (Figure 14.3, right). Studies of the fate of individual cells in the normal embryo show that the missing portions normally develop from the cells that contain polar lobe substances.

We can conclude that one part of the cytoplasm contains a substance not found in another part of the cytoplasm. Usually the distribution of these substances plays an important role in determining which group of cells will form which structures in the embryo.

Operon Theory of DNA-RNA Control. The effects described in the preceding two sections can be explained by the operon theory for which two Frenchmen, François Jacob and Jacques Monod, were awarded the Nobel Prize in 1965.

They hypothesized that there are *operator genes* which function like switches whereby the product of *regulator genes* can turn segments of DNA on or off. Therefore, at any one time not all of the DNA is directing the synthesis of messenger RNA; some of it is switched off.

A regulator gene is a gene that may be located anywhere in the DNA and that through a messenger RNA most likely directs the production of a protein capable of affecting an operator gene. The usual form of this protein prevents (represses) the activity of an *operon*.

An operon is composed of an operator gene and the segment of DNA it controls. Repression occurs when the protein combines with the operator gene and prevents the initiation of messenger RNA synthesis along this segment of DNA (Figure 14.8).

The repressor form of the protein may be changed to an inactive form if a specific substance is present. This substance may be synthesized by other activity in the cytoplasm (for example, proteins) or be derived from the environment (for example, ions and amino acids). Consequently, the presence of this substance will induce the production of specific proteins by turning on the operator gene, or in other words, by removing the repression of messenger RNA synthesis along this portion of DNA.

For example, the DNA in each of the cells in a developing molluscan embryo may be in contact with cytoplasm which contains slightly different substances. These various substances will induce activity in different portions of the DNA by affecting different repressor proteins. Consequently, the makeup of the cells continues to diverge and specialization occurs.

Most of the evidence supporting this theory comes from experiments with bacteria. Indications are strong, however, that the general outlines proposed by this theory also operate in higher organisms. In higher organisms removal of the proteins that surround DNA seems to be an essential part of induction of messenger RNA synthesis.

Nuclear Transplant Experiments.   The most direct way to discover the role the nucleus plays in differentiation is to pull the nucleus out of the cell and replace it with one from another cell or from the cell of another species. This type of experiment has been conducted with *Acetabularia*. In these experiments, however, the nucleus is not removed, but the base of the plant which contains it is cut off and replaced with the base of another plant.

Two species of *Acetabularia, A. crenulata* (*cren*) and *A. mediterranea* (*med*), have frequently been used. The most obvious difference between the two is the shape of the cap. If the cap and stalk are removed from a member of either species, the plant regrows a new cap of its normal variety. If the capless stalk of a *cren* is grafted onto the base of a *med,* the plant regenerates an intermediate cap the first time. If this cap is removed, all subsequent caps will be of the same kind as the nucleus (*med*). (See Figure 14.9.) A reciprocal experiment (*med* stalk, *cren* base), produces a *cren* cap. We can conclude that by control of

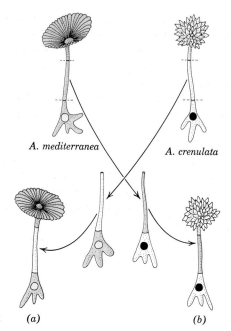

Figure 14.9. Reciprocal transplant experiments in Acetabularia showing nuclear effects on regeneration.

A. mediterranea

A. crenulata

(a)

(b)

the production of new protein the nucleus containing DNA regulates the type of cap regenerated regardless of the type of cytoplasm in the stalk.

How does the nucleus achieve this effect? If we cut the base and the cap from a plant, the piece of stalk regenerates a cap of the same type as the plant *one time only.* After this the plant dies. Obviously some substance of short life span which also contains the information necessary to control regeneration is present in the cytoplasm. Messenger RNA fits these requirements.

During development in midges (a type of insect) all nuclei except those that are eventually going to form gametes in the adult undergo a special kind of division during which most of the chromosomes are lost. The nuclei that will form gametes migrate to one end of the developing embryo where they undergo normal mitosis in an area having special granules in the cytoplasm (polar granules). Thus the gametes retain the normal chromosome number for the species. If the polar granule area is first exposed to ultraviolet radiation, the nuclei that migrate to this area also undergo the peculiar division in which chromosomes are lost. This means that the insect will be sterile because the cells that develop from this irradiated area will not contain the normal chromosome number for the gametes.

Since the area of polar granules has been shown to be rich in RNA, and since, in the cell, nucleic acids are the substances most sensitive to ultraviolet radiation, the evidence indicates that damage to RNA has destroyed this peculiar aspect of the control of development in midges. These data correlate with the control of cellular activity and present a good example of the process whereby the nucleus can control developmental phenomena.

The control system of development involves the hereditary information, DNA, and the carrier of information in the cytoplasm, messenger RNA. How are these inherited? How are they changed from one generation to the next? How has the information in two distinct species become different? These aspects we must leave to our next major topic, genetics.

Principles

1. Development comprises cleavage, morphogenesis, and differentiation.

2. The position of a cell in an embryo determines its developmental fate. This positional effect is caused by the distribution of cytoplasmic materials during cleavage and to changes that occur in the nucleus.

Suggested Readings

Fischberg, Michail and Antonie W. Blackler, "How Cells Specialize," *Scientific American,* Vol. 205 (September, 1961). Offprint No. 94, W. H. Freeman and Co., San Francisco.

Galston, Arthur W., *The Life of the Green Plant.* Second edition. Prentice-Hall, Englewood Cliffs, N. J., 1964, pp. 81–105.

Gray, George W., "The Organizer," *Scientific American,* Vol. 197 (November, 1957). Offprint No. 103, W. H. Freeman and Co., San Francisco.

Spratt, Nelson T., Jr., *Introduction to Cell Differentiation,* Reinhold Publishing Co., New York, 1964.

Steward, F. C., "The Control of Growth in Plant Cells," *Scientific American,* Vol. 209 (October, 1963). Offprint No. 167, W. H. Freeman and Co., San Francisco.

Waddington, C. H., "How Do Cells Differentiate?" *Scientific American,* Vol. 189 (September, 1953). Offprint No. 45, W. H. Freeman and Co., San Francisco.

Questions

1. Would you expect to find cleavage stages in the development of a single-celled organism? How about morphogenesis and differentiation?

2. Differentiation is almost entirely a physiological phenomenon. Is this true of cleavage?

3. During what cleavage stage does differentiation evidently begin?

4. How does the quantity of yolk in an egg affect the type of cleavage it undergoes?

5. Describe an experiment which shows that the differentiation of a cell depends partly on its association with other cells.

6. Does the nucleus of a cell change in some way during development? Cite an experiment to support your answer.

7. What features of *Acetabularia* make it especially suitable for experimentation involving the role of the nucleus in differentiation?

8. What is the significance of the experiment in which gametes of midges were exposed to radiation?

9. Why would it be difficult to argue that heredity is more important than cellular environments during development?

Mendel and the Beginning of Genetics

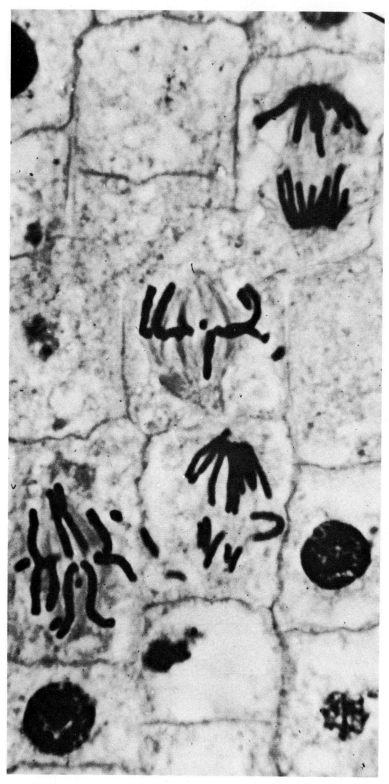

Cell division in the onion root tip. (Ward's Natural Science Establishment.)

Mendel and the Beginning of Genetics

Sexual reproduction, as we have seen, is characterized by the uniting of two haploid nuclei which bring together hereditary material (DNA) from two parent organisms. The result, a zygote, then develops under the control of this DNA material (Figure 15.1). It will not be identical to either parent but instead will be a new, and in a sense unique, organism. Consider for a moment the differences between children in the same family and you acquire the concept of individual differences.

On the other hand, the zygote invariably develops into something quite *similar* to its parents. We can predict with certainty that dogs will produce puppies and human beings will beget human beings.

It is evident that this phenomenon is of universal importance in the living world. To understand it, we must explore how hereditary material passes from parents to offspring, how this material expresses itself in new combinations, and whether principles can be formulated that apply to so complex an event. This exploration is the study of heredity, the branch of biology known as *genetics*.

Historical Background

As a science, the study of heredity is fairly recent. It dates from 1900 to be exact. As a subject of general interest and wide application, it is much older. After all, we do not have to understand the principles of heredity to breed farm animals and attempt to improve crops. It is in these areas of practical usage that some sort of crude applied genetics probably goes back to antiquity. Certainly many domesticated plants and animals were present thousands of years ago, which indicates they had an even earlier origin.

Despite this long history of practical experience, many misconceptions became associated with heredity, some of which persist. Probably the most widespread erroneous concept has to do with the influence of environment in changing or shaping new generations of organisms. Superficially it may seem reasonable to consider this influence a cause-and-effect relationship. Animals that try to hang from tree limbs by their tails should eventually give rise to young with prehensile tails; plants forced to grow in dry habitats should give rise to offspring with reduced leaves; what a mother does or feels should influence her unborn child, and so on. None of this is true, however, as we shall see shortly, because normally the environment has no effect on the structure of the hereditary material. Another common belief associates blood as a hereditary factor, as reflected by terms such as "bloodline," "blue blood," "blood will tell," and so on. Again, this is a misconception arising from ignorance of how hereditary mechanisms really operate.

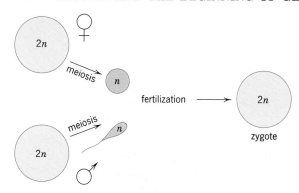

Figure 15.1. The basic scheme of reestablishment of the diploid condition.

Gregor Mendel.   The development of genetics as a scientific endeavor starts with Gregor Mendel (1822–1884), who spent a major portion of his lifetime as a monk in a monastery in Austria. He was also educated in natural science and for many years was a schoolmaster. During this time he cultivated garden plants, primarily peas, in a series of experiments designed to study inheritance in plants. Owing to Mendel's good judgment and some degree of luck, garden peas turned out to be an excellent choice for this type of study. A number of distinct varieties exist—different flower colors, dwarf and tall plants, etc., and they can be cross-pollinated by hand fairly easily, but are self-pollinating otherwise. Moreover, they bear numerous progeny (seeds). Mendel must be credited with the wisdom of studying one trait at a time, repeating his experiments, and maintaining careful records of his findings.

For a better understanding of Mendel's work, it is helpful to study the technique of his experiments with the pea plants. If he wanted to cross a red-flowered plant with a white-flowered one, he first collected seeds from each of the two varieties. He assumed that these seeds always grew true to their respective flower colors, since pea flowers are modified in such a way that the pollen cannot escape from them. Pea flowers then are self-pollinating, which means that, under normal circumstances, there is no cross-pollination between varieties. This is a handy method for assuring that one is working with pure-bred lines of descent.

Mendel then planted their seeds and allowed the plants to grow. Before the flowers matured, he removed the anthers from the flowers of one of the varieties and covered them with small sacks. When the female part of these flowers matured, he pollinated them by hand with pollen from another variety. Later he collected the seeds, the peas, which resulted from this artificial crossing. But, as you probably realize, he still had to plant these seeds and observe *their* flowers before he knew the results of this one cross.

On the surface, this appeared to be a simple experiment, but take a second look at what was involved:

(1) Careful technique in hand-pollinating the flowers at just the right time of anther and pistil development as well as prevention of accidental pollination from the wrong variety.

(2) Close attention and care for the plants between generations, that is, from seed to seed.

(3) Careful record keeping as to the number of plants involved, types of crosses, and number and kind of offspring produced.

Now let us follow one of his experiments and then see if we can reach the same conclusions as Mendel did. When he wished to study the inheritance of flower color, he crossed red-flowered peas with white-flowered ones: the seeds he obtained grew into plants which bore red flowers only. He then let this new generation of peas with the red flowers fertilize itself, collected the seeds, planted them, and observed the results. In one experiment, the results turned out to be 705 red-flowered pea plants and 224 white-flowered ones (Figure 15.2). This is illustrated diagrammatically as follows. The parental generation (P_1) of plants is bred:

P_1:   red-flowered $\times$ white-flowered

This cross yields seeds which grow into the *first filial generation* (F_1):

F_1:   plants bearing red flowers only

When plants of the F_1 generation are crossed,

red-flowered $\times$ red-flowered

the yield is seeds which grow into the *second filial generation* (F_2):

F_2:   red- (705) and white-flowered plants (224)
(approximately a 3:1 ratio)

Mendel performed numerous experiments similar to this one covering various characteristics such as tall and dwarf plants, smooth and wrinkled seeds (Figure 15.3), yellow and green seed color, and so on. Over a period of eight years of experimentation he used twenty varieties of garden peas. Eventually he studied his extensive data, noted the consistent occurrence of

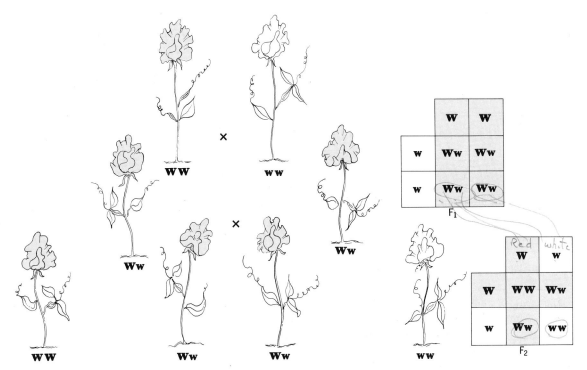

Figure 15.2. A graphic representation of Mendel's red- and white-flowered cross.

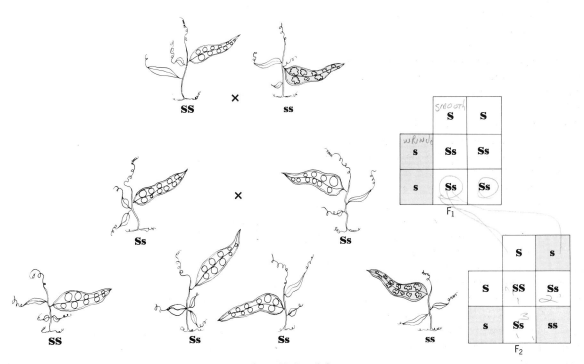

Figure 15.3. Mendel's experiment crossing smooth- and wrinkled-seeded peas.

certain ratios, and realized that an orderly process had to be operating. He finally arrived at some significant conclusions:

(1) Hereditary traits are discrete units which pass unchanged from generation to generation. For example, the trait "white-flower" seems to disappear in the F_1 generation, but reappears in the F_2 progeny. Note also that there are no intermediate colors, only red or white.

(2) Each trait is produced by *two* hereditary factors. This is a necessary assumption to account for the way in which a trait such as flower color appears in successive generations in a predictable ratio.

(3) When two *contrasting* hereditary factors are present in an organism, such as red-flower color and white-flower color, only one will be expressed. One will be *dominant* and the other *recessive*. In the case of the peas, red-flower color is dominant to white-flower color when these two factors occur in the same plant, since only the hereditary trait of red shows in the F_1 generation.

(4) Each parent contributes only *one* of the two hereditary factors to each gamete. When the egg or sperm cells are formed, there is a separation or *segregation* of hereditary factors. For example, an egg may contain either a factor for red color or one for white color, but never both. (This is called *Mendel's law of segregation*.) Moreover, as a consequence of segregation, equal numbers of gametes of each kind are formed.

(5) When gametes unite at fertilization, the two hereditary factors are brought together and again exist in pairs. Fertilization is a random union in the sense that equal numbers of the different kinds of gametes are produced, and it is a matter of chance how they will pair. This being true, it should be possible, on a probability basis, to predict the ratio of various characteristics in the offspring. In the flower-color experiment, for example, the ratio of approximately three red-flowered plants to each white-flowered plant conforms to the expected or predicted ratio of three to one.

Based on these conclusions, the same cross can be diagrammed with symbols, if, as Mendel suggested, capital letters are used for dominant factors and lower case letters for their recessive counterparts. For example, if **W** represents the hereditary factor for red and **w** the hereditary factor for white, then a plant could be **WW** (red), **Ww** (red), or **ww** (white).

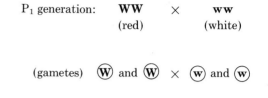

P_1 generation: **WW**   ×   **ww**
                     (red)   (white)

(gametes)   Ⓦ and Ⓦ   ×   ⓦ and ⓦ

F_1 generation: **Ww**
                     (red offspring only)

Crossing F_1's: **Ww**   ×   **Ww**

(gametes)   Ⓦ and ⓦ   ×   Ⓦ and ⓦ

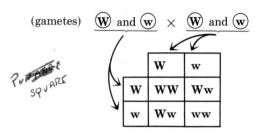

(This set of boxes is termed a Punnett Square and is useful in finding all possible gametic combinations.) Summarizing from the Punnett Square we obtain

F_2 generation: 1 **WW**   +   2 **Ww**   +   1 **ww**
                     (red)   (red)   (white)

                              3 red   1 white

                        Hence a 3:1 ratio

By using symbols we have illustrated how the five points just listed operate. The same rules of procedure apply in crosses dealing with either plants or animals. For example, crossing black and white guinea pigs through the second generation produces a ratio of about three black offspring to each white one.

We need to introduce a few more terms which will be useful in the topics that follow. Hereditary factors are commonly termed *genes*, hence **WW** represents a pair of genes for red-flower color. Also, when the two genes for a trait are alike, as **WW** or **ww**, they are said to be *homozygous*. **WW** is the homozygous dominant state, and **ww** is the homozygous recessive condition. When contrasting genes occur, as in **Ww**, the condition is *heterozygous*. The two letters describe the composition of a gene pair, a *genotype*. **AA**, **Aa**, and **aa** are genotypes. The observed characteristic produced by

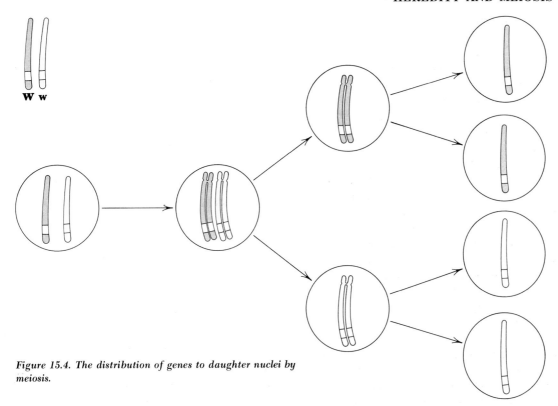

Figure 15.4. The distribution of genes to daughter nuclei by meiosis.

a set of genes is called *phenotype*. Red-flower color is the phenotypic characteristic observable from either genotype **WW** or genotype **Ww**. By way of contrast, there is only one genotype, **ww**, for white-flower color. Finally, contrasting genes such as red-flower color and white-flower color are termed *alleles*. To constitute an allele, two genes must occupy the same sites on a homologous chromosome pair.

Heredity and Meiosis

This is probably a good place to relate Mendel's findings to meiosis, since this is the actual mechanism on which hereditary transmission depends.

Recall that chromosomes occur in homologues in cells; since the genes are located on the chromosomes, the genes also occur in duplicate. Thus the symbol **Ww** means that there is a gene for red color on one chromosome and a gene for white color on its homologue. Only one of these genes, however, will express itself in the organism; this is termed the dominant gene.

In Prophase I of meiosis, homologous chromosomes (and their genes) pair up, then at Anaphase I separate or segregate into daughter nuclei (Figure 15.4). Each pair of chromosomes does this independ-

ently of all other pairs. At the end of meiosis, two of the four resulting gametes contain a **W** gene and two carry a **w** gene. In other words, equal numbers of gametes carrying the **W** gene and the **w** gene are produced: in the diagram on p. 184 a single **W** or **w** represents either an egg or a sperm. Furthermore, the combining of male and female gametes (fertilization) is a random process so that all possible combinations that might occur must be found.

We can predict the most probable outcome of various genetic crosses because hereditary factors segregate independently, equal numbers of different kinds of gametes form, and there is an equal probability of different gametic unions (eggs and sperm). The ratio that is most likely to occur can easily be determined by counting the different combinations in the Punnett Square. Thus, in the example on p. 184, we can see from the Punnett Square that one-fourth of the flowers will be white, one-fourth homozygous red, and two-fourths heterozygous for red. In terms of phenotype, out of every four F_2 progeny, one will bear white flowers and three will bear red ones—thus the 3:1 ratio.

This raises the question of how to determine

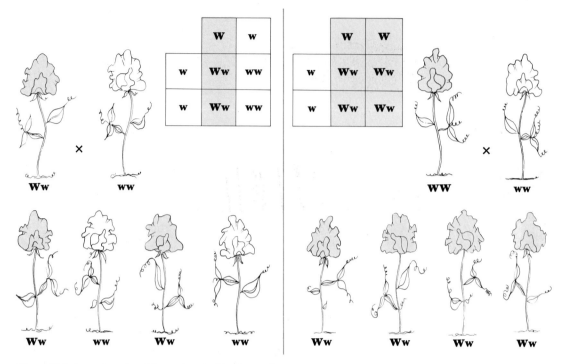

Figure 15.5. A test-cross involving red- and white-flowered peas.

whether an observed phenotype is homozygous or heterozygous. When one has a red-flowered pea plant is it **WW** or **Ww**? To determine this, an additional cross has to be made between the red-flowered pea and a *homozygous recessive* (white-flowered) one. If the phenotype in question is heterozygous, two types of progeny should be produced in approximately equal numbers, as may be seen from the diagram.

$$\text{Ww} \quad \times \quad \text{ww}$$

Gametes:	**W** and **w**	×	**w**
Offspring:	**Ww**	+	**ww**
	(red)		(white)

If, on the other hand, the red-flowered pea is homozygous (**WW**), then *all* of the progeny would have to be red flowered (Figure 15.5). This type of mating or cross is variously termed a *test-cross* or *progeny test,* and is applicable to both plants and animals. It has obvious practical uses to individuals engaged in trying to produce pure-bred varieties of livestock or farm crops.

Some Other Hereditary Patterns

Dihybrid Cross. Thus far we have followed the transmission and expression of one pair of genes, a *monohybrid* cross. What happens if we follow *two hereditary traits* at the same time, that is, a *dihybrid* cross? Actually the principles of the cross remain the same, but now we must work with *two* pairs of genes on separate chromosomes. Mendel performed such experiments and followed the simultaneous transmission of such combinations as flower color (red or white) and height of plants (dwarf or tall).

In order to demonstrate the mechanics of this type of cross and to show that it also applies to animals, let us consider guinea pigs. In these animals black fur color (**W**) is dominant to white fur (**w**) and rough-appearing fur (**S**) is dominant to smooth fur (**s**) (see Figure 15.6). The genes for these traits are located on two pairs of chromosomes. Thus various combinations of these genes may be indicated in the following way:

WWSS: a black guinea pig with rough coat
wwss: white, smooth coat
WwSs: black, rough coat
Wwss: black, smooth coat
etc.

The way in which these genes segregate and then recombine is illustrated in the following diagram which shows mating between a male white-colored, smooth-

	WS	Ws	wS	ws
ws	WwSs	Wwss	wwSs	wwss

wwss	×	WwSs

WwSs	Wwss	wwSs	wwss

Figure 15.6. A dihybrid cross between black, rough, and white, smooth guinea pigs.

coated guinea pig and a female that is heterozygous for both characteristics:

P_1:

♂   ♀

wwss   ×   **WwSs**

Gametes:

(ws) × (WS) and (Ws) and (wS) and (ws)

(Note that a gamete can contain only *one* of each kind of gene.)

F_1:

Mother's Gametes

	WS	Ws	wS	ws
Father's gametes ws	WwSs	Wwss	wwSs	wwss

To summarize, the offspring may be one of the following:

WwSs: black, rough

Wwss: black, smooth

wwSs: white, rough

wwss: white, smooth

According to the Punnett Square, the proportion of offspring is $1:1:1:1$, or, the probability of any one of these combinations in a guinea pig offspring is one chance out of four.

The principles operating here are the same ones used in monohybrid crosses. We are simply working with an additional pair of genes. These principles also apply to *trihybrid* inheritance (three pairs of genes) or as many gene pairs as we wish to consider. Beyond three pairs of genes, the mechanics of working with so many gametic combinations becomes too cumbersome to be practical.

Incomplete Dominance. We have assumed that genes are always either dominant or recessive, but in reality other genetic interactions operate in relation to a pair of genes. It is not uncommon to find examples of a lack of dominance between two genes as in the common garden flower called four o'clocks. Here, a cross between red four o'clocks and white ones yields F_1's (heterozygous) which bear *pink* flowers (Figure 15.7).

A similar situation is met in a variety of tailless cats. If these animals are mated with long-tailed cats, the kittens (F_1) all have short tails. Short tails thus represent the consequence of the reaction between the gene for no tail and the gene for long tail. Additional variations of gene interaction exist, but we shall not consider them.

Analysis of a Human Pedigree. A considerable amount of knowledge has been accumulated concerning hereditary traits in human beings. Of course, a basic problem arises here because experimental matings and test crosses cannot be performed under the control of the investigator. Consequently, human geneticists must utilize indirect sources of evidence

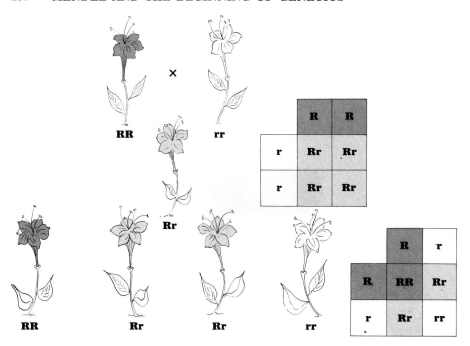

Figure 15.7. An example of inheritance showing incomplete dominance in the four o'clock flower.

such as hospital records, studies of maternal and fraternal twins, and even family histories. It may be possible by use of these sources to follow a characteristic through several generations on a pedigree chart, as indicated in Figure 15.8. By studying a number of pedigree charts for myopia, an investigator can form an hypothesis about the type of inheritance involved. For example, it should be obvious that myopia is not due to a dominant gene and is not restricted to either sex. See if you can formulate an hypothesis to fit the facts observable on the pedigree.

The concepts presented in this chapter should permit a general grasp of the basic hereditary principles discovered by Mendel. In Chapter XVI we build on these Mendelian principles and examine some more recent developments in genetics.

Principles

1. Genetics is the study of the transmission and expression of traits in successive generations of organisms.

2. Gregor Mendel established the existence of discrete hereditary units and some of their simpler interactions including dominance, segregation, and recombination.

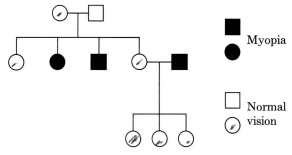

Figure 15.8. The occurrence of myopia in a family. Females are represented by circles, males by squares, a marriage by a horizontal connecting line, and children at the ends of short vertical lines.

Suggested Readings

Mendel, Gregor, "Letter to Karl Nägeli," in *Great Experiments in Biology,* edited by M. L. Gabriel and S. Fogel. Prentice-Hall, Englewood Cliffs, N. J., 1955, pp. 228–233.

Mendel, Gregor, "Experiments in Plant-Hybridization," in *Classic Papers in Genetics,* edited by James A. Peters. Prentice-Hall, Englewood Cliffs, N.J., 1959, pp. 1–20.

Sturtevant, A. H., "Social Implications of the Genetics of Man," in *Classic Papers in Genetics,* edited by James A. Peters. Prentice-Hall, Englewood Cliffs, N. J., 1959, pp. 259–263.

Questions

1. What is the hereditary significance of fertilization?

2. Can you think of some erroneous hereditary concepts not listed in the chapter?

3. Did the development of the basic hereditary principles (Mendel's laws) depend on the improvement in tools and technology as was true of studies of the cell? Defend your answer.

4. For what reasons would Mendel probably have been unsuccessful if he had used animals, such as rats or dogs, instead of garden peas for his studies on heredity?

5. Make a list of the aspects of meiosis which are essential to the understanding of Mendel's principles.

6. In what way are the principles of heredity related to the idea of probability?

Post-Mendelian Genetics

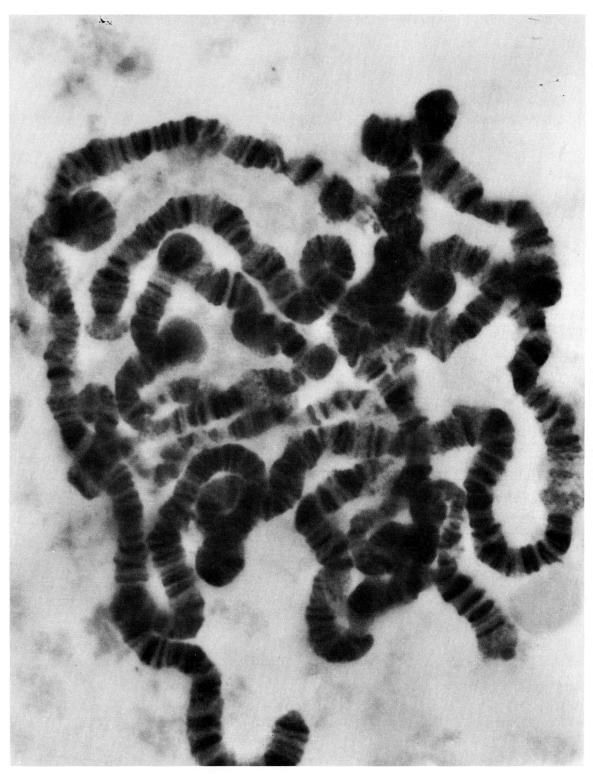

Giant chromosomes in Drosophila.

CHAPTER XVI

Post-Mendelian Genetics

Mendel published his results in 1866 but no one realized their significance until 1900. At that time, several research workers discovered Mendel's publication and linked his explanations with their own findings. From then on genetics advanced rapidly; hence, the title of this chapter, *post*-Mendelian genetics.

Chromosome Theory

In 1902 Walter S. Sutton, a graduate student at Columbia University, noted the similarity between the behavior of Mendel's hereditary factors and the action of chromosomes. After carefully comparing the two he concluded that genes were located on the chromosomes and that one of each gene pair was on one of each member of a pair of homologous chromosomes. Thus, in meiosis, for example, genes must do what chromosomes do. This valuable concept is termed the *chromosome theory*.

Shortly after this (1910), Thomas Hunt Morgan began using the small, common fruit fly, *Drosophila,* in breeding experiments in his laboratory at Columbia University in New York City. Many rapid advances in genetics soon followed; in fact, many of the principles of heredity known today were worked out using this tiny fly. *Drosophila* can be maintained fairly easily in laboratory cultures, it reproduces prolifically, and it exhibits a variety of distinguishable phenotypic features (Figure 16.1). In addition, cells in its salivary glands contain giant chromosomes (Figure 16.2).

These chromosomes are convenient for such experimental uses as correlating genes with specific loci (sites) on chromosomes or for studying the general structure of chromosomes.

While discussing genes and chromosomes we can clarify a matter which frequently puzzles students— what is the precise relationship between genes and chromosomes? A chromosome usually consists of DNA, RNA, and several types of proteins. This is termed a nucleoprotein complex. The DNA portion

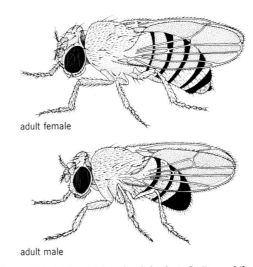

adult female

adult male

Figure 16.1. Male and female of the fruit fly Drosophila.

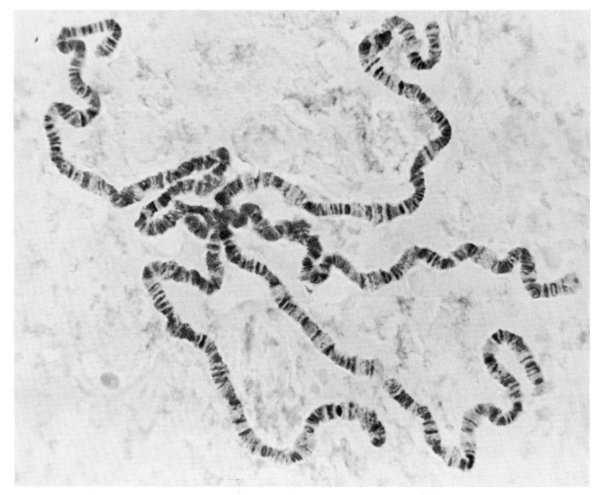

Figure 16.2. Giant chromosomes from the salivary glands of Drosophila. *(Dr. B. P. Kaufman.)*

of this complex is the actual genetic material and will be discussed further in Chapter XVII. It is customary in biology to speak of genes being "in" or "on" chromosomes with the understanding that genes are integral parts of these nuclear structures.

Sex Determination

One of Morgan's many contributions concerned the discovery of a pair of chromosomes in *Drosophila* cells which appeared to determine sex; these are termed *sex chromosomes*. The two in the cell of a female are alike and are known as **X**-chromosomes. The two in male cells are not alike; one is an **X**-chromosome, as in the female, but its partner is different in shape and is termed a **Y**-chromosome. The four chromosomes segregate during meiosis and recombine at fertilization as illustrated in the diagram.

	Female		Male
	XX	crossed with	**XY**
Gametes:	Ⓧ	crossed with	Ⓧ and Ⓨ
F₁:		**XX** and **XY**	

One-half of the offspring receive the **XX** combination and one-half receive the **XY** combination. This accounts for the expected 50–50 ratio of males to females in crosses.

It is convenient to speak of the nonsex chromo-

Figure 16.3. A cross involving the sex-linked trait eye color in Drosophila.

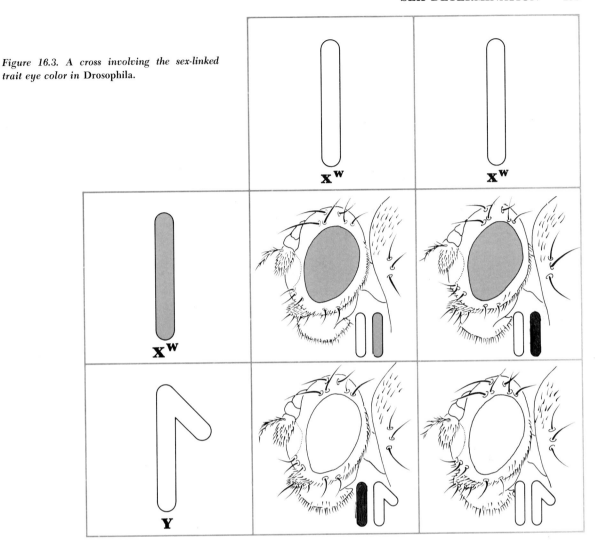

somes, as distinct from the sex chromosomes, as *autosomes*. A human being, for example, has 22 pairs of autosomes and one pair of sex chromosomes for a total of 23 pairs or 46 chromosomes.

Human beings and other mammals have the same type of sex chromosome mechanism, but it is not universal. In birds the sex chromosomes are alike (**ZZ**) in the male but they differ in the female. In bees sex is determined by chromosome number in that females are diploid and males haploid.

Early in his work Morgan discovered that some traits in *Drosophila* were found more frequently in males than in females. White eye color is an example. The gene for eye color is located on the **X**-chromosome, that is, it is *sex linked.* The **Y**-chromosome carries few genes and has none for eye color. Thus we

can consider it blank in our discussion. The gene for red eye (**W**) is dominant over the gene for white eye (**w**). Since they are located on the **X**-chromosome, we can use the symbols X^W and X^w for them. A cross between a white-eyed female fly and a red-eyed male is diagrammed as follows:

	Female		Male
	$X^w X^w$	crossed with	$X^W Y$
Gametes	X^w	crossed with	X^W and Y
F_1:	$X^W X^w$ and $X^w Y$		

Note that the male F_1's are now white eyed and that females are red eyed (Figure 16.3). The **X**-chromosome in males has no homologue so that every gene on it, recessive or dominant, is expressed.

An example of sex linkage in humans is red–green color blindness, a recessive trait. If a color-blind man marries a woman with normal vision, all their children will have normal vision, but the girls will be carriers (heterozygous). Verify this by means of a diagram of the marriage.

Linkage, Crossover, and Chromosome Mapping

In discussing Mendel's work, we considered the mechanism of crossing where the genes were on *separate* chromosomes. What happens when the genes are located on the *same* chromosome? In *Drosophila,* it is known that genes for the recessive traits of black body (**b**) and curved wing (**c**) belong to the same chromosome. The dominant alleles of these two are gray body (**B**) and normal wing (**C**). (See Figure 16.4.) An easy way to diagram a cross involving these traits is to indicate them on little "stick" chromosomes. Genes **B** and **C**, or their alleles, are indicated by dots on the

stick chromosome, as follows:

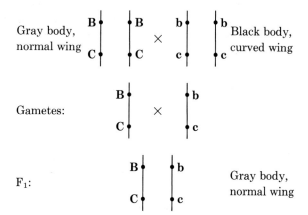

A cross between a fly that is homozygous normal for these traits with one showing the recessive conditions would appear as:

Gray body, normal wing   ×   Black body, curved wing

Gametes: ×

F₁: Gray body, normal wing

Up to this point the phenotypic results (F₁) are identical to the type of dihybrid cross we described earlier. Note what happens if the heterozygous individual is crossed with a homozygous recessive one.

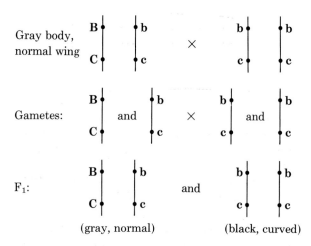

Gray body, normal wing   ×

Gametes: and   ×   and

F₁: and

(gray, normal)   (black, curved)

One-half of the offspring are gray and normal-winged and one-half are black with curved wings. These results are not the same as those that would be obtained if these genes were on separate chromosomes. Then there would be four phenotypes rather than two.

black body — curved wing

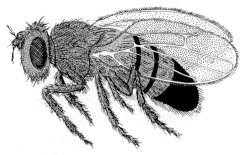

gray body — normal wing

Figure 16.4. Flies showing the traits black body, curved wing (above), and grey body, normal wing (below).

Actual performance of this cross would yield *mostly* gray, normal or black, curved offspring as shown; however, a *few* gray-bodied, curved-winged individuals and a *few* black-bodied, normal-winged members would also result. These two phenotypes are unexpected from the standpoint of the mechanisms we have been using and require a special explanation. Let us therefore refer to meiosis again. Recall that in Prophase I, the homologous chromosomes pair and then pull apart. As they do this, some of the chromatids appeared to stick together at various places; in reality, the homologous chromosomes exchanged homologous parts. In the cross involving body color and wing traits, this exchange can be diagrammed as follows:

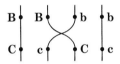

If the crossing chromosomes broke and then rejoined at the crossover point, we would have the following:

We would now have gametes

If we repeated the cross of heterozygous gray, normal with black-bodied, curved-winged, our results would be as shown at the bottom of the right-hand column.

Notice the percentages under each phenotype. Together, they indicate that 74 per cent of the offspring result from the noncrossover gametes, and 26 per cent from the crossover gametes. This is not an accidental occurrence, since a repetition of the cross will give the same proportion of offspring. Other linked genes give other characteristic values. T. H. Morgan and his student, A. H. Sturtevant, hypothesized that if genes were arranged in a linear manner along chromosomes, the genes closest together would undergo crossover less often than those farther apart. There would be a greater likelihood and probability of breaks occurring between genes at opposite ends of a chromosome than

when they are close together. Sturtevant found a way to plot the location of genes, relative to each other, on the chromosomes. With this concept, Morgan's group and other geneticists mapped the chromosomes of *Drosophila* and other suitable organisms. A number of gene locations are also known for human chromosomes.

Let us look briefly at this mapping technique. In the foregoing example, recall that body color and wing shape showed 26 per cent crossover. Let us call this percentage 26 crossover units and map the two genes on a hypothetical chromosome as follows:

Now let us add a third gene, cinnabar eye (**Cn**), which breeding experiments show to be 9 crossover

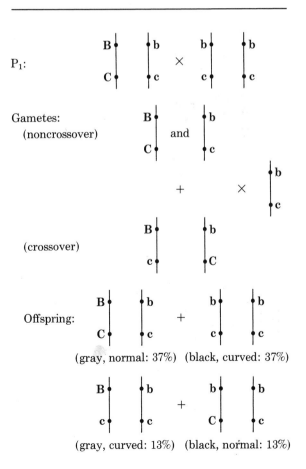

units from **B** and 17 units from **C**. It must be located as follows:

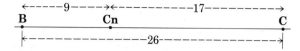

If brown eye (**BW**) were found to be 25 units from **C** and 42 units from **Cn**, it would be positioned thus:

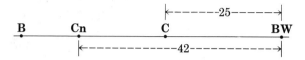

By repeating this procedure many times a virtually complete chromosome map may be constructed.

Quantitative Inheritance

The traits considered previously are discontinuous: red or white flowers, white or red eye color, color blindness or normal vision, and so on. This is an either/or situation; there are no intermediates except in the few instances of incomplete dominance, and even there only one intermediate is possible. Many other traits show numerous intermediate types and are also hereditary: for example, body size, height, weight. These traits are manifested by almost innumerable gradations, and the mechanisms of Mendelian-type heredity do not seem to apply to them. If we hypothesize that height is the result of simultaneous action of a whole series of genes, with a lack of dominance between alleles, then this continuous trait may be explained. Since each gene for tallness adds to the person's height, the accumulative effect determines the height of the individual. This phenomenon is known as *additive gene action*.

Assume that height is due to five pairs of genes. By assigning capital letters to indicate genes for tallness and small letters to indicate genes for shortness, we represent an extremely tall person by **AA BB CC DD EE**, and an extremely short individual by **aa bb cc dd ee**. Different combinations of these genes produce different heights. For example, the combination **Aa Bb Cc Dd Ee** represents a genotype half-way between the two extremes. So would the genotype **AA BB Cc dd ee**.

This type of inheritance also explains another phenomenon commonly observed in nature. If we measure a number of live oak leaves, or weigh a hundred toads, or measure any continuous-type trait in a population, there will be a few of the extreme types and many intermediates. In live oak leaves, for example, a *frequency distribution* might look like this:

Leaf Length (mm)	Number of Leaves
50	1
51	0
52	3
53	88
54	15
55	5
56	4
57	1
58	2
59	2

Generally we attribute this kind of distribution to the additive actions of multiple genes. The role of environment must not be overlooked since it selects which phenotypes can exist. Those phenotypes that function most efficiently for survival of the organism will persist. The optimum leaf length for our live oak in its particular environment lies between 52 and 55 mm. These leaf lengths function best under this set of environmental conditions. Practically all traits reflect this phenomenon.

The Mutation Concept

Even prior to 1900 biologists were aware that new traits occasionally appeared in plants and animals that had not been present in their ancestors. Eventually the term *mutation* was applied to the sudden appearance of a new feature, which thereafter was passed from generation to generation. In other words, mutation denotes an hereditary change.

Geneticists had always been interested in this striking event, but the first real advance in understanding mutation took place in 1927 when the geneticist Herman J. Muller found that he could cause mutations in *Drosophila* flies by exposing them to X-rays. The X-rays in some way changed one or more genes in the reproductive cells of the organism. This technique provided a tool for accelerating the rate of mutation, which normally occurs infrequently. With this tool, biologists could better study mutations and their effects in many types of organisms. For his pioneer work, H. J. Muller received the Nobel prize in 1946.

In Chapter XVII the topic of mutation will be considered again with reference to the different kinds of mutations and their precise relationship to genetic materials.

The Genetics of a Haploid Organism: *Neurospora*

Life Cycle. As mentioned previously, most of our knowledge of the mechanics of genetics has derived from laboratory organisms like *Drosophila* and to a lesser extent from other common laboratory animals. All of these, however, have one major drawback: they are diploid. Every gene is represented at least twice with all the complications of dominance-recessive relations and other interactions. An organism that is haploid during much of its life cycle would not present these problems and thus would facilitate several aspects of the study of genetics. In recent years organisms like the pink breadmold, *Neurospora,* have made this possible.

Neurospora is a common fungus, a pest in some instances, which grows by slender filamentlike extensions called *hyphae*. The hyphae contain nuclei that are haploid: this organism spends most of its life cycle in the haploid condition (Figure 16.5). *Neurospora* reproduces asexually by a series of continually spreading hyphae and by spores, which can be blown about to start new colonies. It also reproduces sexually, which is of importance here. Two mating strains, **A** and **a**, must be present before sexual reproduction will occur. Mating strain **A** will not cross with another **A**, neither will strain **a** cross with another **a**: only strain **A** crosses with strain **a**.

When the two strains are together, some of the hyphae of each form reproductive cells. No meiosis is involved since the nuclei are already haploid. Reproductive cells of opposite strains unite so that the equivalent of a fertilized egg, a diploid nucleus, is obtained. The specialized structure in which it is located becomes an *ascus*. The diploid cell in the ascus undergoes meiosis to form four haploid daughter cells, each of which enters one mitotic division to become two cells; now there is a total of eight haploid cells (*ascospores*) in the ascus. These eight spores will eventually be freed to form new hyphae. The reason that the ascus is so helpful to geneticists is that it is tubelike in form. The meiotic and mitotic products must line up side by side, in order of their formation, like peas in a pod.

The geneticist thus can cross two strains of *Neurospora* showing different characteristics, then remove each individual ascospore, germinate it, and observe the results. This is equivalent to being able to grow

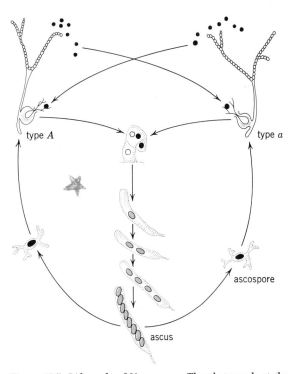

Figure 16.5. Life cycle of **Neurospora**. *The photograph at the top shows the spores oriented within the ascus. The order of spores shows segregation.* (**Dr. David R. Stadler.**)

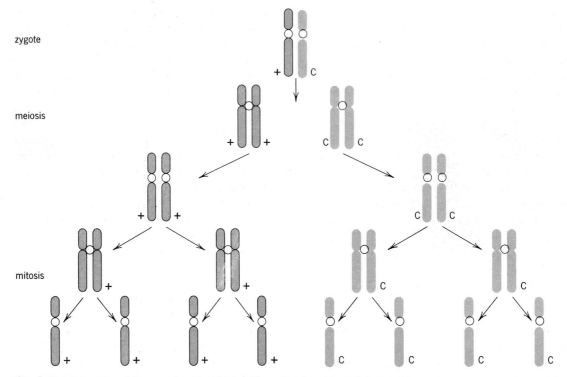

Figure 16.6. Separation of the genes for colonial (c) and spreading (+) growth in ascospore formation.

individual gametes or haploid spores into adult organisms in order to analyze each product of meiosis.

Neurospora contains seven chromosomes in each of its nuclei (haploid or diploid?). One of these chromosomes contains the gene for normal spreading-type growth, denoted by a + symbol. An allele which produces colonial growth is denoted **c**. Hence a cross between a strain showing normal growth with a strain showing colonial growth would be represented as in Figure 16.6.

If the ascospores were separated and then germinated on a culture medium, four would show the normal growth pattern and four the colonial type.

The Work of Beadle and Tatum.   Now let us examine a case of biochemical genetics which was demonstrated by G. W. Beadle and Edward L. Tatum in 1941, for which they received a Nobel prize. Prior to that time it had been postulated that genes controlled the production of enzymes that govern the numerous complex chemical activities in cells, which in turn bring about the phenotypic expressions of the genes. But how could this concept be demonstrated with living organisms? Beadle and Tatum used *Neurospora* for their experiments.

Normally *Neurospora* can be grown on an artificial culture-medium containing only sugar, salts, and biotin (a vitamin). With these basic materials, called a *minimal culture-medium,* the fungus is able to synthesize all of its needed organic compounds such as amino acids, proteins, carbohydrates, fats, and nucleic acids— in short, all of the complex compounds found in living organisms. If these syntheses are controlled by enzymes, and enzymes are controlled by genes, then an altered gene, that is, a *mutation,* should disrupt some stage of this vital chain of events.

Beadle and Tatum proceeded to test this idea by exposing the spores of a normal *Neurospora* to mutagenic agents such as X-rays or ultraviolet light. The exposed spores were then grown into colonies on a culture-medium containing all of the amino acids and vitamins essential to the growth of the fungus. These colonies provided sufficient additional material for carrying out the remainder of the experiment.

A portion of each colony was placed on the minimal culture-medium. If it grew normally, then the sample most likely had not undergone mutation: those that did not grow had been altered in some way, probably by a mutation.

The altered samples (*mutants*) had to be tested to determine which gene or genes had mutated. This was a trial-and-error process in which the mutants were placed in a series of minimal culture-media, each containing a different amino acid. When a mutant survived and grew, it indicated which gene had been altered. For example, in one of the experiments performed by Beadle and Tatum, the mutant grew on a minimal culture-medium when it was supplemented by the amino acid, lysine. Evidently this was a mutation affecting the gene that controlled the synthesis of lysine. To confirm this, the lysine mutant (if it really existed) should yield predictable results when crossed with normal *Neurospora*. Thus:

Parents: normal (+) crossed with
                       lysine mutant (lys)
Zygote: + lys
Meiosis: + + lys lys
Mitosis: (ascospores) + + + + lys lys lys lys

When cultured, all spores should grow on the minimal-plus-lysine medium but only half of them (+ strain) should grow on the minimal medium lacking lysine. This, in fact, happened and confirmed the *gene-enzyme-synthesis hypothesis*.

Beadle and Tatum found many other reactions in which there was a direct gene-enzyme relationship. They also found cases of chain-reaction syntheses where different genes controlled different steps in the reaction. A mutation of one of these genes disrupted the reaction unless the missing substance was added to the culture medium. In diagrammatic form it might appear like this:

Precursor   —Gene 1→   Ornithine   —Gene 2→   Citrulline
material   Enzyme 1   Enzyme 2

                        —Gene 3→   Arginine
                        Enzyme 3

Clearly then, a mutation of any of these three genes would interfere with this stepwise reaction. Experimentation also confirmed this concept.

Studies such as these carried out with *Neurospora*, *Chlamydomonas* (an alga), and bacteria have revealed information that would have been extremely difficult to obtain from more complex creatures like *Drosophila*. Not only did this type of investigation open up a new field of biochemical genetics but it also provided

a frame of reference for some poorly understood hereditary events in higher animals. In human beings sickle-cell anemia—a deficiency of hemoglobin in red blood cells—is now known to be due to an inherited defect in the hemoglobin molecule: the synthesis of hemoglobin is defective because of one "wrong" amino acid in the compound.

Bacterial Genetics

In recent years significant work in genetics has been accomplished through the use of bacteria, which, like *Neurospora*, are haploid. In addition, bacteria reproduce so rapidly that many individuals and generations can be produced in a short time. Although bacteria do not have discrete nuclei, they do contain DNA located in chromosomelike structures. One oddity of the "bacterial chromosome" is that it appears to take the form of a ring. Although fission is the most common form of reproduction, it can be demonstrated that bacteria exchange hereditary material in unusual ways.

Conjugation. Investigators found that in some cases two bacteria temporarily join (*conjugate*) and one (the donor) passes a strand of genetic material into the recipient (Figure 16.7). If the donor and recipient remain in contact long enough, the donor passes a complete strand into the recipient. In this case the recipient is diploid for all genes. At any time during conjugation, however, the two may separate. When this occurs only part of the strand will have been transferred. The recipient is then diploid only for those genes it has received.

Following conjugation, the bacteria separate and recombinations of genetic material take place in the recipient. This bacterium divides and passes the recombinations to the daughter cells. The classic studies which led to an understanding of this process were conducted by Joshua Lederberg and Tatum in 1946 using a bacterium called *Escherichia coli*. They worked out the minimal culture-medium on which normal (wild-type) *E. coli* would grow. They then utilized two mutant strains which would grow on the minimal medium only if certain amino acids and vitamins were added to it. One of these strains required the addition of threonine, leucine, and thiamine; the other strain required phenylalanine, cystine, and biotin. If *mixed* cultures of these mutant forms are grown, some of the resulting colonies are able to grow on the minimal medium. A recombination of genes has evidently taken place so that at least some of the daughter cells received a recombined strand of non-

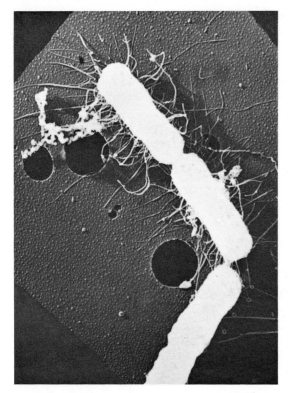

Figure 16.7. Bacteria conjugating. (Dr. Thomas F. Anderson.)

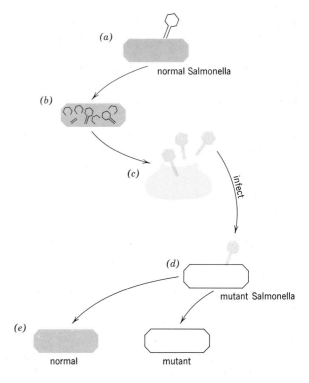

Figure 16.8. Transduction: the transport of genetic material from one bacterium to another by a virus.

mutant genes. This experiment led Lederberg and Tatum to conclude that transfer of genetic material occurred in bacteria. Other experiments and findings have verified this conclusion.

Recall the statement that bacterial chromosomes appear in the form of a ring. Presumably this ring opens during conjugation and passes in a linear manner through the cytoplasmic bridge between two conjugating bacteria. The passage of this chromosome into the female cell takes about two hours. By vigorously stirring the mass of mating forms, the conjugants are separated and the chromosomal strand is broken. Part of the strand will be left in the female and part in the male. The piece received by the female will be passed on to daughter cells and function there. By separating bacteria at different times during mating, it is possible to vary the amount of the chromosome entering the female. By noting the traits of the daughter cells, we can map the chromosome in these bacteria.

Transduction. Another means of genetic transfer between bacteria involves use of a virus as the transmitting agent. Viruses called *bacteriophages* attach to

bacteria, but only the DNA core of each virus particle actually enters the bacterium. The viral DNA directs the synthesis of more phage units until the bacterium is eventually destroyed.

Some types of phage, however, become associated with the genetic material in a bacterium and simply reside there without reproducing or harming the host. This viral guest may be passed through many generations of the bacterial strain in this manner. Some of the virus forms occasionally start reproducing, an event which destroys the host bacterium. In the process, the virus particles retain a copy of part of the bacterial chromosome. If one of these viruses infects another bacterium, the chromosomal fragment brought in from the old host may be recombined with the genes of the new one. Usually only a single gene is transmitted from donor to recipient bacteria, but even one gene may significantly change the genotype (Figure 16.8).

One experiment on *Salmonella* bacteria illustrates how this process, *transduction,* functions. One strain of *Salmonella* grows on a minimal medium only if an amino acid, tryptophan, is added; thus it is a "tryptophan mutant." If a phage is allowed to infect normal *Salmonella*—one which grows on a minimal medium—some of the cells will be destroyed, liberating new phage particles. If the mutant *Salmonella* is then exposed to these new phage forms, some of them become able to grow on the minimal medium without the addition of the amino acid. In other words, some of the tryptophan mutant forms have been transduced by the viruses into the normal or wild-type *Salmonella*. Could this be a mutation converting the tryptophan strain into the wild-type? Mutations do, of course, occur in bacteria, but in the case cited, the mutation rate would not be sufficiently high to account for the number of new forms which appear in the tryptophan population.

With reference to mutation in bacteria, we must note several points. Since most bacteria appear to be haploid, mutations appear immediately, that is, there is no dominant gene to inhibit the expression of the usually recessive mutant gene, as occurs in diploid organisms. Coupled with a rapid reproductive rate, this endows bacteria with tremendous adaptive potential. For example, if streptomycin, is added to a culture of *E. coli*, most or all of the culture will die. There may, however, be a few mutant forms present which can resist the antibiotic; these forms survive and even reproduce. Note that the streptomycin did not *cause* the mutation but rather provided an environment in which the mutant form could express itself, becoming the normal or dominant population. The significance of this phenomenon in areas such as medicine is enormous. Many hospitals, for example, are now encountering *Staphylococcus* infections which resist all normal treatment methods, whereas this type of bacterium was easily controlled previously.

Thus in bacterial genetics, some new dimensions have been added to the study of heredity. Basic hereditary principles still apply, but their adaptations to the microbial world have many unusual aspects.

Principles

1. The behavior of genes and chromosomes during meiosis is parallel. When crossover occurs, the parallel behavior allows us to map the location of genes on chromosomes.

2. Organisms that are haploid in part of their life cycles are used to establish genetic control of cellular activity via control of enzyme production.

3. Studies of heredity in bacteria support the concept that recombination of DNA is the basis for hereditary variation.

Suggested Readings

Beadle, George W., "The Genes of Men and Molds," *Scientific American,* Vol. 179 (September, 1948). Offprint No. 1, W. H. Freeman and Co., San Francisco.

Gordon, Manuel J., "The Control of Sex," *Scientific American,* Vol. 199 (November, 1958).

Jacob, François and Elie L. Wollman, "Viruses and Genes," *Scientific American,* Vol. 204 (June, 1961). Offprint No. 89, W. H. Freeman and Co., San Francisco.

Levine, R. P., *Genetics.* Holt, Rinehart and Winston, New York, 1962, pp. 38–58, 64–90, 100–118.

Mittwoch, Ursula, "Sex Differences in Cells," *Scientific American,* Vol. 209 (July, 1963). Offprint No. 161, W. H. Freeman and Co., San Francisco.

Zinder, Horton D., "Transduction in Bacteria," *Scientific American,* Vol. 199 (November, 1958). Offprint No. 106, W. H. Freeman and Co., San Francisco.

Questions

1. Explain why all the sons of a color-blind mother must also be color blind. Why is it that a male cannot be heterozygous for color blindness?

2. Explain why it is necessary to go back to meiosis to explain crossover.

3. What is the relation between Sutton's chromosome theory and the method used for mapping genes?

4. What is the relation of environment to gene expression? What mode of inheritance illustrates this point particularly well?

5. In what respect is the study of hereditary mechanisms simpler in haploid than in diploid organisms? For instance, why did Beadle and Tatum use *Neurospora* rather than *Drosophila* or white rats?

6. What is the hereditary advantage in being diploid rather than haploid?

7. On what basis could you argue that bacteria like *E. coli* reproduce sexually?

8. For what reasons are bacteria especially useful in studies on mutation?

9. How do bacteria illustrate the concept that the basis for hereditary variation lies in the recombination of DNA?

Chemistry of the Genetic Material

Skip

Chromosomes damaged by radiation. Notice the fragments of chromosomes. (Dr. Arnold H. Sparrow, Brookhaven National Laboratory.)

Chemistry of the Genetic Material

As more and more information became available about inheritance, the chemical identity of the genetic material became an increasingly intriguing problem. Early geneticists knew that the chemical substance had to have a mechanism for duplicating itself as exactly as genetic material had been observed to do. This substance had to have enough different forms to account for all variations in organisms. It needed some way to control the activities of the cell. The Watson–Crick model of the structure of DNA satisfied the first two criteria. Recent studies of RNA control of protein synthesis have satisfied the last criterion.

DNA: The Hereditary Material

Early Evidence. DNA was first considered a possible genetic material because its characteristics seemed to match those known for such material. The evidence to support this early suggestion now comes from several different sources. Early experiments showed that the nucleus had a large concentration of DNA. Later it was shown that the chromosomes were composed of DNA and protein. However, really good evidence for DNA being the genetic material was not available until the amount of DNA present in the cells of an organism was shown to be constant. Since each cell in an organism has the same genetic information, the total amount of the genetic material should be the same in each. Optical techniques for weighing DNA produced this information.

Nucleic acids had been shown to absorb ultraviolet radiation (wavelength of 260 mμ) strongly. This information was the basis for later evidence that a nucleic acid was the genetic material. First, ultraviolet light of this wavelength brought about mutations; that is, it affected the genetic material. Second, many of the processes of development found only in a small number of species could be abolished by treating the cells with ultraviolet radiation, suggesting that interference with genetic control of development had occurred.

During the 1920s some studies of bacteria showed that freshly killed bacteria of one strain could cause a change in the genetic characteristics of another strain. In the 1940s further work in the same field indicated that only the DNA portion of the bacteria could bring about this effect, called *transformation.*

A crucial finding was that digested DNA (free nucleotides) did not cause transformation, whereas intact pieces of DNA did. This showed that the important factor was not merely the presence of the nucleotides but rather something about the relation of these units to one another in the DNA molecule.

Structure and Function. To review, DNA is composed of two long chains of nucleotides which spiral around each other to form a double helix (Figure 17.1). These chains are structurally interdependent. Since, of all the parts, the bases of the nucleotides approach each other closest, the fact that the bases will pair

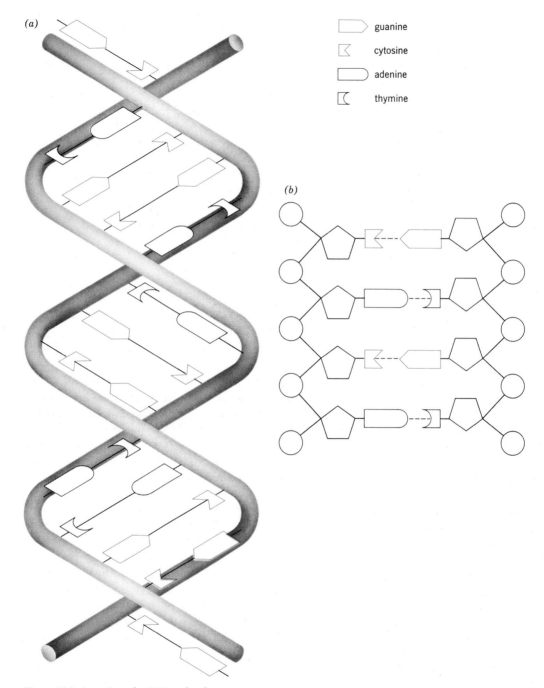

(a)

guanine

cytosine

adenine

thymine

(b)

Figure 17.1. A portion of a DNA molecule.

208

in only one way is very important to the structure of the DNA helix. Because of the specific pairing of bases, through knowing their sequence in one chain, we can predict the sequence in the other chain. The order of bases in the chain is the genetic code itself, the genetic information.

How does this relate to the structure we can see, the chromosome? Except in bacteria and some algae, the long DNA molecule forms the core of the chromosome but not its whole. A coat of protein surrounds the DNA. Although the protein plays no part in the genetic information carried by the chromosome, it is important in repressing the activity of the chromosome (see Chapter XIV).

The exact relationship of the nucleotide units to the visible chromosome is difficult to understand. We do not know how many nucleotide pairs make up a chromosome. Only shrewd guesses can be made. When we talk of nucleotides, we are talking of the biochemical structural units of the chromosome. These are neither the visible cytological unit, the chromosome, nor the functional unit which we discussed as the gene in Chapters XV and XVI.

We have already described the way in which three bases form the genetic unit that determines which amino acid will be located at a particular point in a particular protein. The translation of a triplet-code unit of DNA into an amino acid in a protein requires the presence of two kinds of RNA (transfer and messenger). Messenger RNA is a relatively long molecule which carries the directions for the production of only one kind of protein. Each triplet determines the location of one amino acid. Thus, this RNA represents the genetic information translated into a slightly different form.

Transfer RNAs are evidently produced by short segments of DNA that may be nearly alike in many different species. One kind of transfer RNA may be used in the synthesis of many different proteins. An amino acid becomes attached to a specific transfer RNA, which pairs with bases at the appropriate sites along messenger RNA (see Chapter VII). The formation of peptide bonds completes the synthetic process.

Duplication. One other aspect of DNA structure must be emphasized. If DNA is the basic genetic material, then there must be a method of duplicating its molecules in order to explain the duplication of chromosomes. This method must be characterized by a high degree of precision and reproducibility.

An explanation for the duplication of DNA is indeed available based on the Watson–Crick model for its structure (Figure 17.2). At the time of duplication the two strands of the helix become separated. Each base of each strand becomes associated with the base of a free nucleotide. The kind of base with which each base will pair is, of course, determined by the specific pattern of base pairing—adenine and thymine, cytosine and guanine. As the free nucleotides become associated with those of the old strands, they are joined to each other by sugar-to-phosphate bonds, thereby forming the new strands. Notice that each of the old strands has served as a pattern by which a new complementary strand is produced. This results in two copies of the original double helix.

Mutation. This method of DNA duplication is highly precise but errors occasionally creep in. These may result from misbonding between bases or from temporary altering of the bonding characteristics of a base by internal or external forces. The frequency of the observed errors of duplication, called *point mutations,* are consistent with these possible sources of error in base pairing.

It is easy to see that a modification of the DNA could bring about a change in the RNA, thereby changing the enzymes present and producing a different phenotype. There are many examples of differences in phenotype based on differences in enzymes which can be related to changes in DNA. Remember the discussion of *Neurospora* in Chapter XVI.

Of the three types of mutations, all of which involve a change in DNA structure, point mutations affect DNA the least. These usually involve the replacement of one base in the DNA chain by another, or the loss or duplication of so few bases that the change cannot be detected in the appearance of the chromosome. All these minor alterations are grouped as point mutations because they cannot be distinguished from one another by a change in appearance of the chromosome.

When a large enough segment of the chromosome (a large number of bases) has been duplicated, lost, or turned around, it is often possible to detect the change by the chromosome's appearance. Consequently, these mutations are called duplications, deletions, and inversions, respectively (Figure 17.3).

The severest type of mutation is the loss or gain of a considerable part or all of a chromosome. Most of these occur during meiosis. Usually such a severe loss of genetic material causes death to the cell involved.

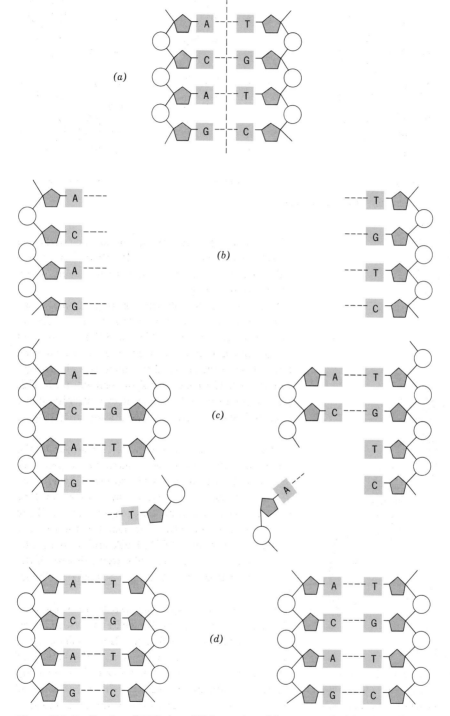

Figure 17.2. Duplication of DNA. (a and b) Separation of the two strands. (c) Free nucleotides joining the strands. (d) Resulting duplicate strands. (Reprinted with permission, Copyright © 1957 by Scientific American, Inc. All rights reserved.)

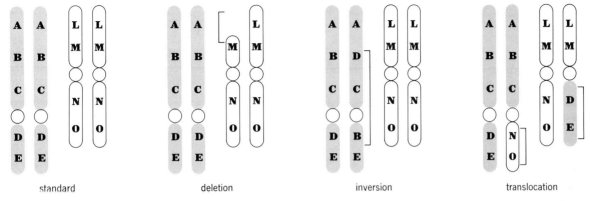

standard | deletion | inversion | translocation

Figure 17.3. Three kinds of mutations that may be detected optically.

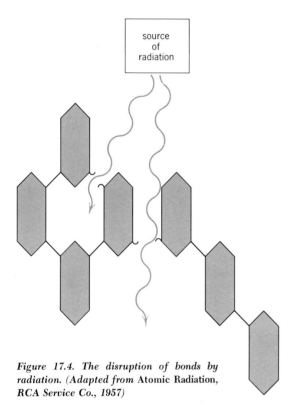

source of radiation

Figure 17.4. The disruption of bonds by radiation. (Adapted from Atomic Radiation, *RCA Service Co., 1957)*

Mutation and Ionizing Radiation

Many mutations occur for no apparent reason, but others are caused by the exposure of the genetic material to certain *mutagenic agents.* One of the most common of these, as shown in the 1920s by H. J. Muller, is *ionizing radiation.*

Ionizing radiation is radiation that forms ions, that is, waveform energy transmissions which will bring about the formation of charged atoms or molecules.

Like visible light, the energy of ionizing radiation travels in the form of waves. It differs from visible light in that it consists of shorter wavelengths and contains more energy.

When a molecule absorbs ionizing radiation, the incoming energy is added to that which is already present in the molecule. This additional supply of energy may modify the bonds in the molecule or even break them (remember that bonds contain energy: Chapter II). If a bond is broken, ions will form. This phenomenon can and does occur in molecules of any size, from water to proteins and nucleic acids. (Figure 17.4.)

If small molecules such as water are struck by the radiation, highly reactive substances such as peroxides or free hydrogen atoms may be formed (Figure 17.5). These substances do not remain in this form for long but react with some other substance in the cell. They may react with any other compound in the cell, but we shall consider only DNA, RNA, and proteins. The same changes in these molecules result directly if the radiation strikes any of these compounds. (Figure 17.6.)

These reactions may cause two types of damage. The molecules may be broken or the bonding pattern in the molecule may be changed. If either happens to DNA, then one of the types of mutations we have listed could occur. Such changes can kill the cell by interfering with mitosis or the cell's metabolism. If the cell lives, these changes will be duplicated in each succeeding cell division. Consequently, such damage to the cell would be permanent. If RNA is affected, temporary changes can result in the protein produced. As the DNA produces more RNA, however, a new supply of normal RNA replaces the defective RNA.

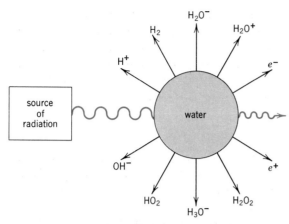

Figure 17.5. *Highly reactive substances formed by the irradiation of water. (Adapted from* Atomic Radiation, *RCA Service Co., 1957)*

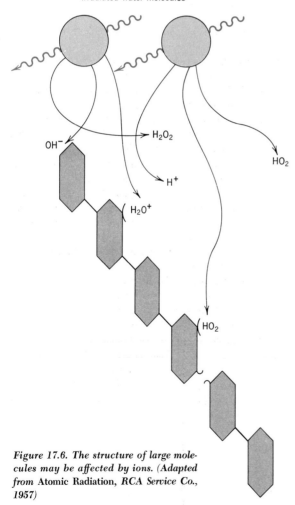

irradiated water molecules

Figure 17.6. *The structure of large molecules may be affected by ions. (Adapted from* Atomic Radiation, *RCA Service Co., 1957)*

Two other important kinds of effects on the cell may be brought about if its proteins are modified. If the proteins that are enzymes (or parts of them) are changed in shape, they may no longer fit together with the molecules upon which they usually act, and therefore their activity will be altered. Since new enzymes will later be formed by the cell, this change is temporary. Permanent damage is done to the cell if the altered protein is a portion of a chromosome. This could result in modified behavior of the chromosome at cell division and in drastic changes in the distribution of genetic material. Of course, any loss of material would be permanent. (Figure 17.7.)

With such diverse possibilities for damage to the cell by radiation, it is possible to understand the many derangements of homeostatic mechanisms in an irradiated organism. *Radiation sickness* results from the cumulative effects of direct damage and the abnormal but highly reactive substances produced by the radiation. The first symptoms are nausea and vomiting, reddening of the skin, and general fatigue. Later, bleeding (for example, from gums or nose), congestion of the lungs, and ulceration of the intestine with salt and water loss may develop. Low immunity to disease and anemia are also common. Active cells are more susceptible to radiation than relatively inactive ones. It may be noticed that the cells affected are dividing fairly rapidly.

An animal might recover from these symptoms yet die or be seriously affected by the long-term effects of exposure to radiation. Cancer or leukemia, continued anemia, cataracts, sterility, and nerve damage may appear after considerable time has passed.

Genetic damage in the gamete-producing tissues will not appear until the next generation. Larger numbers of mutations, mostly to deleterious alleles, and increased fetal or young animal deaths result. This kind of damage is the most dangerous to the species in the long run and is the most difficult to detect. Because low doses of radiation over a long period of time can cause these genetic effects, this form of damage is also the most insidious.

Since radiation sources such as X-rays, radioactive fallout, radioactive substances on watch dials, and natural radiation are so common, the problem of the effects of radiation on biological systems is an impor-

212

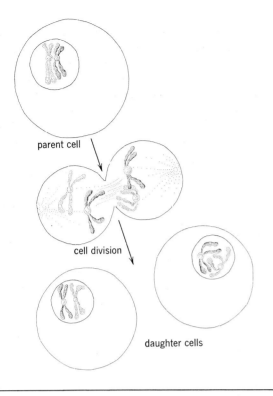

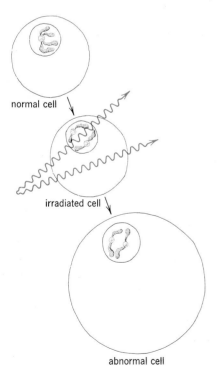

Figure 17.7. Modification of the genetic contents of a cell by radiation. (Adapted from Atomic Radiation, *RCA Service Co., 1957)*

tant one. What can be done? At present facts are being gathered but there are still no satisfactory answers. Even if there were, the final answer would be dependent on public acceptance of the danger and of the solutions. The problem is not only scientific but also psychological and sociological.

Principles

1. DNA has been established as the genetic material because the Watson–Crick model provides an adequate explanation for duplication, mutation, and control of cellular activity.

2. Ionizing radiation alters the structure of DNA as well as the structure of other molecules such as RNA, protein, and water.

Suggested Readings

Alexander, Peter. *Atomic Radiation and Life*. Penguin Books, Baltimore, 1965.

Beadle, George W., "Structure of the Genetic Material and the Concept of the Gene," in *This Is Life*, edited by W. H. Johnson and W. C. Steere. Holt, Rinehart and Winston, New York, 1962, pp. 185–211.

Beerman, Wolfgang and Ulrich Clever, "Chromosome Puffs," *Scientific American*, Vol. 210 (April, 1964). Offprint No. 180, W. H. Freeman and Co., San Francisco.

Lindell, Bo and R. Lowry Dobson. *Ionizing Radiation and Health*. World Health Organization, 1961.

Hollaender, Alexander and George E. Stapleton, "Ionizing Radiation and the Cell," *Scientific American*, Vol. 200 (September, 1959). Offprint No. 57, W. H. Freeman and Co., San Francisco.

Levine, R. P., *Genetics*. Holt, Rinehart and Winston, New York, 1962, pp. 8–22, 120–135.

Loutit, John F., "Ionizing Radiation and the Whole Animal," *Scientific American*, Vol. 201 (September, 1959).

Muller, H. J., "Radiation and Human Mutation," *Scientific American*, Vol. 192 (November, 1955). Offprint No. 29, W. H. Freeman and Co., San Francisco.

Platzman, Robert L., "What Is Ionizing Radiation?" *Scientific American*, Vol. 201 (September, 1959).

Spiegelman, S., "Hybrid Nucleic Acids," *Scientific American*, Vol. 210 (May, 1964). Offprint No. 183, W. H. Freeman and Co., San Francisco.

Questions

1. What early evidence indicated that DNA was the basic hereditary material?

2. What did Watson and Crick contribute to this idea? Why was this important?

3. What is a chromosome? What is the relationship between DNA and chromosomes?

4. If the bases in one chain of DNA are known, can we predict the sequence of bases in the other chain? How?

5. Trace the steps involved in the translation of a DNA code in the nucleus into a enzyme out in the cytoplasm.

6. Name the ways in which mutations occur. Can man deliberately cause any of these mutations? How?

7. Explain how ionizing radiation can produce changes in cells.

8. Does radioactive fallout material constitute a source of ionizing radiation? Explain.

Population Genetics:
An Introduction to Evolution

A winter aggregation of Monarch butterflies.

Population Genetics: An Introduction to Evolution

In attempting to learn how traits are inherited we mate two individuals that differ in one or more respects and observe the characteristics in their offspring. Although this technique has been useful in discovering the basic laws of heredity and the mechanism for inheritance of traits, it does not provide a genetic basis for understanding evolution.

Since an individual's genetic makeup does not change during his life span, we must look at the unit that does change over time. This unit, which is composed of all individuals that can interbreed and their offspring, is a reproductive unit called a *Mendelian population*. The unit is characterized by a changing genetic composition throughout an existence which may span millions of years.

This change and the consequent modification in the phenotypes constitute evolution. The population, not the individual, evolves. Therefore, if we wish to understand the genetic basis of evolution, we must understand the genetics of populations.

In previous chapters the Punnett Square was used to combine gametes from two parents to show all possible types of offspring. The same technique can be applied to population genetics if we use in proper number all the gamete types from all parents in the population. In other words, we shall select gametes from a pool containing all the genes in the population. We call this the *gene pool* of the population.

The Hardy-Weinberg Law: Populations in Equilibrium

Let us imagine a population of hamsters composed of 100 males and 100 females. There are 49 homozygous gray, 42 heterozygous gray, and 9 homozygous black animals of each sex. Gray coat color (**B**) is dominant over black (**b**). If each individual produced ten gametes, the gametes produced by the *males* should appear as in Table 18.1.

Table 18.1

Genotypes of the Males	Gametes		
	B	**b**	Totals
49 **BB**	490	0	490
42 **Bb**	210	210	420
9 **bb**	0	90	90
	700	300	1000
	or	or	or
	70% (0.70)	30% (0.30)	100% (1.00)

The heterozygous individuals should produce as many gametes carrying recessive genes as they do gametes carrying dominant genes, since the genes are present in equal numbers in these individuals. The homozygous individuals will produce only one kind of gamete in each case. The figures 0.30 and 0.70 in

217

the table are gene frequencies (or gamete frequencies, since they are equal). They tell us that 30 per cent of the genes of this population are recessive genes while 70 per cent are dominant. The females in the population should produce the same number of the same types of gametes since they contain the same genes in identical proportions. A Punnett Square can also be constructed showing how often fusion occurs among the various combinations of gametes.

	Gametes from the Males		Summary
	0.7 **B**	0.3 **b**	0.49 (49%) **BB**
Gametes from the Females 0.7 **B**	0.49 **BB**	0.21 **Bb**	0.42 (42%) **Bb**
0.3 **b**	0.21 **Bb**	0.09 **bb**	0.09 (9%) **bb**
			1.00 (100%)

The Punnett Squares for problems in the previous chapters assumed that the number of each type of gamete produced by each individual would be equal. Since the homozygous gray individuals far outnumber the homozygous black individuals, this population will *not* produce equal numbers of the two kinds of gametes. We have therefore inserted in the foregoing diagram the frequency of each kind of gamete along with its symbol.

Since the probability of any two types of gametes fusing depends on their frequency, the percentages of resulting genotypes are computed by multiplying the frequency of the gamete from one parent by that of the gamete from the other parent. The results are summarized at the right of the Punnett Square.

If we examine the offspring in this population, we find that 49 per cent are homozygous gray, 42 per cent heterozygous, and 9 per cent are black. These are the same percentages observed in the parental generation. If we now allowed these to reproduce, the gene frequency would be the same in each succeeding generation. Two men, G. H. Hardy, a British mathematician, and W. Weinberg, a German physician, noticed this fact independently and stated what is known as the *Hardy–Weinberg law: under certain conditions, gene frequencies and genotype frequencies remain the same from one generation to the next in sexually reproducing populations*.

Obviously most populations cannot be controlled in a manner that will result in each individual contributing only a given number of genes to the next generation. The same kind of reasoning can be used, however, to set up a formula that will apply to a general population if we substitute p and q for the frequency of the dominant and recessive genes, respectively.

	Gametes from the Males		Summary
	p (**B**)	q (**b**)	p^2 = freq. **BB**
Gametes from the Females p(**B**)	p^2 (**BB**)	pq(**Bb**)	$2pq$ = freq. **Bb**
q(**b**)	pq(**Bb**)	q^2 (**bb**)	q^2 = freq. **bb**
			100% (1.00)

In this Punnett Square p equals the frequency of the dominant gene (0.7 in the last example) and q equals the frequency of the recessive gene (0.3 in the last example). We now see that there will be p^2 homozygous gray animals, $2pq$ heterozygous animals, and q^2 black animals. (Verify this by substituting 0.7 for p and 0.3 for q and checking against the results in the table.) We may use this method of calculation as long as each individual has an equal chance of reproducing, and the offspring have an equal chance of surviving.

A second look at the substitution shows that since there are only two kinds of genes (**B** and **b**), then $p + q = 1$. This can be restated as: the frequency of the dominant genes plus the frequency of the recessive genes equals all the genes in the population. Similarly, since there are only three possible genotypes (**BB**, **Bb**, and **bb**), $p^2 + 2pq + q^2 = 1$. These two equations are useful in calculating the gene and genotype frequencies for a population.

For example, if we are studying a simple recessive trait like vestigial wing (very short wing) in *Drosophila,* which is present in 4 per cent (0.04) of a laboratory population, we can complete all the genotype and gene frequencies for the population provided the conditions are met for a Hardy–Weinberg equilibrium. We define the letters from the two equations in the usual fashion.

p = the frequency of the dominant gene
q = the frequency of the recessive gene
p^2 = the frequency of the homozygous dominant genotype
$2pq$ = the frequency of the heterozygous genotype
q^2 = the frequency of the homozygous recessive genotype

Since vestigial wing is a recessive trait, we know that all individuals showing it must have a genotype **vv**.

The frequency of this group is q^2 by definition and is equal to 0.04. Since

$$q^2 = 0.04$$
$$q = 0.2 \text{ or } 20\%$$
$$p + q = 1$$
$$p + 0.2 = 1$$
$$p = 0.8 \text{ or } 80\%$$
$$p^2 = (0.8)(0.8) = 0.64 \text{ or } 64\%$$
$$2pq = 2(0.8)(0.2) = 0.32 \text{ or } 32\%$$

In summary, 80 per cent of the genes are the dominant (**V**) for normal wings, while 20 per cent are recessive (**v**) for vestigial wings. Sixty-four per cent of the flies are homozygous dominant (**VV**), 32 per cent are heterozygous (**Vv**), and 4 per cent are homozygous recessive (**vv**) (Figure 18.1).

Forces Changing Populations

In the statement of the Hardy–Weinberg law there is an important qualification—"under certain conditions." All of our calculations have assumed that:

(1) No selection was occurring.

(2) Migration into or out of the population did not occur.

(3) No mutations were occurring (or that mutations in the two directions were equal).

(4) The population was large enough not to be affected by random changes in gene frequencies.

These assumptions had to be made since the absence of any one of these conditions would cause a shift in the gene frequencies. Since a change in the gene pool constitutes evolution, we shall examine the first three of these four conditions separately. If the fourth one is not met, a condition commonly called genetic drift may result. This does not occur often enough to be important to us.

Natural Selection.   Selection for the best adapted individuals is the most potent force that serves to change the characteristics of populations. It is the basic driving force of evolution. We can divide selection into three types on the basis of the phase of the life cycle at which this occurs: before the organism reaches reproductive age, during mate selection and actual mating, or during fertilization and embryonic life.

Figure 18.1. Distribution of vestigial wing in a population of Drosophila.

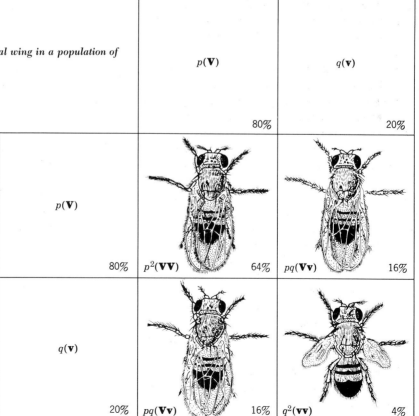

Figure 18.2. A spawning starfish. Gametes released into the water have a small chance of surviving. (Dr. Alfred Chaet.)

Probably the type of natural selection easiest to envision is that which occurs prior to reproduction. It is obvious that if the organism does not survive to reproduce, it will not pass genes to the next generation.

Selection during mating can occur only if the organism survives to reproductive age. The mechanism of this type of selection varies; the females may select one type of mate in preference to others, the pollen may not be carried as far, the flowers may not be as attractive to pollinators, or most of the population may have already completed their breeding before this individual is ready. In any of these cases the effect may vary from complete prevention of breeding to an only slightly lessened chance.

The third type of selection operates on the gametes or embryos. Gametes are often infertile or at a disadvantage in reaching or being reached by other gametes (Figures 18.2 and 18.3). Even if fertilization occurs, death of the zygote or embryo from genetic causes may occur at any time.

To illustrate, let us return to the population of hamsters (p. 217), starting with the same basic ratios of individuals. This time, rather than assuming equal reproductive success of all genotypes, let us place the homozygous **BB** hamsters at a disadvantage by allowing only five gametes from each to be involved in the

Table 18.2

Genotypes of the Animals	Gametes		
	B	**b**	Total
49 **BB**	245	0	245
42 **Bb**	210	210	420
9 **bb**	0	90	90
	455	300	755
	or	or	or
	approximately	approximately	
	60% (0.60)	40% (0.40)	100%

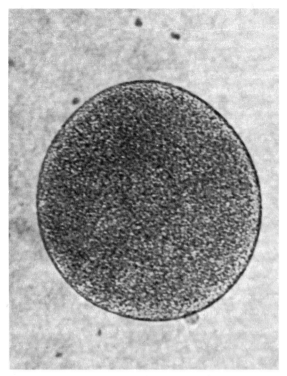

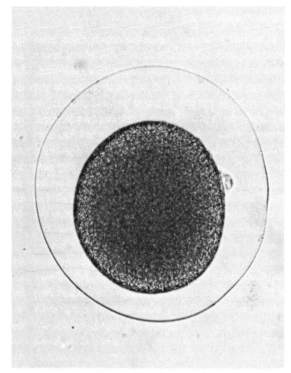

egg without fertilization membrane

egg with fertilization membrane

Figure 18.3. Starfish eggs. The egg on the right has been fertilized and is beginning normal development. The one on the left has failed to develop despite fertilization.

production of the succeeding generations. This is half the number contributed by each **BB** individual in the calculations in Table 18.1. The other two groups continue to contribute the same number of gametes. See Table 18.2. The result of our interference is as follows:

		Gametes from the Males		Summary
		0.6 **B**	0.4 **b**	0.36 (36%) **BB**
Gametes from the Females	0.6 **B**	0.36 **BB**	0.24 **Bb**	0.48 (48%) **Bb**
	0.4 **b**	0.24 **Bb**	0.16 **bb**	0.16 (16%) **bb**

In just one generation the frequency of the genes has shifted appreciably owing to a 0.5 selection factor against the homozygous dominant individuals. This is rigorous selection but by no means extreme. On some occasions the selection may completely eliminate any carrier of the gene.

Migration. The second factor that modifies gene

frequencies is immigration from a population characterized by different gene frequencies or selective emigration of one genotype from its population. In most widely distributed species the semi-isolated populations are kept as integral parts of the species by the frequent migration from one group to another of individuals or gametes and the genes they contain. Such exchange of genes prevents the differentiation of the gene pools of the populations and their division into distinct species.

Mutation. Mutation is the third factor modifying the genetic characteristics of the population. Mutation alone is, however, usually unimportant because its rates commonly fall between one in 100,000 and one in 100,000,000 gene duplications. Even if mutations were common, the mutation of the new gene back to the original allele would tend to moderate the effect on gene frequencies. But mutation combined with selection is a potent force in modifying populations because mutation supplies the only new source of variation upon which selection may act.

Some Applications

If so many factors in nature modify the gene frequencies predicted by the Hardy–Weinberg law, what good is this concept? It has many different uses. The law provides a model with which to compare populations found in nature. If these natural populations do not conform to the Hardy–Weinberg predictions, one or more of the conditions stated in the law has not been fulfilled. Calculations based on the Hardy–Weinberg law are also of interest in studying human populations. Couples that have an inherited disease somewhere in their families often want to know the likelihood of one of their children being affected. Even couples that do not have any family history of undesirable traits often want to know the chances of their having children with one of these characteristics. Questions are often asked about albinism because the complete lack of pigment in the skin, hair, and eyes causes the person to differ markedly in appearance from most of the population. In order to predict the chance that a child in a given family may be an albino, it is essential to know the prevalence of the trait in the general population, the history of the trait, if any, in the two families, and the method of inheritance of the trait.

This simple recessive trait is present in about one person out of 5,000 in the population. This means that $q^2 = 1/5000$ or 0.0002 if the letters are defined in the usual way. The frequency of the recessive gene (**a**) would be 0.014.

$$p + q = 1.0$$
$$p + 0.014 = 1.0$$
$$p = 0.986 \text{ or } 98.6\% \text{ of the genes are}$$
$$\textbf{A} \text{ (for normal trait)}$$
$$p^2 = (0.986)(0.986) = \text{approx. } 0.972$$
$$\text{or } 97.2\% \text{ of the population are } \textbf{AA}$$
$$2pq = 2(0.986)(0.014) = \text{approx. } 0.028$$
$$\text{or } 2.8\% \text{ of the population are } \textbf{Aa}$$

If the prospective parents were both normally pigmented and had no known history of albinism in their families, we could tell them that the chance that both of them were heterozygous would be (0.028)(0.028) or about 8 chances in 10,000. Even if they were both heterozygous, only one child in four should be albino. As in all cases where no family history of a relatively rare recessive trait occurs, the chance of this couple having a child with the recessive trait is very low.

Of more interest to us for its theoretical implications is the study of the frequencies of traits in different populations. Many human groups in the past were quite isolated from one another for long periods of time. This isolation allowed differences in gene frequencies to develop between groups. We are familiar with differences such as skin color, which according to the existing evidence are an adaptation to the amount of sunlight in the ancestral environment. But other marked differences occur in the frequencies of traits, such as the frequencies of the A—B—O blood groups, for which we know only indirect adaptive significance.

The nationalities from central Europe all show fairly similar blood group frequencies. We would expect this because of relatively free intermarriage. A sample of Belgians and a sample of Germans form the most widely divergent groups in this area but are still not very different (see Table 18.3). On the other hand, two tribes of Indians from Montana show extreme divergence. Evidently little intermarriage has occurred between these tribes. This information helps our knowledge of evolution by demonstrating that differences in relatively nonadaptive traits can arise between isolated populations and by giving us information on the degree of isolation which these human groups have experienced.

Table 18.3. Frequencies of the A-B-O Blood Groups in Various Populations (Modified from W. C. Boyd, Genetics and the Races of Man, Little, Brown and Co., Boston, 1956)

Population	Place	Percentage of			
		O	A	B	AB
American Indians					
Utes	Mont.	97.4	2.6	0	0
Blackfeet	Mont.	23.5	76.5	0	0
Navaho	N. M.	77.7	22.5	0	0
Flatheads	Mont.	51.5	42.2	4.7	1.6
Belgians	Liège	46.7	41.9	8.3	3.1
Spaniards	Spain	41.5	46.5	9.2	2.2
Frenchmen	Paris	39.8	42.3	11.8	6.1
Germans	Berlin	36.5	42.5	14.5	6.5
Greeks	Athens	42.0	39.6	14.2	3.7

Many people are interested in controlling or eliminating the reproduction of individuals possessing so-called undesirable characteristics. Reproductive control unfortunately does not provide a quick answer to the problem of eliminating undesirable recessive traits. If we modify the Hardy–Weinberg equations to include the effects of such selection on gene frequencies, we can use the basic idea of population genetics to show

how long selection would take to eliminate or reduce the trait to any particular level. In Japan a recessive gene was found that caused the homozygous individual to be deaf and mute. The frequency of this gene in the population was 0.009 (9 recessive genes out of every 1000 genes). If *all* the individuals showing the trait were prevented from marrying and having children, the frequency of the recessive gene in the population would be reduced at the rate shown in Table 18.4. These calculations indicate that reduction of the frequency of a recessive trait is very slow. Is control worth all the problems it entails? Society must make that judgment.

Table 18.4. Frequency of One Gene for Deaf-Mute in Japan

Generations of Selection	Frequency of the Gene	Frequency of Homozygous Individuals
0	0.009	0.000081
14	0.008	0.000064
32	0.007	0.000049
139	0.004	0.000016

Principles

1. In sexually reproducing populations the gene frequencies and genotype frequencies remain the same from one generation to the next if certain conditions prevail.

2. This genetic equilibrium may be altered by selection, migration, mutation, and genetic drift.

Questions

1. State the Hardy–Weinberg law.

2. Is this only a useful theoretical model, or a realistic statement of conditions as they occur in nature? Defend your viewpoint.

3. Is a *gene pool* an abstract concept or a reality? Explain.

4. If provided with the frequency of a certain gene in a population, how do you determine the frequencies of the genotypes in which it may occur?

5. List the major forces that act to change gene frequencies in populations.

6. Which of these forces plays the dominant role in directing the course of evolution? Explain how it works.

7. Which of these forces introduced entirely new genes into the population?

8. Using the Hardy–Weinberg concept, explain why eliminating an undesirable recessive phenotype from a population reduces the frequency of the gene only slightly.

9. Find out whether the state in which you live has any "eugenic" laws aimed at reducing the frequencies of undesirable genes. If so, are the laws really effective from a biological viewpoint?

Adaptation and Speciation

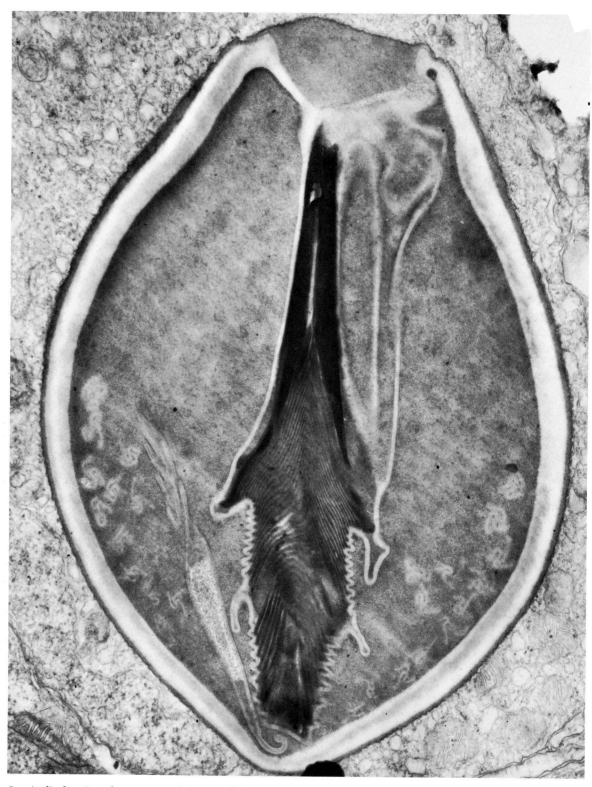

Longitudinal section of a nematocyst (stinging cell) from Hydra. (Dr. George B. Chapman.)

CHAPTER XIX

Adaptation and Speciation

Although the gene pool of a population tends to remain the same, selection, mutation, and migration produce shifts in the gene frequencies. Since selection is the force that gives direction to these changes, the organisms in the population become progressively better adapted to their environment.

In what ways do organisms become better adapted? We can classify adaptations into three general categories: (1) morphological, (2) physiological, and (3) behavioral. At first it seems that examples should fall cleanly into one of these categories. Careful examination of the examples confirms what our knowledge of the interrelations of parts of organisms leads us to suspect—that adaptations in the structure, function, or activity of an organism are generally accompanied by related adaptations in the rest of the organism.

Types of Adaptations

Morphological adaptations are the most noticeable (Figures 19.1 to 19.3). Protective devices in plants such as thorns are obvious examples. Another example is the bulliform cells in the leaves of grass. These large, specialized cells permit the folding of the leaf under dry conditions. This device is a water conservation mechanism in addition to the ones discussed in Chapter X (Figure 19.4). Why is it adaptive?

At one time the treatment for Red Scale, an insect which attacks citrus, was cyanide gas fumigation of the trees. After several years of this treatment, a strain of scale appeared that was resistant to the concentrations of cyanide which had been used. Concentrations of cyanide strong enough to kill this new strain of scale also caused severe damage to the trees. This is a good example of a *physiological adaptation* brought about by artificial selection, that is, selection controlled by man. An explanation for this phenomenon can be advanced using mutation and selection as factors modifying the Hardy–Weinberg equations, as in the last example in Chapter XVIII. Another physiological adaptation is shown in Figure 19.5.

Since the study of behavior is new in biology, it is more difficult to find simple examples of *behavioral adaptations*. Many of the best examples involve subtle modifications. (See Figure 19.6.) The release of a black fluid called "ink" by a squid is a clear example. When threatened by a predator, the squid shoots its ink into the water, usually becomes paler in color, and swims away. The ink assumes a roughly squidlike configuration in the water. Together with the paler color of the squid which makes it less noticeable, the black ink tends to draw the attention of the predator away from the squid and helps the prey to escape.

One animal that shows all three types of adaptations in one related set is the skunk. This distinct coloration, the ability to produce scent, and the pawing of the ground and ejecting of the scent are all important adaptations in the skunk's mechanisms for self-protection. Which adaptation should have arisen first? Why

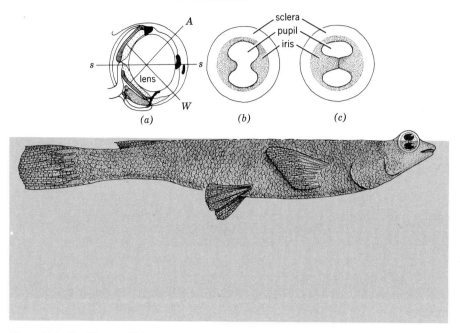

Figure 19.1. The "four-eyed" fish. The upper diagrams show development of the two pupils in an eye. The two lenses allow the fish to see simultaneously in and above the water. (a—Adapted from A. Pütter, Handbuch der gesamten Augenheilkunde, 1912. Aufl., Bd. 2; *b and c—Schneider and von Orelli,* Mitt. d. naturt. Ges. in Bern., 1907.*)*

would natural selection, that is, selection by nature, not by man, then favor the other adaptations?

Mechanisms of Adaptation

Variations in Environment. Even though we have treated the environment as though it were uniform, it is probable that no two points in an organism's entire geographic range have exactly the same environmental conditions. Slightly different traits will be adapted for each set of these conditions.

As a result, the forces of natural selection differ from one area to another, and the direction in which the gene pools change varies from one population to the next. This, of course, means we shall find distinct adaptations for each area that has a markedly different environment.

Color in a small mammal such as the beach deer mouse (*Peromyscus polionotus*) in northern Florida illustrates this point. It is important that the color of these animals be closely matched to the color of the soil if the animals are to survive. A coat coloring that is distinct from the soil color will allow predators to spot the animals much more easily.

In northern Florida the soil color varies from reddish near the east coast, to dark in the central part, to very light sand along the Gulf coast. The color of the mice follows this same pattern. Since the populations of mice from all these areas can interbreed and are much alike except for color, we assume that they came from ancestors which all looked very much alike. The observable differences among populations have arisen because the differences in the environments of these areas have selected individuals best adapted to each. We are able, therefore, to identify the population to which various mice belong.

Certainly more differences than color occur among these populations. If we were to measure the mice and the environments on the east and Gulf coasts, we could probably enumerate a good number of distinctions in each. Under existing conditions, genes from the population on one coast can be exchanged with genes from the population on the other coast through the interbreeding of mice from each population with individuals from the population in the central part of the state. What would happen if the genes in each of the two groups were prevented from crossing to the other?

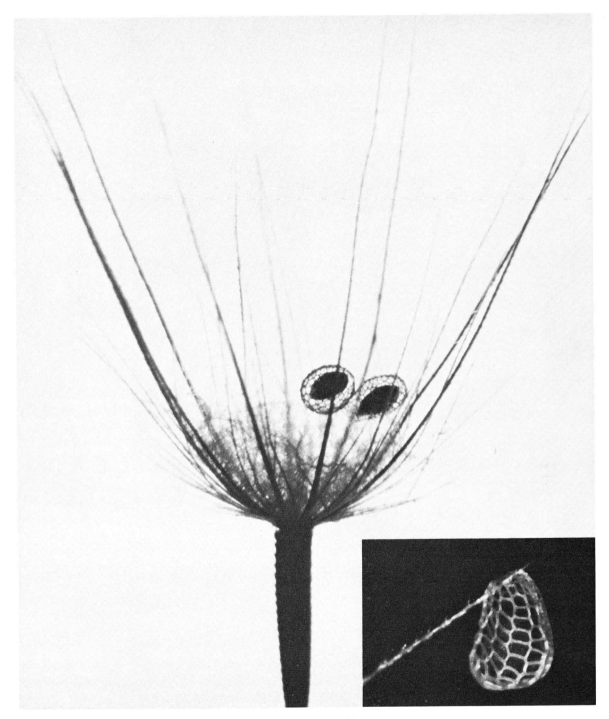

Figure 19.2. Coordinated seed dispersal in a parasite and its host. The netlike structure surrounding the seed of the parasite often catches on the bristles of the host's seed. (Mr. P. R. Atsatt.)

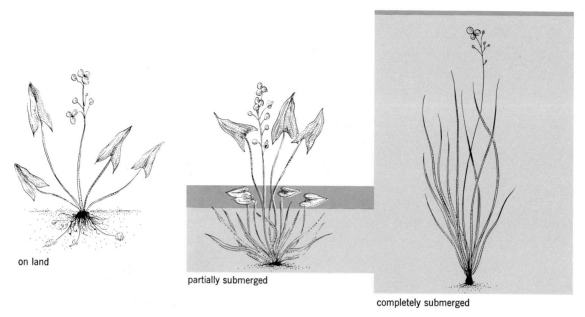

on land

partially submerged

completely submerged

Figure 19.3. The leaf shape in the arrowleaf plant is modified in different environments. (Redrawn from Bruce Wallace and Adrian M. Srb, Adaptation, *second ed., 1964, Prentice-Hall, Englewood Cliffs, N. J.)*

Barriers.   A barrier would be effected if the mice were all removed from the central area of the state. Then the only possible way in which gene exchange could occur between the two coastal populations would be the migration of individuals from one coast to the other. The distance is too long for this to occur often. Consequently, *reproductive isolation* (lack of gene exchange) would result. With no exchange of genes between the two populations, the mutations occurring in one could not reach the gene pool of the other.

The tendency of natural selection to cause the two groups to become dissimilar would continue unabated. The counterforce of migration and gene exchange would no longer slow down the divergence of the two populations. They would become progressively more dissimilar. It is impossible for this to occur unless a barrier to gene exchange has arisen.

In most cases the first barrier that prevents gene exchange is a *geographical barrier.* The organisms are prohibited from reaching one another by some feature of the environment between them. It may be a river, ocean, mountain, desert, forest, or any unsuitable habitat. As the two groups become more dissimilar through time, other barriers to reproduction may arise. Examples of these are temporal, ecological, behavioral, and hybrid inviability barriers. These names all refer

to barriers that prevent effective gene exchange, but they function at different times in the life cycle or in different ways.

In the first two instances, temporal and ecological barriers, the two organisms do not even meet during the breeding times. One group breeds earlier than the other (*temporal*) or in a different type of habitat (*ecological*). An interesting example of ecological isolation is found in some small birds living in Mexico. Two species, the Red-eyed Towhee and the Green Towhee, live very close to one another in some areas. In one area in southeastern Mexico, the two species live on the same mountain without any apparent inter-breeding (Figure 19.7). The Red-eyed Towhee lives in the brushy growth in oak and oak-pine forests at lower elevations, whereas the Green Towhee lives in the brushy plants in fir and oak-pine forests at higher elevations. Even though they live near each other, they do not live in the same environment, and therefore do not interbreed.

Farther north in Mexico, the two species again come into contact. However, in this area man has changed the environment a great deal by cutting the virgin forests. The brushy regrowth is an optimum habitat for both species. Consequently, both nest in these areas and interbreeding occurs. Here the population is

Figure 19.4. A cross section of a Poa *leaf showing bulliform cells. Under dry conditions these lose water and allow the leaf to fold.*

quite variable and intermediate between the normal appearance of the two species. Obviously, the two species can interbreed but differences in habitat have usually kept them apart.

Behavioral barriers often prevent the interbreeding of individuals of different species that do meet during the breeding season. Some important factor in the courtship differs between the two. Consequently, the displays necessary to initiate mating are not all present and mating does not occur.

The Eastern and Western Meadowlarks look almost identical. In the midwest, where their ranges overlap, the male of one species may court the females of the other. All may go well with the courtship until just before the male mounts the female. As he approaches the female, he gives a call note that is different in the two species. The female, hearing the wrong note, will not allow courtship to proceed.

Hybrid inviability does not prevent interbreeding. It only prevents interbreeding from generating gene exchange. The hybrid may die at any stage of development up to the onset of reproduction. In fact, even if

the hybrid lives but is incapable of reproducing because of sterility or its unattractiveness to other members of the species, the result will be the same.

An instance involving flax represents one end of this range. If two species are crossed, the hybrid seeds fail to germinate. However, perfectly normal germination occurs and luxuriant fertile plants are produced if the seedcoats are first removed from the embryos. Here the seedcoat which comes from the tissue of the maternal plant interacts with the hybrid embryo in some way that prevents germination.

In nature, these hybrids would not grow. Any plants that interbred with members of the other species would leave no offspring. Therefore, natural selection would favor plants that did not interbreed and more barriers would be introduced to reinforce this one of hybrid inviability.

Speciation: The Results of Adaptation

Let us now assume that the two groups of mice are again able to reach each other. What will happen? Will the groups be able to interbreed again or not? The re-

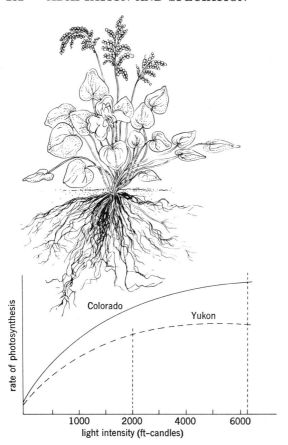

Figure 19.5. The rate of photosynthesis in Oxyria *is adapted to the plant's environment. (Dr. H. A. Mooney.)*

sult will depend on the extent to which barriers have been built up. If, when the geographic barrier breaks down, other barriers are sufficiently developed to prevent gene exchange, the two groups will remain distinct and continue to be affected by their own selective pressures. The changes in the gene pool of one that has been brought about by selection and mutation will not be transmitted to the other gene pool and will not affect its evolutionary path.

If, on the other hand, the two groups do interbreed, genes from the two pools will become intermingled and the differences between the groups will become less marked than before. Distinctions between some individuals may be even greater because of recombinations of the greater variety of genes, but most individuals will resemble some intermediate form.

In reality we have been discussing the method by which two species may develop from one. This process is called *speciation.* When the two populations make contact again, a lack of interbreeding indicates that each is now, in fact, a distinct species. This lack of interbreeding is a meaningful test to show distinct species in sexually reproducing organisms because two populations that cannot interbreed, cannot affect the course of each other's evolution. The most favored formal definition of a species includes this idea of lack of gene exchange: *a species is an interbreeding population or group of populations that is reproductively isolated from other such populations.*

Speciation can occur in other ways; one other deserves mention. In plants, and possibly in animals, doubling of the chromosome number results in rapid, one-step introduction of reproductive barriers between individuals and therefore brings about the development of a new species. Closely related species of plants often interbreed to some extent in nature. These hybrids are sterile or nearly so if the chromosomes derived from the two parents do not pair normally in meiosis. This results in the chaotic distribution of chromosomes to the gametes and generally death of these gametes. On occasion, however, some of these hybrid plants show a doubling of chromosome number. When this occurs, all chromosomes can pair at meiosis and viable gametes result. Note that these gametes contain twice the number of chromosomes found in gametes from the parent plants. These *tetraploid* (four sets of chromosomes) plants may now be fertile and reproduce readily, but they will be incapable of interbreeding with the parents. Usually the new species resembles the parent species closely, yet such a population would meet the requirements necessary to be called a new species by our definition since it would be reproductively isolated. Note that external differences are not necessary between different species.

Adaptive Radiation

Let us now expand the model from two isolated populations to several reproductively isolated groups. Earlier we stated that the environment was certain to be distinctive in each place in the range of an organism. Each of the isolated units is therefore exposed to its own selection pressures and different adaptations arise. If the isolation persists long enough, several distinct species result. The differences in structure that we would see in the various groups would be related to the adaptation of each group to its own environment. Since all of these groups come from a common ancestor, becoming different as they adapt to new

Figure 19.6. (a) *A sea otter carrying a rock on its stomach. He opens his food (sea urchins,* b) *by cracking them against the rock.*

environments, this process is called *adaptive radiation.*

Because of their respective adaptations, each group would probably be doing something unique in its environment, for example, feeding in a slightly different place; nesting in a special spot; growing on another soil; etc. Since the groups exploit different parts of the environment, they are said to occupy separate niches. As soon as these niches become distinctive enough to avoid undue overlap, the groups can come together without interbreeding or severe competition (Figure 19.8).

Comparison of groups of living organisms and study of the fossil record reveal large numbers of examples of adaptive radiation. Evidently any time a group developed a new major adaptation (flying in birds, body temperature control, etc.) or reached an area with many unoccupied niches it could fill, it evolved in many directions and became adapted to many niches. Such adaptation resulted in organisms which may be very different superficially, but whose basic structural similarity indicates their close relationship. On the other hand, two unlike organisms in different areas may become adapted to the same niche and superficially appear similar. Examination of their basic structure shows that they come from different kinds of ancestry. It is obvious that if we wish to have the classification of organisms indicate the degree of relationship caused by sharing a common ancestry, we must find basic characteristics upon which to construct the classification.

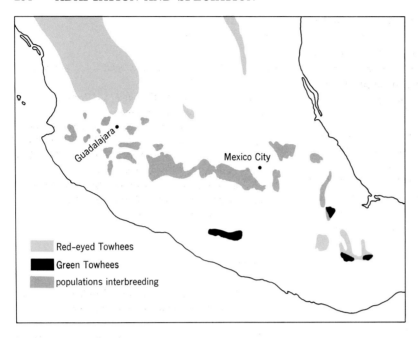

Figure 19.7. Distribution of towhees in Mexico.

One more point must be made about the operations of natural selection. It cannot select characters that are not present. It works only with available materials and structures or with those that happen to develop because of mutation or genetic recombination. The clearest examples of this are shown by comparing two completely unrelated organisms adapted to similar environments.

Whales and fish live in the same general environment and their general body form is much the same (Figure 23.1). Their respiratory systems contain marked differences, however. When a lung-breather like the whale becomes adapted to life in the water, a system such as gills that allows gas exchange to be carried out under water would be most useful. This acquisition was not available to whales, because no mutation for the development of gills occurred. Instead, mutations occurred which modified the utilization of oxygen and enabled long periods between breaths. Lungs are still the means of gas exchange and these can accommodate rather large supplies of air. The real adaptations are found in the operation of the circulatory system and in the ability of certain cells to tolerate low oxygen supplies—but not in the respiratory system. When the animal dives, the heart rate drops and most of the blood is shunted to the nervous system with little going to the extremities. The sensitive nervous system receives sufficient oxygen to

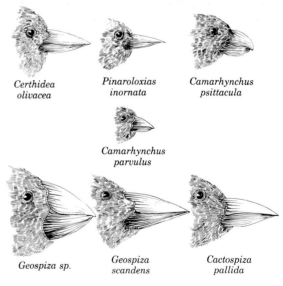

Figure 19.8. Shape of beaks in Darwin's finches. A group of small finches reached the Galapagos Islands where no other land birds lived. The radiation to feed in the available habitats has resulted in the marked differences in beak shapes.

prevent damage and to allow respiratory movements to be suspended. Cells in the extremities receive little oxygen and must tolerate a low oxygen supply. This type of adaptation to life in the water does not appear to be as advantageous to the organism as the development of gills. However, lungs were already present and gills were not.

Natural selection operating on the variability present in the genotypes of populations can cause better adaptation of organisms to their environment. Coupled with reproductive isolation, these adaptations bring about speciation. To determine the relationships of species to one another, however, we need to know the types of evidence for evolution and their possible meanings.

Principles

1. Selection adapts a population to its environment by choosing the fittest individuals available.

2. Populations adapted to different environments may undergo speciation if they are isolated from one another for a sufficient period of time.

Suggested Readings

Savage, Jay M., *Evolution*. Holt, Rinehart and Winston, New York, 1963, pp. 66–93.

Sheppard, P. M., *Natural Selection and Heredity*. Harper and Row, Publishers, New York, 1960.

Stebbins, G. Ledyard, *Processes of Organic Evolution*. Prentice-Hall, Englewood Cliffs, N. J., 1966, pp. 1–127.

Wallace, Bruce and Adrian M. Srb, *Adaptation*. Second edition. Prentice-Hall, Englewood Cliffs, N. J., 1964.

Wecker, Stanley C., "Habitat Selection," *Scientific American*, Vol. 211 (October, 1964). Offprint No. 195, W. H. Freeman and Co., San Francisco.

Questions

1. In light of the previous chapters, does heredity act as a conservative force in evolution or as an agent of change? Why?

2. Name three categories of adaptation and provide an example of each. Can you think of some examples in addition to those in the chapter?

3. Why is it incorrect to say that the environment *causes* organisms to change (adapt) in order that they may better survive? Can you think of an experiment to test this idea?

4. List some of the ways in which reproductive isolation might occur. Does this always lead to speciation? Why?

5. What is the best evidence that two populations have become two species?

6. How can polyploidy bring about speciation in only one generation?

7. What is the relation between speciation and adaptive radiation?

CHAPTER XX

Evolution: Evidences and Theories

A fossil starfish. (Smithsonian Institution.)

Evolution: Evidences and Theories

Evolution in its simplest and broadest sense means changes in gene frequency over a period of time. Natural selection guides these changes. Only those changes persist that will better adapt organisms to their environment. The origin of *new* characteristics lies in mutation. In mutation there is also a change in gene frequency (from zero to some small percentage), and the survival of these changes is likewise subject to the test of adaptability.

Over long periods the accumulation of changes may be sufficient to separate once similar populations into distinct groups. In the course of evolutionary history this divergence has apparently led to different classes (mammals, birds, fish, etc.), different phyla (insects and corals, for example), and even different kingdoms (plants and animals).

Evidences of Evolution

How extensive has evolution been? What information can be used to show which groups are closely related and which are distantly related? The same evidence can be used to answer both questions.

The evidence may be divided into two classes: *direct* or fossil evidence and *indirect* evidence. Since the fossil evidence is the most important to our knowledge of the history of life, we shall discuss it first.

Fossils. A fossil is any evidence of pre-existent life (Figure 20.1). Many people think of fossils as organisms turned to rock. Such fossils are relatively rare.

More often, the organism has been slowly replaced by sand, mud, or a mineral. In a few cases part of the organism itself is still present. In other cases only an impression of the organism remains. Regardless of the method of preservation, the important fact is that preservation has occurred. Consequently we have information about an organism that existed in the past. The information varies, but allows us to say that a particular kind of organism did exist at some definite time. We have the remains and are therefore certain of its existence. For this reason we consider fossils direct evidence that evolution has taken place.

If we can discover the approximate age of the fossils, we can arrange them in order of their appearance on the earth. By carefully noting the details of the structure of fossils and the time at which they existed, it is possible to construct a history for many groups of organisms. This history tells us when they existed, in what forms, and the relationships among members of the group.

Dating techniques that utilize radioactive substances are the most widely known. We shall illustrate the process for carbon, which is used for dating recent materials. The process is essentially the same for any radioactive substance—a substance that emits energy, particles, or both, all of which are measurable. Other radioactive substances used for dating older remains include uranium and radioactive potassium. A sample of the fossil to be dated is analyzed for two carbon

239

isotopes, C^{14} (carbon 14 or radioactive carbon) and C^{12} (carbon 12 or ordinary carbon). If the organism being dated has died recently, the ratio of C^{14} to C^{12} would be the same as it is in the atmosphere today. The earlier in the earth's history the organism died, the greater will be the amount of C^{14} that will have decayed to C^{12} through the loss of energy and particles (Figure 20.2). Thus the ratio of C^{14} to C^{12} will necessarily be lower. By using the rate of decay for C^{14} to C^{12}, which is already known, we can calculate how old the fossil must be. The age that we obtain is not com-

pletely accurate but the range of error is small enough to make this technique a valuable tool.

Since not all fossils can be readily dated by radioactive methods, we must use some other methods as well. In studying fossil materials it has been found that certain <u>fossils occur only in rock of one age</u>. These fossils are called *indicator species*. After several rock formations bearing these species have been dated by the radioactive methods, the presence of these indicator species may be used to identify other rock formations of the same age.

It is important to emphasize the detail sometimes found in the fossil record. Sections of some plant fossils have even shown detail within their cells. In a few cells we can identify the stage of mitosis by the appearance of the chromosomes. The changes that occurred as mammals arose from reptiles are also recorded in fine detail in fossil form (Figure 20.3). There are fossils which show almost every minor change in skull structure.

If all groups of organisms showed such fine fossil records, many of the problems concerning the history of life would be settled. Just as the record is rich in some areas, it is noticeably impoverished in others. The organisms that do not have hard parts (for example, a skeleton of some kind) such as most worms, algae, and jellyfish, do not often appear as fossils. When we consider the events which must occur for an organism to become a fossil, the comparative rarity of soft-bodied forms is reasonable.

For an organism to become a fossil, it must be buried before it has decayed. Hard body parts decay less rapidly than soft parts, increasing the chance of fossilization for an organism with hard parts. In addition, after burial hard parts are better able to withstand the pressure and heat in the rock. Soft parts are frequently reduced to a thin layer of carbon. The chance

Figure 20.1. A fossil fern leaf. (John H. Gerard, Monkmeyer Press Photo Service.)

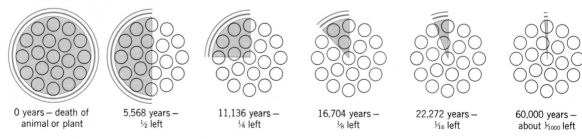

| 0 years — death of animal or plant | 5,568 years — $\frac{1}{2}$ left | 11,136 years — $\frac{1}{4}$ left | 16,704 years — $\frac{1}{8}$ left | 22,272 years — $\frac{1}{16}$ left | 60,000 years — about $\frac{1}{1000}$ left |

Figure 20.2. The proportion of carbon 14 remaining in fossils of different ages. (Adapted from an illustration by Adolph E. Brotman for TIME-LIFE BOOKS, 1962, Time Inc.)

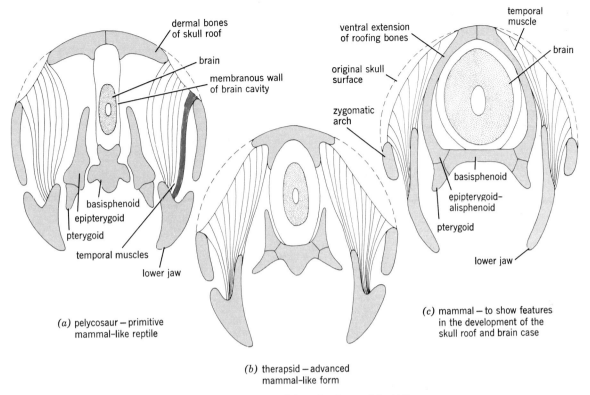

Figure 20.3. Changes in details of skull structure determined from fossil materials. (After Alfred S. Romer, The Vertebrate Body, third ed., 1962, W. B. Saunders Co., Philadelphia.)

of finding this thin layer is small. In many instances, even if it is found, little information is available about the organism the layer represents.

Evidences from the distributions of organisms and from their comparative structure, development, and function are indirect. If we assume that evolution has occurred, these many facts present a coherent and intelligible picture. If we assume that evolution has not occurred, these facts become a confusing array of disconnected observations. As evolution enables us to explain more facts about organisms in terms of known phenomena, our explanation of the history of life in evolutionary terms becomes more certain.

Biogeography. The distribution of organisms (*biogeography*) is an indirect evidence. Some distributions show patterns that are exactly as we would expect them to be if the various species of the group had originated from a common ancestor through a long series of minor changes. For example, nearly all species of sheep are represented in Central Asia, which seems to be the place of their origin. The area of origin is often the place where the majority of the species of any group live, because the longer the group has lived there, the more opportunity there has been for speciation. In addition, the older fossils of sheep and their relatives are found in Central Asia. As the sheep spread north and east through Siberia during recent glacial times, they found a route to North America by way of the land bridge across the Bering Strait. The bighorn sheep of the Rocky Mountains is more closely related to the sheep in northeastern Siberia than to any of the other nine species of sheep. This is the distribution we would expect if the sheep, when isolated, differentiated into distinct species. (See Figure 20.4.)

In two further examples from biogeography we shall look at some patterns of distribution of closely related groups which seem to argue against evolution from a common ancestor. However, as we examine all the evidence, including fossil remains and the habitat requirements of the species, these examples also show the exact distribution we would expect if evolution had occurred.

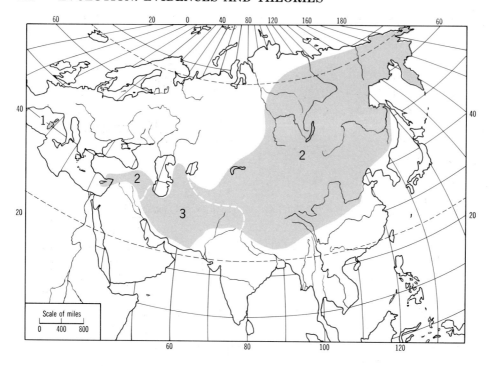

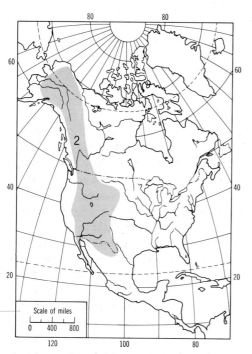

Figure 20.4. Distribution of bighorn sheep. The numbers indicate how many species of bighorns inhabit each area.

The distribution of magnolias presents a problem that is difficult to solve (Figure 20.5). How can closely related species be found in widely separated localities with no relatives anywhere between? The fossil record gives us the clue to this distribution. Earlier in the earth's history the magnolias were widely spread over Europe, Asia, and North America. During the glacial periods, the ice sheets forced the plants into small refuges in southeastern North America and Asia. In Europe, the Mediterranean Sea and the mountains of Asia Minor prevented the plants from moving farther south to areas in which they could have survived. After the glaciers retreated, the magnolias spread back to the north in Asia and North America but could not reach the areas of Europe they had occupied before because intervening areas were too dry or too high.

The plants and animals of extreme southern Florida also show an interesting and apparently contradictory pattern. Almost all of the plants and marine fish of southern Florida are related to forms found in the West Indies, whereas the birds, mammals, amphibians, and reptiles are nearly all related to forms found over more northerly parts of the United States. The water between the West Indies and Florida was a *barrier* (preventing organisms from crossing) or a *corridor* (a means of distribution) depending on whether the organism could tolerate exposure to salt water. Neverthe-

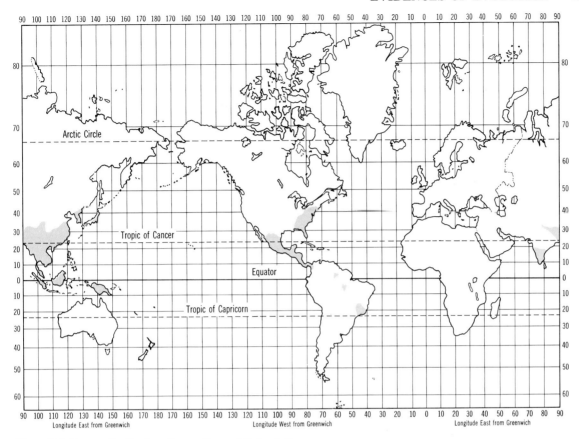

Figure 20.5. Present distribution of magnolias and their relatives.

less, some birds and many insects have come from the West Indies to southern Florida, many of them being blown across by hurricanes.

Comparative Structure and Development.   Comparison of living organisms provides considerable information for use in deciding the degree of relationship among groups. This information is particularly helpful in working with groups that are not well represented in the fossil record and with relationships among major groups (phyla) where fossils are few.

Most comparative information is obtained from the study of the structure of embryonic and adult organisms. We assume that if evolution has occurred, those groups that have developed more recently from a common ancestor should resemble one another more closely in their development and adult structure than those that have been distinct groups longer.

Some seemingly nonadaptive structures occur in the embryos of higher organisms, but through modification become distinct adaptive structures in the adults of different groups. In the more primitive forms, the adult structure is not markedly different from the structure of the embryo. This is not to say that the embryos of higher groups resemble the adults of lower groups, but that they resemble the embryos of the lower groups from which they have descended. The gill slits of all vertebrate embryos are a good example (Figure 20.6). In fish most of the gill-slit structure develops into gills and gill slits in the adults. The embryos of all amphibia, reptiles, birds, and mammals have gill slits. In later development, parts of these structures become modified into parts of the ear and parathyroid and thymus glands. Not only does this evidence indicate a close evolutionary relationship among the many vertebrate groups, but it also seems nearly inexplicable on any other grounds.

Some plants of the nightshade family superficially appear to be quite different from others. Yet tomatoes, potatoes, tobacco, nightshade, and jimsonweed (*Datura*) all belong to this family. The flowers and

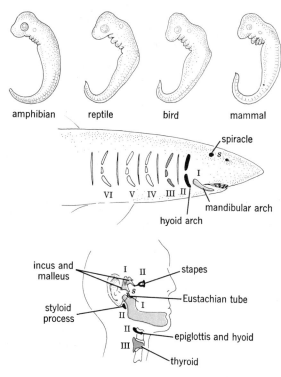

Figure 20.6. All vertebrates have similar gill slits as embryos (upper diagrams). The different fates of the structures associated with the gill slits in a shark and in man are illustrated in the lower diagrams.

fruits of these groups of plants are similar (Figure 20.7). This factor and other similarities support the idea that these plants are all closely related and should be included in the same family.

One caution must be repeated about the interpretation of similarities. The two preceding examples illustrated similarities in basic structures that are present because the organisms had a common ancestor. Distinctions among the groups have arisen through natural selection by different environments, a pattern of evolution called divergence. Since the similarities in the structures are similarities in basic form and are due to a common origin in the embryo, the two structures are homologous.

It is easy to mistake superficial similarities such as the spiny, water-storing, leafless stems of some of the cacti and euphorbs (another group containing desert adapted plants) for homologies (Figure 20.8). Observations of the flowers show that the two groups are unrelated (Figure 20.9). Both are selected for desert environments but on different continents and from different kinds of ancestors. The increasing similarity

of two groups due to selection for similar environments is called convergence.

Within the cacti and euphorbs at least two different kinds of spines are found. In the euphorbs the spine is a reduced leaf, whereas at least some of the cacti have spines that are modified bud scales and therefore not as closely related to foliage leaves. The tissue of the stem which stores water is also of two different types. In euphorbs it is derived from the cortex, a tissue which would in most plants be only a thin layer within the structure we call bark. In cacti this water-storage tissue is derived from the pith in the center of the stem and other tissues nearby.

Since these adaptations have different basic structures and different embryonic origins in the plant, the term analogous is applied to the structures. Such similarities do not indicate evolutionary relationships.

Comparative Physiology. Some evidence may be adduced for the evolutionary relationships of almost all living things. This evidence is partly based on the remarkable similarities in the structure of cells and their process of dividing. It is also based on similarity in the metabolic pathways of nearly all organisms. Cellular respiration occurs in approximately the same way regardless of the type of organism under study. Methods for the control of protein synthesis are also nearly identical. Such evidence from comparative physiology argues for the common origin of all living things.

Classification. Over the hundreds of millions of years that life has existed on the earth, natural selection acting on available variability has brought about a tremendous number of different kinds of organisms. By the eighteenth century many scientists in Europe had given much thought to naming and grouping plants and animals by schemes that attempted to place similar organisms together. Most of their efforts failed. In the middle 1700s the Swedish naturalist Carolus Linnaeus introduced a useful system for classifying organisms. He gave each organism two Latinized names—the first representing its genus and the second its species; for example, Homo sapiens, the scientific name for man. Linnaeus then ordered these names into a sequence of increasingly larger categories (see Table 20.1), each containing a greater variety of organisms than the preceding one. This system of branching categories allowed Linnaeus to indicate relative degrees of similarity. Thus two organisms, such as the coyote and the red fox, placed in the same family are more like each other than they are like any

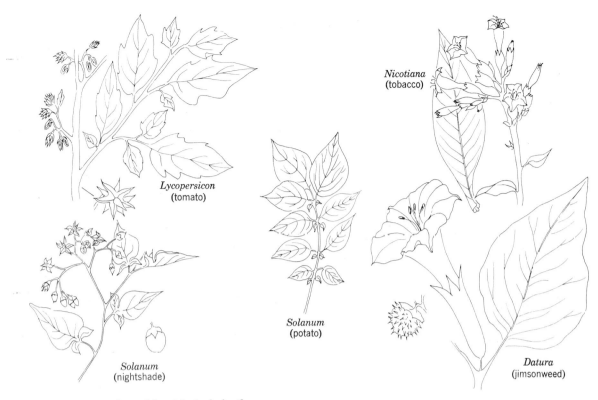

Figure 20.7. Some members of the nightshade family.

Table 20.1. Classification of Some Organisms

	Common Names				
	Domestic Dog	Coyote	Red Fox	White-tailed Deer	Gray Squirrel
Kingdom	Animalia	Animalia	Animalia	Animalia	Animalia
Phylum	Chordata	Chordata	Chordata	Chordata	Chordata
Class	Mammalia	Mammalia	Mammalia	Mammalia	Mammalia
Order	Carnivora	Carnivora	Carnivora	Artiodactyla	Rodentia
Family	Canidae	Canidae	Canidae	Cervidae	Sciuridae
Genus	*Canis*	*Canis*	*Vulpes*	*Odocoileus*	*Sciurus*
Species	*familiaris*	*latrans*	*fulva*	*virginianus*	*carolinensis*

	Leopard Frog	House Fly	White Oak	White Pine	Pine Moss
Kingdom	Animalia	Animalia	Plantae	Plantae	Plantae
Phylum	Chordata	Arthropoda	Tracheophyta	Tracheophyta	Bryophyta
Class	Amphibia	Insecta	Angiospermae	Gymnospermae	Musci
Order	Salientia	Diptera	Fagales	Coniferales	Polytrichales
Family	Ranidae	Muscidae	Fagaceae	Pinaceae	Polytrichaceae
Genus	*Rana*	*Musca*	*Quercus*	*Pinus*	*Polytrichum*
Species	*pipiens*	*domestica*	*alba*	*strobus*	*commune*

Figure 20.8. A euphorb (left) and a cactus (right) which show marked similarities, the result of convergent evolution. (From Fuller and Tippo, College Botany, revised ed., 1954, Holt, Rinehart and Winston, New York.)

other organism that is placed in a different family. A third organism, the gray squirrel—dissimilar enough from the first two to be placed in a different family and a different order—still has enough similar characteristics to be placed in the same class with them.

When Linnaeus first proposed his systems, he classified the organisms on the basis of characteristics that seemed fundamental to him. The concept of evolution played no part in his choices. Since the process of evolution by natural selection was discovered, biologists have tried to select those characteristics that indicate a common ancestry for the organisms for use in classification. This work on classification modified Linnaeus' work but did not discard it. A modern version is presented in the Appendix. Because of the accumulation of knowledge about plants and animals, Linnaeus, without knowing anything about evolution, was able to select characters which indicated evolutionary relationships. This is one evidence for evolution which is obtained from classification.

As we compare the various sources of evidence in any group of organisms, we find that almost all of it points to the same general kind of relationship. This coincidence is another strong argument for evolution.

Trends in Evolution

Detailed presentation of any one theory of the evolutionary relationships among organisms is beyond the purpose and scope of this book. There are certain general characteristics of evolution, however, that are found throughout the history of life, which we shall discuss.

The most obvious characteristic is probably that of *change* itself. Since environments are always changing, the species that inhabit them must change in order to remain adapted and alive. Sometimes these changes are striking and at other times they are more difficult to observe. Remember that these changes have resulted from natural selection acting on variation that was more or less random and spontaneous.

Some of this variation allowed individuals to *invade new environments,* the second characteristic of evolution. Consequently the history of life shows organisms confined at first to relatively few habitats but progressively moving into more and more of them.

With the invasion of additional habitats and progressive adaptation to them, new and increasingly

Figure 20.9. A euphorb (a) and a cactus (b) in flower. (General Biological Supply House, Inc.)

complex structures appeared. As complexity increased, the organisms often became specialized to utilize only a small part of their original environment. This allowed other species to utilize the remaining portions. Although *increasing complexity* is a third general characteristic of evolution, it is not universal. Those organisms that have become adapted for certain kinds of parasitic niches become progressively simplified in structure.

The fourth characteristic, *expansion,* follows from the first three. As more environments can be inhabited and the organisms become increasingly adapted to more specialized portions of these environments, the total number of species and of individuals increases. This combination of trends allows living things to utilize a growing percentage of the earth's total energy input. This energy input is the final barrier to expansion.

The total number of living things has increased through time but many groups of organisms first showed expansion and then extinction. At one time the dinosaurs were the dominant type of animal life.

They have been extinct for seventy-five million years. At about the time the dinosaurs began to decline, the number of mammals began to increase. Increases in groups like this have offset the decrease in other groups and maintained the expansion of life.

Theories of Evolution

All the evidence at hand has not by itself yielded any theory of this history of life. Men looked at the evidence available and constructed an explanation they thought accounted for it. Others compared the theory with this evidence and additional evidence that subsequently became available. If the explanation seemed to fit the evidence, the theory was retained; if not, it was discarded and replaced by another.

The success of each of the various theories of evolution has depended partly upon the amount of evidence available to the man propounding a theory and also upon his attitude and those of the people judging his theory.

The germinal concepts of the theory of evolution were present in the minds of many men before 1800. These ideas did not attract much attention because the evidence to support them was sparse and the prevailing ideas of the time were against them. Nonetheless, these theories did cause some men to look for evidence and to think about the problem of the history of life.

Lamarck's Theory.   Shortly after 1800 Jean Baptiste Lamarck attempted to explain evolution by his theory of the *inheritance of acquired characteristics.* Briefly summarized this theory states the following:

(1) The environment introduces a *need* for some structure in the organism.

(2) The organism attempts to meet this need.

(3) In response to its efforts the structure of the organism is changed.

(4) The change in the structure of this organism is passed on to its offspring.

The classic example used to explain this theory is the development of a long neck in giraffes. Short-necked ancestors of the giraffe needed to reach foliage in the trees in order to obtain food. To meet this need they stretched their necks as far as possible. Stretching the neck resulted in longer necks in the offspring. The continuation of this process through many generations resulted in the long-necked giraffe as we know it today. Although this is untenable in view of our current understanding of heredity, no information on heredity

was available to contradict the theory when Lamarck propounded it.

Darwin's Theory.   By the time that Charles Darwin completed his investigations in 1858, two important works in other fields had provided clues to another solution. To Charles Lyell, the origin of the geological formations of the earth did not need to be considered mysterious but rather as something that could be understood in terms of the natural processes which affect these same forms today. This means that the changes in the earth's surface have been brought about by uniform physical forces acting throughout the history of the earth. No cataclysmic events need to be postulated to account for the earth's surface features. In addition to explaining the appearance of the surface of the earth, Lyell's theory implied that the earth was considerably older than had been supposed up to that time.

Thomas R. Malthus, an economist, published an essay on the relationship of human populations to the resources supporting them. He stated that since resources increased arithmetically and populations increased geometrically, some forces obviously operated to check population growth. He listed war, famine, and pestilence. In this Darwin found the idea of competition between organisms for the available resources.

In the 1830s Darwin spent five years as the naturalist on a round-the-world expedition. During this trip he noticed variation among organisms and the adaptability resulting from some of the variations. Over a number of years of further study he developed a theory of the origin of species by *natural selection.* This theory contained four major points.

(1) Within a population individuals show considerable variation. For instance, not all seeds of a species of plant are exactly the same color; some are a little lighter than the average, others a little darker.

(2) Populations tend to produce more offspring than can possibly survive, because the available resources are limited.

(3) The offspring must compete for the resources that are available.

(4) Of the offspring those individuals that are best fitted will survive. Because the selection of the individuals that are to survive is made by the environment, Darwin called this natural selection.

Modern Modifications.   Darwin, like Lamarck, had little understanding of the basis of variations even though Mendel was his contemporary. With the rediscovery of Mendel's work in about 1900, the physical basis for this point of the theory was supplied. It is now possible to discuss sources of variations and the means of selection in a meaningful manner, as we have done in Chapters XVIII and XIX.

Although Darwin's four points are still used as a general statement of the means by which organisms evolve, the meaning of the phrases is somewhat different from what it was in Darwin's time. By survival of the fittest Darwin meant the survival of those specimens that were largest and strongest. Consequently, the discussion of competition tended to be limited to physical strife.

We now think of survival of the fittest in the sense that the organisms best suited to leave the most offspring will survive. It is not merely the ability to survive but the ability to survive and reproduce that is important. The combination of genes that enables its bearer to produce the highest number of offspring will be found most frequently in the subsequent generation.

Competition is no longer thought of in the narrow sense of direct physical combat but involves the utilization of any necessary resource and acquisition of mates. The competing organisms may never see each other, or, like plants, may be quite incapable of combat. Such competition is less bloody but no less real and effective.

Why do most biologists believe that this explanation of evolution is the correct one? On the basis of the evidence, it seems to offer the most reasonable theory to account for what is at hand. It will indeed be modified by new evidence in the future but probably will not be completely discarded. Too much available evidence fits well with this theory for us to suppose that complete rejection will be required.

Principles

1. Charles Darwin proposed a theory of evolution based on variation, competition, and consequent natural selection.

2. The basic mechanism of evolution is now known to be changes in gene frequencies of populations through time, guided by natural selection.

Suggested Readings

Cain, A. J., *Animal Species and Their Evolution.* Harper and Row, Publishers, New York, 1960.

Deevey, Edward S., Jr., "Radiocarbon Dating," *Scientific American,* Vol. 186 (February, 1952). Offprint No. 811, W. H. Freeman and Co., San Francisco.

Eiseley, Loren C., "Charles Darwin," *Scientific American,* Vol. 194 (February, 1956). Offprint No. 108, W. H. Freeman and Co., San Francisco.

Hurley, P. M., "Radioactivity and Time," *Scientific American,* Vol. 181 (August, 1949). Offprint No. 220, W. H. Freeman and Co., San Francisco.

Kettlewell, H. B. D., "Darwin's Missing Evidence," *Scientific American,* Vol. 200 (March, 1959). Offprint No. 842, W. H. Freeman and Co., San Francisco.

Lorenz, Konrad Z., "The Evolution of Behavior," *Scientific American,* Vol. 199 (December, 1958). Offprint No. 412, W. H. Freeman and Co., San Francisco.

Newell, Norman D., "Crises in the History of Life," *Scientific American,* Vol. 208 (February, 1963). Offprint No. 867, W. H. Freeman and Co., San Francisco.

Simpson, George Gaylord, *Life of the Past, an Introduction to Paleontology.* Yale University Press, New Haven, Conn., 1964.

Stebbins, G. Ledyard, *Processes of Organic Evolution.* Prentice-Hall, Englewood Cliffs, N. J., 1966, pp. 132–175.

Questions

1. Are footprints or leafprints from the past considered fossils? Why?

2. Why are indicator species useful for dating rock formations?

3. Fossilization is often called a rare event, yet fossils are abundant in some areas. How do you explain this?

4. How does biogeography provide evidence to support evolution?

5. What is the basis for the idea that similar structures in organisms indicate relationship?

6. Give an example of convergence among plants.

7. Dehydration synthesis and hydrolysis are universal chemical events in the living world. In what category of evidence would you place this?

8. List the major trends in the course of evolution.

9. Explain the meaning of "Lamarckian evolution."

10. How did Darwin describe natural selection? Describe natural selection as viewed by modern biologists.

11. The establishment of evolution as a biological principle is said to be the major unifying concept for all areas in biology. Can you defend this statement?

Ecosystems:
Physical Aspects and Structure

CHAPTER XXI

Ecosystems:
Physical Aspects and Structure

The final five chapters of this book, beginning with this one, present some of the major concepts derived from studies that view organisms and their environment as a biological unit. This area of biology is known as *ecology*. In a sense, we introduced the ecological approach in the chapters on population genetics and evolution, since they dealt with populations interacting with their environments through natural selection. These topics provide the historical basis for understanding many of the organismic-environmental relationships we see at the present time.

Most people feel at home with the topic of environment, since it is part of their everyday experience. Everyone has observed a number of different environments, from woodlands to bodies of water. In fact, we can step into the backyard and immediately observe a community of grass, shrubs, and trees reasonably well adapted at that particular moment to its physical and biotic surroundings. It even seems easy to predict what will happen in this artificial community if environmental conditions such as temperature or rainfall change drastically. Studying the environment may seem to be simply a matter of measuring all of these factors and noting their influence on the organisms in it. This is a deceptive assumption, as biologists have demonstrated many times. For example, the success or failure of a backyard community may also depend

on subtle environmental factors like the presence or absence of certain trace elements in the soil, the pH (acid-base relations) of the soil, the amount of humus present, and the kinds of insect populations which may appear, to name only a few such factors. In addition, organisms themselves may change the environment in many ways, for example, by increasing the moisture content of the soil or by fixing nitrogen (changing atmospheric nitrogen into nitrates which can be utilized by plants). Thus, understanding the backyard community requires an investigation of not only the influence of factors on organisms but also the influence of the organisms on the environment. Furthermore, the reciprocal interactions of communities of organisms and their environment results in varying degrees of self-regulation. This mechanism enables a community to function smoothly despite fluctuation in the physical environment caused by weather, seasons, etc.

It is especially important for us to realize that man is not only a manipulator of his environment but also a functional *part* of the environment, since he depends on biological processes for food, water purification, oxygen, and many other of his vital needs. To achieve short-term gains by modifying natural environments, he must become aware of the long-term effects of his power to bring about radical changes in the living world. He must learn to interact properly with the environment or suffer drastic consequences. Most of you have read of the tragic dust bowl era in the plains, of polluted rivers, exploited pasture lands, and other examples of man's failure to consider the intricacies of natural communities. One of the objectives of this section is to help you make intelligent decisions about such matters as air pollution, sewage disposal, drainage projects, and the like.

Ecology has been traditionally defined as the study of relationships between organisms and their environment. A modern viewpoint, enunciated by a contemporary ecologist, Eugene Odum, defines ecology as "the study of the structure and function of nature." This definition attempts to avoid the distinction between organisms and environment by treating them as an integral unit. This is the viewpoint we propose to develop. First, we need to present some background material on the major physical aspects of the environment (*abiotic factors*) so that we can better develop the modern concept.

Physical Aspects of the Environment

Heat and Light.   *Solar radiation* is the most important of the abiotic factors because it is the sole energy supply for life. It reaches the earth as sunlight, a mixture of short and long wavelengths partially screened or filtered by the atmosphere. The ecologically important wavelengths are infrared (heat), light, and ultraviolet.

Heat, recorded in terms of temperature, is obviously important in the activities and distribution of many living things. Most forms of life lack an internal temperature controlling system; they are *poikilothermal.* These forms often compensate for temperature changes with behavioral activities and other adaptations. Generally, poikilothermal forms function best at temperatures between 41° and 93° Fahrenheit, which limits their distribution. A few forms of life exhibit extreme heat hardiness (tolerance) such as the blue-green alga which lives in hot spring water of 162°F in Yellowstone National Park. A few also have extreme cold tolerance, particularly certain plant seeds, spores, and protozoan cysts which survive temperatures far below the freezing point.

Only birds and mammals are *homoiothermal,* that is, have a relatively uniform body temperature. They are less restricted in their distribution by temperature extremes; however, their metabolisms require more energy, and this may become a limiting factor. A few groups like bats are able to exploit the advantages of both poikilothermy and homoiothermy by alternating these states to adjust to different temperatures or different seasons. Generally speaking, all living things operate most efficiently at temperatures somewhere between the freezing and boiling points of water. Thus a considerable portion of the earth, including all the oceans, presents hospitable temperatures for plants and animals.

Forms of life that inhabit areas subject to drastic changes of season frequently show adaptations for temporarily avoiding detrimental extremes. Many plants become *dormant* during very cold or very dry seasons. Animals may *hibernate,* that is, become physiologically inactive during the colder seasons. Animals in extremely hot, arid areas may escape environmental crises during hotter portions of the year by *estivating,* that is, by entering a similarly inactive state.

Organisms display many additional adaptations to heat or cold, including body size, length of extremities, coloration, number of young, and other physiological manifestations (Figures 21.1 and 21.2). We might expect metabolic reactions to be considerably influenced by temperature. For example, the rate of development of eggs or the growth of plant seedlings usually shows a definite relation to temperature, as indicated in Figure 21.3.

Another important aspect of solar radiation is *light,* a factor with complex ecological effects. Probably the most obvious and most important role of light is in relation to photosynthesis, described in Chapter IV. Virtually all forms of animal life have evolved light receptors of some sort, an indication of the importance of light. In terms of their response to light, animals can be divided into *nocturnal* (night-active), *diurnal* (day-active), and even *crepuscular* (twilight-active) types. A majority of mammals are nocturnal, the majority of birds are diurnal, and bats, many moths, and a few birds are crepuscular. The many-colored patterns throughout the animal kingdom are another indication of the importance of the receptor-light relationship and are related to the functions of protection and mating (Figure 21.4). Even plants respond to light by growth movements, although they lack specific light receptors.

In another type of light reaction, many plants and animals exhibit seasonal changes in response to the number of daylight hours in a twenty-four-hour cycle; this response is called *photoperiodism.* In plants, it often determines the flowering and fruiting time. In animals the breeding cycle often functions in relation

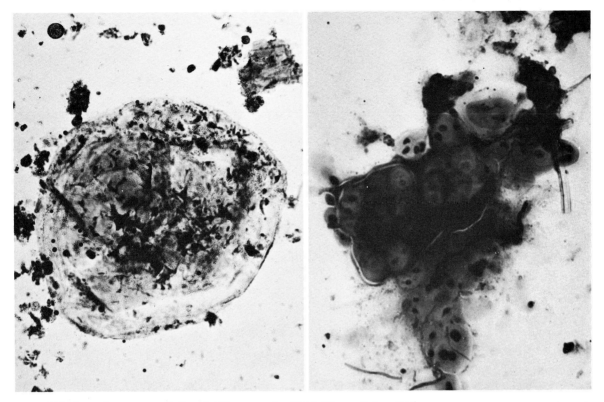

Figure 21.1. Cysts of a protozoan (left) and a blue-green alga (right). These cells have thick protective walls which enable them to withstand extreme temperatures.

Figure 21.2. The arctic fox maintains a constant body temperature despite the cold temperatures of its environments. (© Walt Disney Productions.)

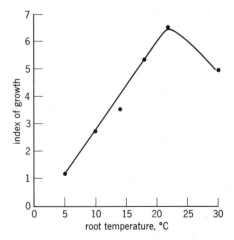

Figure 21.3. Effects of temperature on rate of development of some roots. (Data from A. H. Gibson, Aust. Jour. Biol. Sciences, 19(2), 1966.)

(a)

(b)

Figure 21.4. Protective coloration in two species of insects. (Dr. Edward S. Ross.)

to seasonal day length. This is well illustrated in birds, since their gonads become extremely small during winter months and then enlarge greatly during the spring of the year (see p. 106). Experiments have related biological events in birds to day length. This interaction sounds simple until we consider that it involves hormonal changes occurring in response to day length as perceived through the eyes of the bird. In other words, this is the sequence: eye → hypo-

thalamus → neurohormones → pituitary → gonads (Figure 21.5).

Gases. The atmospheric gases *oxygen* and *carbon dioxide* are vital components of an organism's surroundings. Animals and plants constantly remove oxygen, while photosynthesis restores it as fast as they use it. For soil- and water-dwelling organisms, the situation is different. These environments contain far less oxygen and its concentration varies.

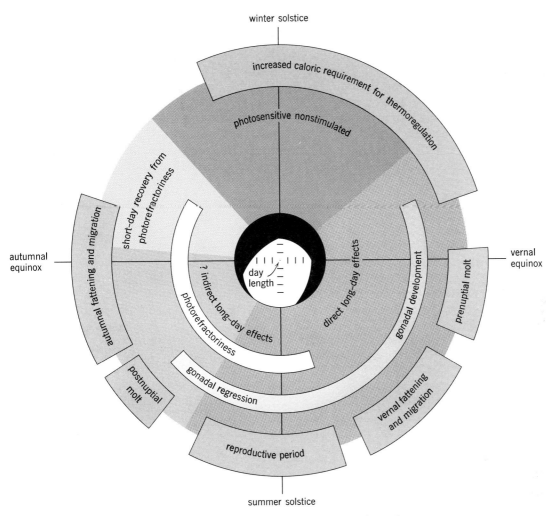

Figure 21.5. Effects of seasonal day length on the annual cycle of a bird. (Redrawn from Donald S. Farner, Photoperiodism in Animals, BSCS Pamphlet 15, D. C. Heath and Co., Boston, 1964.)

Carbon dioxide constitutes only a fractional part of the atmosphere, yet is vital to the photosynthetic process as well as to many physiological reactions in plant and animal tissues. It is readily soluble in water, where it forms carbonic acid. In this form it influences the pH of the surroundings or may be combined with calcium to help form bones, shells, and limestone formations such as coral reefs. Carbon dioxide reaches the environment from the respiration of living things. Moreover, industrial processes release large amounts of it into the atmosphere. Here we encounter a consequence of human activity which could change the environment of an entire planet. The smog situations in London and California perhaps provide an uncomfortable preview of the kinds of atmospheric changes that do take place.

Water. Water constitutes a major factor in the environment and in the lives of organisms. It enters the atmosphere by evaporation, eventually returning to the terrestrial environment as rain or snow. As lakes, rivers, and oceans it forms major habitats for living things. As ice and snow, or as moisture in the atmosphere, it influences many aspects of plant and animal ecology. Of course, water is also the most abundant compound within living tissues. The basic anatomy and physiology of all forms of aquatic and marine life are highly modified through adaptations to the liquid medium in which they live. Terrestrial organisms must adapt to the problem of preventing excess loss of water from their bodies; special body coverings, various respiratory devices, and excretory organs may serve this need. Dehydration is a major limiting factor for life in terrestrial communities just as the absence of oxygen limits life in aquatic environments.

Chemical Substances. Chemical substances, both organic and inorganic, are important environmental factors in soil and water. One category of these substances, dissolved salts, serves as vital materials for sustaining life. These substances are termed *biogenic* salts or nutrient materials and consist of chemicals such as nitrogen and phosphorus salts as well as potassium, calcium, sulfur, and magnesium. They are primarily substances necessary for maintenance of green plants which provide the basic source of nutrition for other forms of life. The term *nutrient* is misleading, since these salts are used in various parts of the photosynthetic process rather than as a source of energy. In other words, plant nutrients do not serve as food materials for plants but as building units or catalysts for synthesizing energy-rich organic compounds.

The so-called "plant food" (fertilizer) that can be bought in a garden shop contains the three chemicals that are most often lacking in soil—nitrogen, phosphorus, and potassium. The label on the bag bears numbers such as 6–8–4, which refer in sequence, to the percentages of nitrogen, phosphoric acid, and potash in the fertilizer. This knowledge of plant nutrients is tremendously important in the production of food crops, since soils that are poor in certain elements can be fortified by the application of the proper fertilizer. These nutrients function in the same way for freshwater and marine plants. By applying ordinary commercial fertilizer to a small lake the microscopic plant life soon becomes so abundant that the water turns cloudy. If this is practiced seasonally, the yield of animal life (fish) increases greatly. This has been done in salt water bodies along the coast of Scotland to increase the numbers of flounder.

This presentation has barely touched on the vast topic of chemicals in the environment, but perhaps now the complexity and importance of these materials in nature becomes clear. In Chapter XXII we shall consider the cyclical movement of chemicals through the environment.

Structure of the Ecosystem

Let us return to Odum's modern definition of ecology—*the study of the structure and function of nature.* In this definition nature includes all of the populations of an area functioning with their nonliving environment. Nature is thus perceived as an ecological system, in other words, an *ecosystem.* This is an extremely useful concept since it is feasible to study the structure and function of an ecosystem in a quantitative manner.

One way to describe the features of an ecosystem is through a familiar example such as a lake or pond (Figure 21.6). These are convenient, self-contained units, needing only the input of energy (sunlight) to function. From the structural standpoint of a pond ecosystem, four major elements can be distinguished.

(1) The *nonliving* components. These nutrient salts and other chemical agents (water, bottom sediments, etc.) constitute the abiotic portion of the system.

(2) The *producer* organisms. These are always green plants and, in aquatic habitats, consist mostly of microscopic algae of many kinds. They must have sunlight for photosynthesis and nutrient salts for making proteins. The term *autotrophic* (self-feeder) is frequently applied to photosynthetic organisms.

(3) The *consumer* organisms. These include the animal life of the pond from microscopic protozoans to fishes. Those that feed on plant life are called *primary consumers* or *herbivores.* The *secondary consumers* or *carnivores* feed on herbivores and sometimes on one another. There may be a whole series of consumer levels depending on the complexity of the ecosystem.

(4) The *decomposer* organisms. These are the bacteria and fungi which break down the complex compounds of "dead" protoplasm to release simpler substances into the environment.

This structural description is based on the general functional aspects of the ecosystem. Producers are living units which convert radiant energy (light) into organic materials and thus provide the basic energy supply for all other life in the pond. The consumers derive their energy needs, directly or indirectly, from the producers. The decomposers act to cycle many vital chemical substances back into the system. Many organisms have more than one function in this system. Thus many consumers are also decomposers, especially such animals as feed on litter or organic wastes. In addition, many algae are partly autotrophic, partly

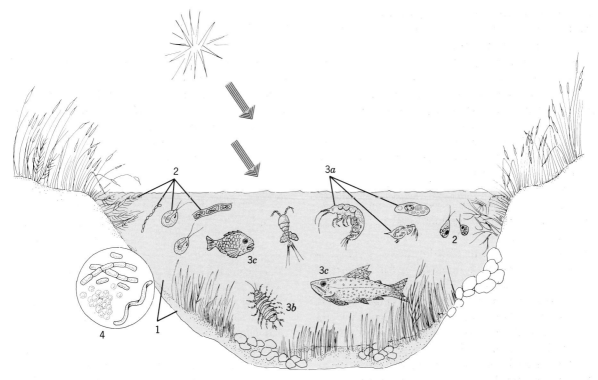

Figure 21.6. A pond ecosystem. (1) nonliving components, (2) producers, (3a, b, c) successive consumer levels, (4) decomposers. (Redrawn from Eugene P. Odum, Fundamentals of Ecology, second ed., 1959, W. B. Saunders Co., Philadelphia.)

heterotrophic, or are able to alternate between the two. The same description applies to a terrestrial situation like a forest or a grassland. In fact, we suggest that you attempt to apply this idea to a community with which you are familiar.

As mentioned before, the ecosystem concept is especially useful because each portion of it can be studied quantitatively. The amounts of biotic and abiotic materials, the *standing crop,* present at any given time can be accurately determined by appropriate methods. The rates of change, that is, turnover rates, of these substances can be closely estimated. The producer-consumer pattern of organisms can be ascertained.

A simple example will illustrate some of these points. A study made in a grasslands area showed that grasshoppers ate grass but in turn were devoured by grasshopper mice. These were eaten by striped skunks and, finally, the great horned owl preyed on the skunks. Here then we have a food chain:

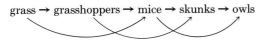

The curving arrows indicate additional feeding relations which probably exist. Further study revealed that it took 5,000 tons of grass to support 900 tons of grasshoppers, which supplied food for 100 tons of mice, which were eaten by 1 to $1\frac{1}{2}$ tons of skunks. The skunks in turn supported $\frac{1}{2}$ ton of horned owls. A *pyramid of mass* constructed from this sequence and diagrammed would look like Figure 21.7.

In addition to the standing crop at each level, the diagram reveals many other things. An enormous mass of grass is required to support a relatively small mass of owls; each stage in the pyramid has far less mass than the preceding one; and an imbalance in any part of the pyramid necessitates adjustments in the rest of it. It is also possible to construct a *pyramid of numbers* by counting the organisms in a food chain. This is not as useful, since the form of this pyramid depends on whether the producers are small or large.

A third type, the *pyramid of energy,* shows the amount of organisms in terms of their energy content. This gives the best functional picture of a community

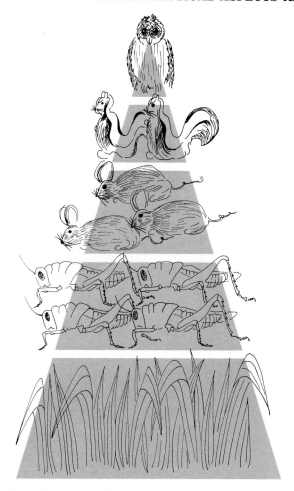

Figure 21.7. A pyramid of mass for a grassland community.

Suggested Readings

Anderson, A. J. and E. J. Underwood, "Trace-element Deserts," *Scientific American,* Vol. 200 (January, 1959).

Knipling, E. F., "The Eradication of the Screw-worm Fly," *Scientific American,* Vol. 203 (October, 1960).

Odum, Eugene P., *Ecology.* Holt, Rinehart and Winston, New York, 1963, pp. 1–36.

Plass, Gilbert N., "Carbon Dioxide and Climate," *Scientific American,* Vol. 201 (July, 1959). Offprint No. 823, W. H. Freeman and Co., San Francisco.

Storer, J. H., *The Web of Life.* New American Library of World Literature, New York, 1956.

Wald, George, "Life and Light," *Scientific American,* Vol. 201 (October, 1959). Offprint No. 61, W. H. Freeman and Co., San Francisco.

Woodwell, George M., "The Ecological Effects of Radiation," *Scientific American,* Vol. 208 (June, 1963). Offprint No. 159, W. H. Freeman and Co., San Francisco.

Questions

1. What is an ecosystem? Name two which are present in the area where you live.

2. Name the major abiotic factors functioning in ecosystems.

3. In what respect is light the most fundamental abiotic factor in an ecosystem?

4. Can you think of a large community of living things that is perpetually dark? How does it obtain its energy supply?

5. What are the four major *structural* elements of an ecosystem?

6. How would you classify man in this structural arrangement?

7. Provide an example of human activity damaging an ecosystem in your area.

8. Provide an example of how man has probably improved an ecosystem.

since it reflects some of the major functional aspects of ecosystems (see Chapter XXII). As we discovered when we studied cells, it is necessary to consider both structural and functional characteristics if we are to understand any biological system.

Principles

1. An ecosystem is a large unit in nature made up of the populations in an area interacting with their nonliving environment and with each other.

2. The major structural features of an ecosystem consist of abiotic materials and populations of producers, consumers, and decomposers.

3. Man or any other organism must interact properly with the rest of his ecosystem if he is to survive, because he is an integral part of that ecosystem.

Ecosystems: Functional Aspects

Ecosystems: Functional Aspects

Two major functional events of importance to ecosystems are the energy relations within it, and the cyclical passage of materials through it.

Energy flow and utilization constitute a major topic in ecosystems. Energy is defined as the ability to do work. It may manifest itself in a variety of forms: light, heat, chemical, mechanical, and electrical. All may function in ecological systems although some, such as light and heat, are more important than others. The behavior of energy is described by two laws.

Energy Flow in the Ecosystem

The *First Law of Thermodynamics* holds that energy may be transformed from one type to another but that it can be neither created nor destroyed. It is frequently transformed into an unusable form like heat, and is thus lost to the ecosystem, but the energy itself has not been destroyed.

The *Second Law of Thermodynamics* says that an energy transformation is never entirely efficient. When energy is changed from one form to another—for example, light energy to chemical energy in photosynthesis—some of the energy is dispersed into unusable heat. In other words, this law concerns the change of energy into increasingly less available forms.

These two "laws of energy" function in ecosystems as they do throughout the physical world. As we shall see, the ecological pyramids mentioned in Chapter

XXI are reflections of the second energy law. For this reason, it is possible to construct a pyramid of energy as well as of mass or numbers for a community.

Ecologists sometimes speak of the *energy flow* through communities, which also illustrates the second law of energy. The heavy black line in Figure 22.1 represents the community or ecosystem. Energy enters the system as sunlight to be converted by the producers, through photosynthesis, into potential energy. Observe that a considerable amount of this energy is lost to the system as heat and is thus shown leaving. Cellular respiration also accounts for some of the energy loss. The potential energy that remains is then utilized by the primary consumers (herbivores). Again, a large portion of it is lost to the system, and so it continues to the final consumers, the carnivores. The striking feature of the energy-flow concept is that tremendous quantities of energy are necessary to support the vital activities of the community, since large quantities are converted during the process into an unusable form.

If the energy demands of the community become greater than the supply, the consequences are evident. If carnivores become more abundant than their food supply, the dynamics of the community will be disturbed. The disturbances become severe if all the carnivores are removed. This actually happened some years ago when all large predators were removed by man from the Kaibab plateau in Arizona. Within a

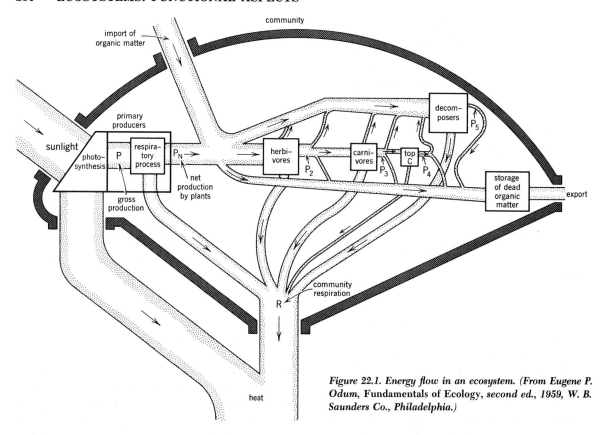

Figure 22.1. Energy flow in an ecosystem. (From Eugene P. Odum, Fundamentals of Ecology, *second ed., 1959, W. B. Saunders Co., Philadelphia.)*

short time the deer (primary consumers) became too abundant to be supported by the vegetation (primary producers). The entire area took on the appearance of an overgrazed pasture and thousands of deer eventually starved. Unfortunately, this is a common consequence of man's attempts to reorganize ecosystems to suit his whims.

Chemical Cycles in the Ecosystem

Between thirty and forty chemical elements are required by living things. Some, like carbon, hydrogen, oxygen, and nitrogen, are needed in sizable amounts, others are necessary only in small quantities. Whatever the case, most of the elements circulate in characteristic paths from environment to organism and back to environment. These pathways are known as inorganic-organic cycles, or *biogeochemical* cycles. A description of the phosphorus cycle demonstrates some of their functional aspects.

Recall from the chapters on metabolism that phosphorus played a key role in the formation of ATP. In addition, phosphorus is an important structural com-

ponent of teeth and bones. The movement of phosphorus in and out of the living world is diagrammed in Figure 22.2.

Let us begin the cycle with the large reservoir of phosphorus found in rock deposits formed over long periods of time. Central Florida, for example, contains one of the largest known deposits of this type. By erosion and weathering phosphates are released, some to be utilized by plants and then by animals. Phosphatizing bacteria serve in an important decomposing role to keep dissolved phosphates circulating in ecosystems. A considerable amount of phosphate material is washed into the sea by rivers to form marine deposits. This material becomes an important component in marine communities since phosphates, along with nitrates, appear to be the major nutrients for marine plant life. Marine birds return some of the phosphorus to terrestrial communities as indicated on the diagram. In addition, man utilizes various marine creatures and recycles small amounts in this way. Much of the phosphate, however, ends up in marine sediments where it remains out of circulation until a geological upheaval

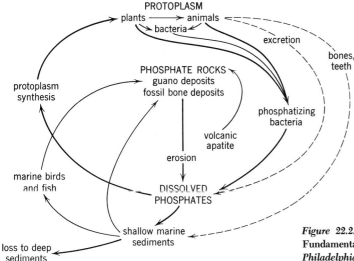

PROTOPLASM

Figure 22.2. The phosphorus cycle. (From Eugene P. Odum, Fundamentals of Ecology, second ed., 1959, W. B. Saunders Co., Philadelphia.)

converts the sea bottom into a land mass. Then weathering and erosion continue the cycle. At present it appears that more phosphorus is being "bottlenecked" in marine deposits than is re-entering the cycle, but this is difficult to judge on a short-term basis. Large amounts of phosphate are mined at present for agricultural and industrial use.

Additional examples of chemical cycles are shown in Figures 22.3 and 22.4. All cycles have several features in common. Specialized micro-organisms, such as the phosphatizing bacteria, have essential functions in mineral cycles. Plants are also basic units and are generally responsible for converting the mineral into a form which animals can utilize. In fact, most cycles could probably function without animals.

Let us digress briefly to describe how experimental procedures can be used in ecological studies. When techniques were found for producing and detecting radioactive isotopes, ecologists acquired a tool by which they could introduce a "tagged" chemical into the environment and follow its fate. In several instances, radioactive phosphorus was put in lakes and then traced as it entered the phosphorus cycle. It was observed in some instances to pass from organisms into mud sediments and then back into organisms again. Other data such as rate of uptake, which could not have been determined by any other technique, were also obtained.

Changing Communities: Succession

One additional aspect of ecosystems concerns the way that communities (or the ecosystem itself) change through time. This is the topic of *succession,* the orderly, and frequently predictable, changes a community undergoes until it reaches the *climax* stage, a fairly stable stage. Everyone has observed succession: the yard near a house which is no longer being maintained, an abandoned field, a stagnant pond. All of these illustrate the idea of changing communities. Ecologists have studied the succession stages of many types of communities. Their findings indicate that communities have a life history during which they go through a sequential period of development, attain some sort of maturity, and eventually may be replaced by another set of producers and consumers.

Many people are familiar with the

bare rock → lichens → fungi and
    ferns → herbs → shrubs → trees

type of succession. This is a long-term development beyond the experience of human lifetime, but there are examples of much shorter duration. Along the coast of Florida and other areas, channels are frequently dredged to facilitate the passage of large boats along the coastline. The mud from the dredging operation is deposited in mounds at the side of the channel. This creates small barren islands. Eventually the seeds of salt-tolerant grasses and herbs find their way to these islets and germinate. This sparse cover will likely be joined shortly by mangrove plants whose seeds are dispersed by tides and currents. These plants grow into a dense, shrubby border around the islands. Their peculiar root system holds the mud in place and may even enlarge the perimeter of the island (Figure 22.5).

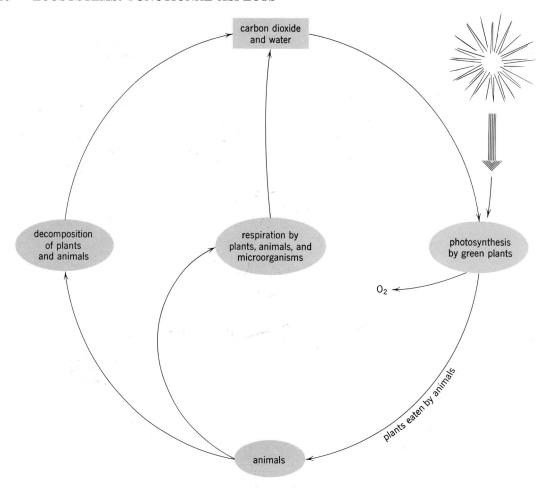

Figure 22.3. The carbon cycle. (After A. Nason, Modern Biology, *1965, John Wiley and Sons, New York.)*

If the island has sufficient elevation to be permanently above water, the grasses and herbs may be gradually replaced by shrubs such as sea grape, groundsel, and even trees, especially pines. But if it is frequently flooded by salt water, mangroves cover the entire island and form a climax community. This type of succession takes place over a relatively few years, but can disappear in a matter of hours in a severe storm.

Most of the detailed studies on succession have concerned larger communities such as the broadleaf forests of the eastern United States, the grasslands of the midwest, and aquatic environments. In the eastern United States, the climax community consists of various types of broadleaf forests such as the oak-hickory or beech–maple forest. In the southeast, succession creates a problem for the pulpwood industry since pines are more desirable than other trees for making

paper, but when pines are harvested from an area, broadleaf trees may succeed or replace the pines so that a former pinewood forest becomes a hardwood forest. Only by restraining the young broadleafs can the timber grower assure another crop of pines; in other words, he must interfere with succession.

What principles can be derived from studies of succession? First, that organisms change the physical and chemical aspects of the environment in which they live. Mice burrowing in the soil, or leaves accumulating and decaying are examples. As the environment changes, so do the kinds of plants and animals inhabiting it. This is the most noticeable feature of the process; hence the term, succession. Accompanying the succession of changing forms is an increase in the diversity of species and an increase in the amount of organic matter in an ecosystem. The excess organic

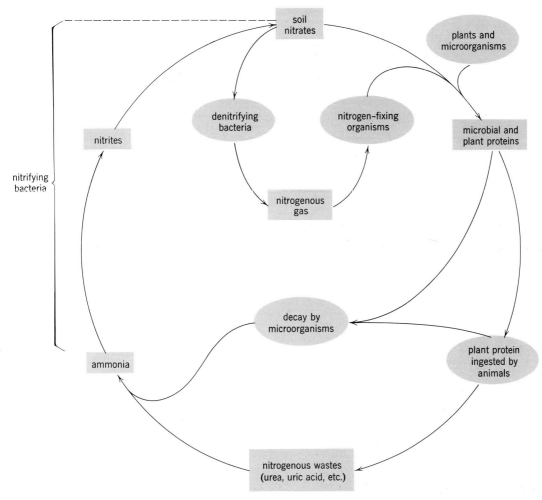

Figure 22.4. The nitrogen cycle. (After A. Nason, Modern Biology, 1965, John Wiley and Sons, New York.)

material (decaying plant and animal remains) plays a dominant role in changing the physical and chemical nature of an area. Finally, as a community becomes stable, there is a decrease in the net production of living matter. In other words, as succession slows in a community, a balance obtains between the utilization of energy (respiration) and the formation of new organic matter. For this reason man requires *early* succession stages for the production of food crops or for certain crops like the pines just described.

Man has experienced a mixture of success and failure in his attempts to modify ecosystems for his long-term benefit. Activities like the misuse of soil, excessive timbering and grazing practices, and indiscriminate use of insecticides represent failures. Success has

been attained in a few areas like wildlife and forestry management. Rice cultivation is an example of the successful manipulation of the marsh ecosystem. Unfortunately, misuses from overexploitation and pollution are increasing at an alarming rate as the result of man's greater power to change the face of the earth and his rapid increase in numbers.

As biologists have attained a better understanding of ecosystems, they have attempted to integrate man's activities with those of nature. Problems associated with water pollution, erosion, overgrazing, and mining are receiving serious attention. The effects of the Second Law of Thermodynamics are inevitable, and perhaps man is now ready to delay rather than hasten the consequences.

Figure 22.5. Red mangrove showing the root system. (W. H. Hodge.)

Population Dynamics

We have used the term *population* in various places throughout this book, assuming that the meaning was correctly understood. Thus a genetic population referred to a self-perpetuating group of organisms, whereas in ecology a population is defined as all of the members of a species inhabiting a particular area. A population, however considered is an important biological unit and in this section we discuss a few of its major features.

A population consists of individuals, and thus many of its features are a reflection of the characteristics of its members. A population also has a number of unique traits which are an outgrowth of its being a numerical concept or entity. We shall consider these quantitative aspects first.

Density. Density refers to the number of individuals per unit of area (or volume). Five meadowlarks per acre, two thousand diatoms per liter of pond water, 10,000 people per square mile are all expressions of density. This is an important aspect of population study in view of the prior discussion of energy relations and structure in the ecosystem.

Natality. This term refers to the production of new individuals, the ability of a population to increase. The natality rate (birth rate) observed in a population living under natural conditions is usually not the maximum rate possible under ideal conditions.

Mortality. The inevitable fate of all organisms in a population is death, which can be expressed in terms of a mortality rate. Mortality is obviously a major factor in population control, but its measurement in wild populations is often difficult unless the organisms have a characteristic feature from which it is possible to tell the age of the individual. For example, the scales of some fish have growth rings, and mountain sheep have horns from which age can be determined. But unfortunately these instances are rare.

Age Distribution. If we study birth and death rates, we find a pattern of age groups. A new, growing population consists of many young members and few old ones. In a mature population the number of older members may become greater than the young ones.

Age is important in relation to both natality (in terms of reproductive age) and mortality. Again the ecologist encounters difficulty in determining age classes in natural populations unless the structure of the individual organism provides a clue.

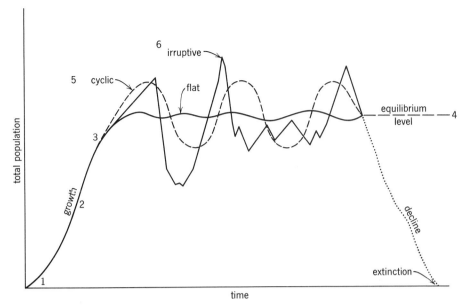

Figure 22.6. Some possible patterns for growth curves. For stage numbers (the arabic numerals) see the text. (After G. Clarke, Elements of Ecology, 1954, John Wiley and Sons, New York.)

Population Growth Rate and Form. At this point we can summarize these brief comments about populations in a growth curve, as shown in Figure 22.6. This curve is also termed a *sigmoid* curve, owing to its S shape, or a *logarithmic growth curve* because of the rapid increase in numbers during stage 2. Curves of this type indicate what happens to a population with the passage of time. Although the curve shown is theoretical, similar curves have been plotted for many laboratory and natural populations. The following statements refer to the numbered stages on the diagram.

(1) Stage *one* is the establishment of the population and involves adaptations to the environment, survival, and initial reproduction. Since relatively few individuals are involved, the rate of increase is slow.

(2) Stage *two* is obviously a time of rapid growth. Here the maximum theoretical reproductive rate may be attained, or at least closely approximated.

(3) In stage *three,* the population encounters environmental resistance of various sorts and thus levels off.

(4) Stage *four* is a theoretical equilibrium position around which the population may oscillate or fluctuate. This is the mean or average size of the population if measured at various intervals of time.

(5) Stages *five* and *six* illustrate two kinds of departures from the equilibrium stage. Relatively symmetrical changes (stage five) are called *oscillations* and result from events such as changes in natality and mortality rates or predator-prey interactions. Those oscillations are often the result of *density-dependent* factors within the population, since they are a function of numbers of organisms. Stage six shows sharp and irregular fluctuations in numbers owing to changes in the physical environment. These often result from *density-independent* factors operating on the population from without. The increase in a mosquito population during the rainy season is an example.

Poor planning and hasty modification of environments by man tend to increase the amplitude of fluctuation creating "boom or bust" situations instead of the more desirable equilibrium levels. Sudden, drastic changes in an environment often produce explosive eruptions of insects or other organisms to make pests out of species which had previously been rare. Finally, of course, the population may decline and die.

This brief treatment should give some idea of the quantitative nature of populations. This topic has become an important field in itself, and the interested student may find an extensive body of literature available concerning it.

Some ecologists contend that a population shares many biological attributes with its members. For example, a population, like an individual, has a specific structure and composition. Populations exhibit growth, adulthood or maturity, and sometimes senescence and death. Populations have an heredity, which we previously termed a gene pool. Then, of course, a population interacts with its environment.

Principles

1. The basic function of an ecosystem is to capture and utilize energy.

2. The laws of energy apply to ecosystems as they do in the physical world as illustrated by energy flow diagrams or pyramids of mass and energy.

3. Chemicals circulate through ecosystems in characteristic pathways termed biogeochemical cycles.

4. Communities of organisms in an ecosystem go through a series of changes termed succession, until a fairly stable stage, the climax, is reached.

5. A population like an individual shows growth, maturity, and senescence.

Suggested Readings

Arnold, James R. and E. D. Martell, "The Circulation of Radioactive Isotopes," *Scientific American,* Vol. 201 (September, 1959).

Carson, R., *Silent Spring.* Houghton Mifflin, Boston, 1962.

Comfort, Alex, "The Life Span of Animals," *Scientific American,* Vol. 205 (August, 1961).

Deevey, Edward S., Jr., "Bogs," *Scientific American,* Vol. 199 (October, 1958). Offprint No. 840, W. H. Freeman and Co., San Francisco.

Deevey, Edward S., Jr., "The Human Population," *Scientific American,* Vol. 203 (September, 1960). Offprint No. 608, W. H. Freeman and Co., San Francisco.

Leopold, A. S., "Too Many Deer," *Scientific American,* Vol. 193 (November, 1955).

Odum, Eugene P., *Ecology.* Holt, Rinehart and Winston, New York, 1963, pp. 37–64, 77–93.

Wynne-Edwards, V. C., "Population Control in Animals," *Scientific American,* Vol. 211 (August, 1964). Offprint No. 192, W. H. Freeman and Co., San Francisco.

Questions

1. What is the relation between the Second Law of Thermodynamics and the ecological pyramids described in Chapter XXI?

2. What is the ultimate fate of energy which is converted into unusable forms such as heat?

3. Can you relate the idea of energy flow through communities to the concepts of energy production in cellular respiration as presented in Chapter V?

4. In the geological past a large quantity of carbon was "bottlenecked" in one place in the carbon cycle. In what form do we find this today?

5. Is carbon still being trapped this way? Why?

6. What are some examples of ecological succession in the locality where you live?

7. Does a field of corn represent an early or a late stage in succession? What concept about energy production at different succession stages does this illustrate?

8. What characteristics do populations and individuals share?

9. What characteristics do populations have that an individual cannot possess?

10. If population growth curves have a characteristic S-shape, is it possible to predict at which point a rapidly growing population (as humans, for example) will level off? Why?

Interaction in Ecosystems

Baboons grooming. (Dr. I. DeVore.)

Interaction in Ecosystems

". . . the structure of every organic being is related in the most essential yet often hidden manner to that of all other organic beings, with which it comes into competition for food or residence, or from which it has to escape, or on which it preys. This is obvious in the structure of the teeth and talons of the tiger; and in that of the legs and claws of the parasite which clings to the hair on the tiger's body." **Charles Darwin, The Origin of Species**

This statement by Darwin illustrates the theme of the chapter, since we wish to explore some of the ways in which organisms interact and react with one another and with their physical environment. These interactions have their beginnings in evolution, since they represent adaptations which have enabled populations to survive through time. As discussed in earlier chapters, the mechanism of this adaptation is natural selection, and the outcome is a population adapted to interact more effectively with its biotic and physical environment.

The interactions between organisms and their environment are recognized by many people. As a mental exercise, consider a familiar organism and then think of ways in which its structure is adapted to the environment: locomotion, nutrition, protection, and so on. Here are a few examples to illustrate the point.

Water, owing to its density, presents problems of locomotion to organisms that live in it. It is no coincidence that the problem was at least partially solved by the evolution of streamlined bodies, even in diverse groups, as illustrated in Figure 23.1. Here a shark, a reptile, and a mammal have evolved similar body forms as an adaptation for movement through a dense medium.

On an even larger scale we can consider the consequences of the evolutionary event known as adaptive radiation, illustrated in Figure 23.2. Here interactions between organisms and their environment lead to divergent body forms rather than similar ones.

One of the most interesting aspects of biology is the many ways in which organisms live in relation to other organisms, ranging from beneficial to detrimental associations. As we saw in the preceding chapter, interactions between producer and consumer populations form a vital part of the ecosystem. Now we want to consider various types of organismic interactions in greater detail.

Adaptation to Competition

Competition. Competition is the outcome of organisms' requiring the same materials from the environment. For plants, these are sunlight, water, minerals, and growing space. For animals, it involves food, nesting sites, and mates. In most instances there is a subtle interaction: the two competitors may never even see

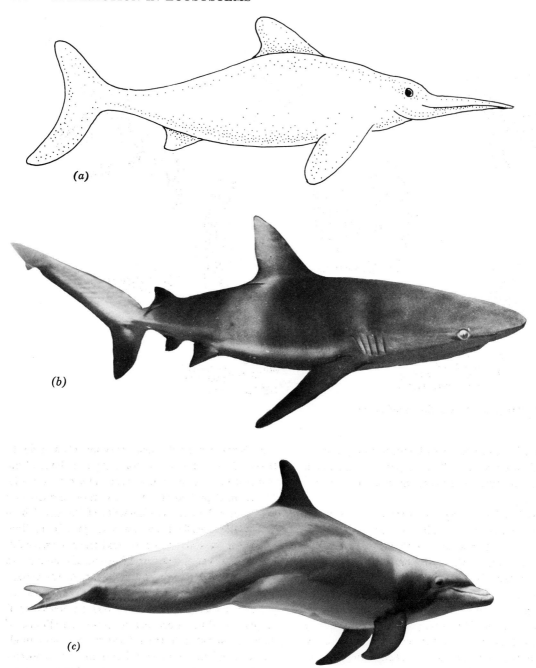

Figure 23.1. Convergent evolution of body form shown by an extinct reptile (a), *a shark* (b), *and a mammal* (c). *All are adapted for an aquatic mode of life.* (c—*Marineland of Florida.*)

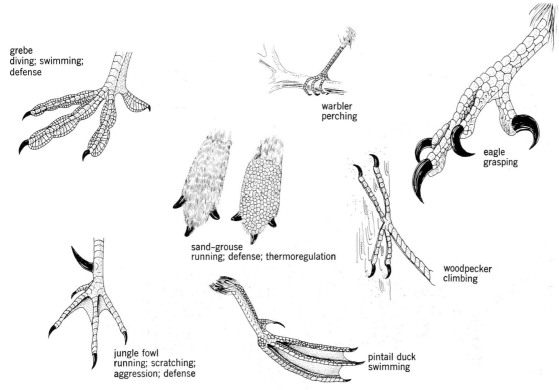

grebe
diving; swimming;
defense

warbler
perching

eagle
grasping

sand–grouse
running; defense; thermoregulation

woodpecker
climbing

jungle fowl
running; scratching;
aggression; defense

pintail duck
swimming

Figure 23.2. Divergent shapes of feet found in birds.

each other. For example, grasshoppers, mice, rabbits, sheep, and antelope may all act as primary consumers in the same community. Several carnivores may utilize the same prey.

One result of studying competition was Gause's *competition-exclusion* principle. In essence, this principle states that two species with identical requirements cannot live in the same habitat: one will be driven away (excluded) or will change its requirements. In reality, related species, with similar requirements, often inhabit the same community. Various conditions make this possible. Frequently they utilize slightly different food sources or, in the case of plants, require different nutrients from the soil. Many animals may utilize the same food but at different times of the day, for example, butterflies and moths. Related organisms often occupy different parts of the same habitat as in a woodland where some organisms forage and live in the tree tops, while their relatives live on or near the ground.

Since manifestations of competition are largely historical—we assume that a present-day distribution pattern is the consequence of competition in the past—

investigators work with laboratory models in order to observe the event while it is taking place. Some of the most fruitful models involve species of the flour beetle, *Tribolium*. Experiments with them were conducted by Dr. Thomas Park at the University of Chicago. These small beetles live, feed, and breed in a jar of flour. Two species can be started in a jar and their progress followed. Moreover, the physical features of their habitat can be regulated. One of the outcomes of the experiments using two species of *Tribolium* was that one species eventually died out. It was an unsuccessful competitor. When Park manipulated the climate of the flour habitat in terms of temperature and humidity, he found that he could determine which species would be successful and which would fail. For example, when *Tribolium castaneum* lived with *T. confusum*, it was found that a hot-wet flour environment always led to survival by *T. castaneum*. A cool-dry one always led to survival by the other species, *T. confusum*. Each species had an optimum climate in which its population dominated the environment. Note that this was a subtle action; neither species directly attacked the other, yet both were competitors.

(a)

Figure 23.3. Elephant seals. During the breeding season the males fight (part a) to defend their territories, their mates, and their young (foreground of part b).

Experiments also have been made using plants. In one, seeds of two competing clovers, *Trifolium repens* and *Trifolium fragiferum,* were germinated and studied in the laboratory. Subtle differences were found in their development, even though the mature plants appeared similar. *T. fragiferum* had larger seeds than *T. repens,* an advantage in nourishing germinating seedlings. However, the seedlings of *T. repens* grew their foliage leaves more quickly. Seeds of *T. repens* germinated more rapidly at temperatures of 25° C and below, but seeds of *T. fragiferum* were capable of more rapid germination at 35° C. In later growth *T. fragiferum* continued to form new leaves later than *T. repens* but bore its leaves higher on the stems. Also, the stem of *T. repens* became prostrate early in development while the stem of *T. fragiferum* remained vertical. Presumably these features aided the plants as they competed in nature.

We have been considering cases of competition between different species. Members of the *same* species also compete. They constitute a population in which all members have identical requirements. Obviously this competition must be carefully regulated in various ways so that it will not harm the population. Let us examine a few examples of how this is done.

Territoriality. Territoriality is a behavioral activity exhibited by many animals (Figure 23.3). In general, the animal, usually a male, defends a circumscribed area from other males, then eventually courts the female there, and perhaps raises young. This behavior is particularly noticeable in birds and can be observed in any backyard in the springtime. Usually the male bird uses a singing perch, his song identifying the area to other males and females of his species. In an aquarium, one can observe male fish defending certain areas of the tank against the other fish. Even domesticated animals like dogs show territorial behavior as exemplified by a small dog chasing a much larger one out of its yard—but no farther!

Territorial behavior apparently serves a variety of functions depending on the animal. It avoids conflict between members of the population since the auditory and visual signals serve as forms of communication. In some cases territoriality limits population size in accordance with the ability of the area to supply food and nesting sites.

Peck Order. Peck order is another behavioral adaptation which functions to decrease intragroup strife. It is most commonly observed in social aggregates such as flocks and herds where members of the group

(b)

become arranged in social hierarchies. Usually the strongest, largest, or maturest individual dominates the other members, who, in turn, dominate individuals below them in the hierarchy, and so on. In a flock of chickens, for example, the dominant ones eat first at the feed trough, get first choice of roosting sites, etc. After the hierarchy is established, the flock functions with a minimum of internal strife. Most gregarious animals exhibit this pecking order and it is even tempting to apply it to human beings!

Symbiosis

The term symbiosis, which literally means living together, may be familiar. We use it in this context to apply to any intimate association between two forms, regardless of the harmful or beneficial outcomes of the relationship.

Commensalism. Symbiotic interactions in which only one of the organisms benefits and neither is harmed is termed commensalism. We shall describe only a few examples (Figures 23.4 and 23.5). Interested students can find additional ones in most ecology textbooks.

A classic example of commensalism is the remora fish, commonly called a "shark sucker." These fish have a suction disk in the head region by which they attach themselves temporarily to much larger forms like sharks, whales, or sea turtles. This does not damage the host yet allows the remora to share tidbits left over from the host's meals. So far as is known, neither does the host gain any advantage from this relationship.

Many plants have adapted to an epiphytic way of life, that is, they grow upon the trunks or limbs of other plants deriving only support but not nourishment from them. Residents of the southeastern coastal areas are familiar with the gray, streamerlike, Spanish moss which drapes so many trees. This epiphyte, a flowering plant rather than a moss, does no damage to its host unless it become thick enough to shade its leaves.

In many of the sandy ridge areas of Florida, a small deer mouse, *Peromyscus polionotus,* lives in burrows which it digs in the sand. A lizard utilizes the opening of the mouse burrow from which it digs a short side tunnel slanting almost to the surface of the soil. When disturbed, the lizard can burst up through the soil to escape a predator. The mouse is neither harmed nor helped by this arrangement, but the lizard's shelter conditions improve.

These few examples illustrate that commensalism occurs among diverse organisms and may involve feeding arrangements, shelter, or support.

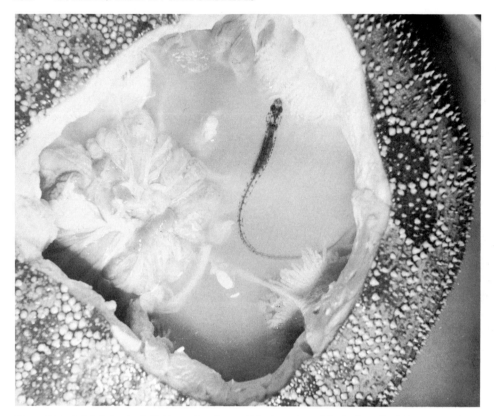

Figure 23.4. A fish living in the body cavity of a starfish. A portion of the body wall of the starfish has been removed.

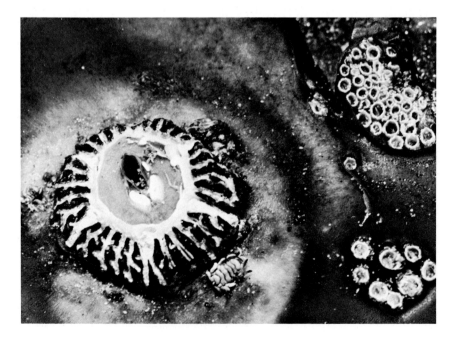

Figure 23.5. Barnacles living on a whale's back.

Mutualism.   It would not be difficult to imagine a commensal relationship evolving into a mutually beneficial one. An interaction in which both populations benefit is termed mutualism. As in all of these relations, there is a wide range of interactions from voluntary mutualism, as in a flock of birds, to inseparable types like the combination of an alga and a fungus known as the *lichen.*

Lichens consist of a mass of fungal cells that contain cells of a green alga. The fungus holds moisture and provides minerals for both members; the algal cells make carbohydrates by photosynthesis, which provides energy to both members. Neither member exists alone in nature.

Many trees including pines, oaks, hickories, and maples have a mutualistic arrangement with a fungus in the soil. The fungus forms a covering (mycorrhiza) around the roots and facilitates the absorption of water and nutrient salts. The fungi are nourished by organic material from their host. Young pine seedlings seem particularly dependent on this mycorrhiza for normal growth since it helps them extract mineral nutrients from the soil.

Many species of ants have evolved a mutualistic arrangement with aphids. Ants feed upon a material which exudes from the body of this small insect. Some species of ants keep aphids in their colonies, feeding and maintaining them while utilizing their exudation.

Other species carry the aphids to plants during the day (aphids feed by sucking plant juices) and return them to the ant hill at night. Both ants and aphids benefit by these arrangements although both can live quite well alone. This is not an obligatory mutualism as is the case with lichens.

In marine habitats a number of small creatures are involved in a "cleaning symbiosis." For example, at least six species of small shrimps, frequently brightly colored, crawl over fish, picking off parasites and cleaning injured areas. This is not an accidental occurrence, since fish are observed to congregate around these shrimp and stay motionless while being "inspected." The shrimp may even forage among the gills and mouth cavity of the fish. Several species of small fish are also cleaners, and nearly all of these show adaptations for this way of life, namely, long snouts, tweezerlike teeth, and bright coloration. This type of mutualism involves a number of species.

The dependency of many plants on insect pollination (Figure 23.6) and the association of nitrogen-fixing bacteria with the roots of leguminous plants indicate that mutualism is a basic biological principle. Even members of the same species which aggregate for purposes of food gathering, protection, or reproduction are practicing a form of mutualism.

It is unfortunate that interactions such as competition have received so much attention in the past be-

Figure 23.6. An insect visiting a flower. (© Walt Disney Productions.)

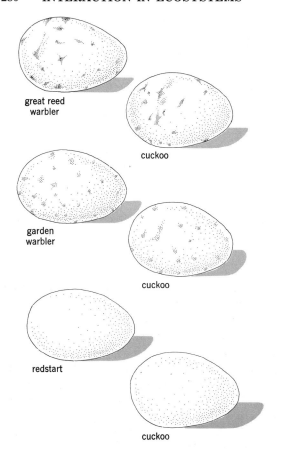

great reed
warbler

cuckoo

garden
warbler

cuckoo

redstart

cuckoo

Figure 23.7. Social parasitism. The eggs of the European cuckoo tend to resemble those of the host. (Adapted from an illustration by Louis Darling for TIME-LIFE BOOKS, 1963, Time Inc.)

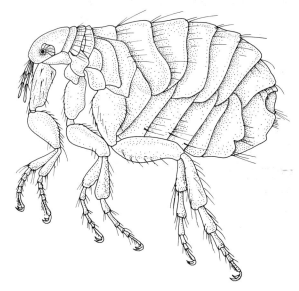

Figure 23.8. A common ectoparasite, the flea.

cause this has tended to overshadow the biological importance of mutualism. Both are vital in the evolution of living things.

Parasitism. It may have occurred to the reader that intimate associations like commensalism and mutualism could become parasitic if one of the members begins to utilize the other as a food source. Perhaps this is how parasitism evolved. Parasitism is a relationship in which an organism spends part or all of its life cycle on or within another organism and uses the food or the tissues of the host for nourishment. There are many degrees of parasitism and some barely fit the definition. Thus, in "social" parasitism the female brown-headed cowbird does not build a nest, but rather, she deposits her eggs in the nests of other birds. The young cowbird is cared for by the host bird, sometimes to the detriment of the host's own progeny. Thousands of species of wasps utilize a similar method by depositing

their eggs in the bodies of other insects. The larvae use the internal tissues of the host for food. One large group of wasps even uses plants as the host tissue.

Parasites can be divided into *ectoparasites,* such as fleas or lice, which live on the exterior of the host, and *endoparasites,* which dwell inside. These highly specialized ways of life require many structural adaptations. Thus fleas have laterally flattened bodies for crawling through their host's fur, and legs adapted for clinging to hair (Figure 23.8). Internal parasites are even more modified. Parasitic worms, for example, frequently show a drastic reduction in all body systems except the reproductive apparatus. This latter system is usually complex and extremely fecund. Not infrequently the life cycles of internal parasites include a stage of asexual reproduction. Since the evolution of internal parasitism was probably long and precarious, internal parasites are often highly specific in choice of hosts. Diagrammatic life cycles for two common parasites are shown in Figures 12.8 and 12.9.

Parasitism is evidently a successful way of life judging by the large number of forms in both plant and animal kingdoms which utilize it to some degree. The term "successful" as used here means that the parasite must not damage its host too severely or its way of life would become untenable—if the host dies, so does the parasite. There are even instances of parasitism within the same species. In several of the abyssal (deep-sea) fishes the male becomes permanently attached to the much larger female. Do you see the adaptive advantage of this arrangement in the lightless depths of the ocean?

Predation

Predation is another type of exploitation of one species by another. In a way it is a form of parasitism, except that the predator does not use its host (prey) as a habitat. Commonly the term predator refers to animals that feed on other animals. Predation has been studied extensively in natural environments and in the laboratory so there is abundant literature on the subject.

In Chapter XXI we presented the food chain

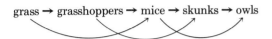

This is also a chain of predators. A number of studies indicate a close correlation between the abundance of a predator and the abundance of its prey. A study by D. A. MacLulich many years ago showed a correlation between population fluctuations in hare and lynx over a number of years. As the hare population rose, the lynx population also increased. As the hare population declined, the lynx population did likewise. An example of the same kind of activity is shown in Fig. 23.9, which graphs the effect of predators on mealy bugs which live in citrus trees. Here again the predator-prey populations are evidently tied to each other, as can be observed from the graph. It is tempting to conclude that the predators *cause* the decline in prey. This cannot be assumed in every instance because there are many factors other than predation that bring about periodic population fluctuations. For example, one of the mealy bug's predators was handicapped by cold weather and thus was less abundant during the winter months. This predator's population changed in response to seasons rather than abundance of its prey.

Predation is a natural and necessary occurrence in a community's energy flow. It benefits the prey population when acting as a control on population numbers. Moreover, if the victims of predation are the sick, old, or less well-adapted members of the prey population, their loss in the long run may benefit the gene pool of the species.

There are examples of predation in the plant kingdom, such as the familiar Venus fly trap. Other animal-catching plants include the vaselike pitcher plant into

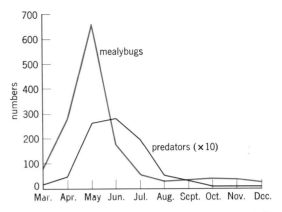

Figure 23.9. *Population changes in mealy bugs and their predators. (Dr. P. DeBach.)*

which insects fall and then are digested, and certain soil fungi which entrap nematode worms. In all of these examples the plants are thought to derive certain nutrient materials, primarily nitrogen compounds, from their prey.

Finally, we might consider briefly the role of man as a predator. First, he is the most voracious and wasteful of all predators. Second, he has frequently attempted to interfere with other predator-prey relationships, especially with respect to game animals. Seldom have these attempts led to any beneficial ends, as shown earlier with the example of the deer on the Kaibab plateau. Rachel Carson's *Silent Spring* presents many cases of the catastrophies that follow inadvertent poisoning of insect predators and parasites when insecticides are used to control the prey species; upon removal of predators, prey often increase to higher levels than existed prior to the control attempt.

We hope the reader realizes that all interactions are solutions to the problem of survival. All presumably arose by natural selection as adaptations for obtaining nutrition, protection, and mates. As man continues to utilize natural communities and ecosystems, he should recognize the importance of *all* interaction and avoid manipulations which suit only his preconceptions of what is "good" and "bad" in these associations.

Principles

1. Two common forms of interaction among organisms are competition and predation. Forms of interaction which lessen competition, such as territoriality and symbiosis, have been favored by natural selection.

Suggested Readings

Argo, Virgil N., "Insect-trapping Plants," *Natural History,*
Vol. LXXIII (March, 1964).

Carson, Rachel, *Silent Spring.* Houghton Mifflin, Boston,
1962.

DeBach, Paul, "Population Studies of the Long-tailed Mealy-
bug and Its Natural Enemies on Citrus Trees in Southern
California," *Ecology,* Vol. 30, 1949, pp. 14–25.

Guhl, A. M., "The Social Order of Chickens," *Scientific
American,* Vol. 194 (February, 1956). Offprint No. 471,
W. H. Freeman and Co., San Francisco.

Harper, John L. and J. N. Clatworthy, "The Comparative
Biology of Closely Related Species.   VI. Analysis of the
Growth of *Trifolium repens* and *T. fragiferum* in Pure
and Mixed Populations," *Journal of Experimental
Botany,* Vol. 14 (February, 1963), pp. 172–190.

Limbaugh, Conrad, "Cleaning Symbiosis," *Scientific American,* Vol. 205 (August, 1961). Offprint No. 135, W. H.
Freeman and Co., San Francisco.

Odum, Eugene P., *Ecology.* Holt, Rinehart and Winston,
New York, 1963, pp. 93–109.

Questions

1. Why is it difficult to observe competition occurring between two different species in nature, that is, under natural
conditions?

2. Name two types of *intraspecific* competition. Why is it
easier to observe this type of competition than the inter-
specific type?

3. What evidence could you provide to support the idea
that territoriality and peck order are present in human
societies?

4. Can you provide examples of mutualism, commensalism,
and parasitism not mentioned in the chapter?

5. Name some ways in which man is a predator in the
ecosystems. How could he be a *beneficial* predator in an
ecosystem?

CHAPTER
XXIV

Ecological Geography of Terrestrial Environments

Ecological Geography of Terrestrial Environments

Communities of plants and animals vary over the surface of the earth, largely in relation to climatic differences. These communities are not haphazard assemblages; the same general types of producers and consumers appear together in similar climatic zones. In this chapter we examine the distribution of these major ecosystems over the earth, their general composition, and some of the principles which influence their distribution.

Terrestrial ecosystems are classified on the basis of their biotic components; thus they are often called *biomes*. They are named according to their dominant plant forms: Tundra, Coniferous Forest, Temperate Deciduous Forest, Grasslands, Desert, Tropical Forest, and Temperate Rain Forest. Some authorities subdivide these thus making a longer list. Recognition of these seven will serve our purpose, however. The world distribution of these biomes is shown in Figure 24.1.

Tundra

The Tundra is a vast, treeless zone bordering the Arctic Ocean in North America, Europe, and Asia (Figure 24.2). It generally extends from the treeline to the areas perpetually covered with ice and snow. Obviously this area has a cold climate: the ground remains permanently frozen to within a few inches of the surface, and the growing season is only about sixty days. There is also an alpine Tundra on the peaks and high slopes of mountains, as in the western Rocky Mountains, the Alps, and the Himalayan Mountains.

In general, tundra vegetation consists of lichens, mosses, grasses, and dwarfed woody plants. The composition of the vegetation in any particular portion of the tundra varies with the thickness and fertility of the soil. Grasses and sedges compose the alpine Tundra. In all cases numerous adaptations for survival in this extreme environment are found: dwarfism, small hairy leaves for water conservation, ability to survive in the frozen state even when flowering, and means of vegetative reproduction.

We might suppose that animal life would be sparse under these conditions, but this depends on the time of the year. During the summer great numbers of waterfowl nest in the tundra, and several species of insects—especially mosquitoes and black flies—are abundant. Permanent residents are few. Small rodents including the well-known lemmings are the most abundant mammals. Other characteristic forms of animal life are caribou (reindeer in Eurasia), arctic hare, arctic fox (Figure 24.3), gray wolf, grizzly bear, polar bear, and the snowy owl. These forms show adaptation for winter survival, including white coloration, ability to hibernate for periods of time, and means for burrowing under the snow.

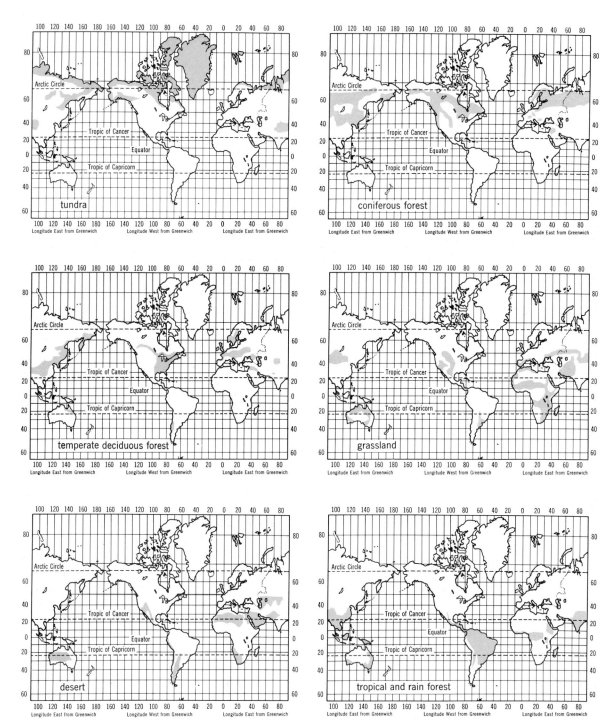

Figure 24.1. Distribution of major biomes.

286

Figure 24.2. Tundra. (© Walt Disney Productions.)

Northern Coniferous Forest

The Northern Coniferous Forest is also called Boreal Forest or Taiga. It consists of a vast belt of evergreen forest which crosses North America, Europe, and Asia south of the Tundra. Large "fingers" of this biome stretch southward in North America and Eurasia. In this area the winter climate is cold and severe, similar to the tundra; however, the growing season is much longer—three to five months.

Vegetation in this biome is composed mostly of needle or scale-leaved evergreen trees: spruces, firs, pines, and cedars. Their dense growth habit produces a deep shade which serves to inhibit the growth of herbs and shrubs on the forest floor. The leaf shapes of conifers (cone-bearing trees) prevent excessive evaporation of water and freezing. Even the flexible branches and cone-shaped form of the trees aid them in avoiding snow damage during the winter. Not uncommon are thickets of broadleafed plants like birch

and alder. The heavy concentration of plants in this biome presents an abundant food supply of leaves, wood, and seeds. Consequently, it supports a considerable assemblage of consumers (Figure 24.4).

Along the west coast of North America from Alaska to central California is a luxuriant, humid, coniferous forest with a warmer climate than the remainder of the biome. Hemlock, cedar, fir, and arborvitae compose much of this forest, with the spectacular redwood trees present in restricted areas of northern California. Coastal fogs frequently drift through these forests and the resulting moisture functions as precipitation. These forests are sometimes called Temperate Rain Forests.

Animal forms of the Northern Coniferous Forest include moose (called "elk" in Eurasia), snowshoe hare, rodents, wolf, fox, lynx, porcupine, and birds such as crossbills, siskins, and evening grosbeaks. Crossbills are uniquely adapted for this ecosystem; the tips of the bill cross, rather than meet, as a device for removing

Figure 24.3 Arctic fox. (© Walt Disney Productions.)

seeds from cones. This biome is of considerable economic importance because of its extensive, exploitable pulpwood, lumber, and fur resources (Figure 24.5).

Temperate Deciduous Forest

The term *deciduous* refers to plants which drop their leaves during a part of the year, a trait common to many of the trees and shrubs in this biome. These trees are sometimes spoken of (in the vernacular of the lumber industry) as broadleafs or hardwoods in contrast to coniferous, narrow-leafed softwoods.

Deciduous forest communities originally formed a continuous band across eastern North America, the British Isles, Central Europe, large portions of China, and southeastern Siberia. Areas in Australia, Japan, and the southern tip of South America also contain

Figure 24.4. Northern coniferous forest. (U.S. Forest Service.)

communities of this type. Today much of this area is occupied and utilized by human beings so that the biome no longer exists in its original form. Its initial boundaries should be kept in mind, however, since they form the basis for the present distribution of many organisms.

The term *temperate* very generally describes the climate of the biome, although this is misleading to some extent. In many instances temperate forests have a distinct seasonal pattern with cold winters and hot summers, but on the average, the climate is moderate. A significant aspect of the climate is the moderate rainfall (30–60 inches per year), which is evenly distributed over the seasons. Among other things, this accounts for the broadleaf forest climax that is typical of the ecosystem.

Figure 24.5. Snowshoe hare. Like many animals of the Northern Coniferous Forest, this hare has a different coat color in summer than in winter. Notice the streaks of dark fur remaining on the head. (© Walt Disney Productions.)

Figure 24.6. Deciduous forest. (U.S. Forest Service.)

Figure 24.7. Bobcat.
(© Walt Disney Productions.)

This biome consists of a series of community types, each with a different set of dominant plants. Thus an oak–hickory forest is most abundantly populated by species of oaks and hickories. A beech–maple community is dominated by beech and maple trees. All of these communities share the striking seasonal contrasts of being leafless during the winter and heavily foliaged during the summer. This trait alone has a considerable influence on the animals that inhabit these communities. Common trees include beech, tulip tree, sycamore, maple, oak, hickory, elm, birch, basswood, and a variety of conifers (Figure 24.6).

Larger animals typical of the biome include the familiar white-tailed deer in North America and other species elsewhere; a number of large cats such as mountain lions and wildcats; foxes; and black bear. Many species of rodents, including squirrels, chipmunks, and mice, inhabit the biome in addition to familiar forms like raccoons and opossums. The birds of temperate forests are largely arboreal and tree-nesting. In North America, warblers, flycatchers, woodpeckers, vireos, and wrens are common, although these are but a few of the long list of species. Tree frogs, salamanders, and numerous snakes are typical. All told, these communities have a rich fauna. Tree dwelling is facilitated by the sharp claws of squirrels and woodpeckers, movable scales of some snakes, and various nesting habits adapted to trees. In the colder portions of the biome, many forms either migrate during winter or else "den up" under the ground or in dead logs to escape the cold. Woodchucks, bats, chipmunks, and numerous insects spend the winter in

hibernation. Others, like the black bear, undergo semi-hibernation.

The southeastern United States is usually included in the Temperate Deciduous Forest ecosystem even though it contains two large vegetation units that are not deciduous. The magnolia–oak forest is one of these, although it also contains some deciduous species. Some ecologists term this forest a broadleafed, evergreen, subtropical forest, although the local designation for these woodlands is *hammock*.

Extensive areas of the southeastern coastal plains are occupied by pine forests known as pine flatwoods. These frequently occur on poorly drained flat areas and are dominated by longleaf, slash, or loblolly pine. A visitor to this forest gets the impression of a scattered array of pines and a sharply delimited shrub layer consisting predominantly of saw-palmettos. This ground layer, however, may contain a large variety of shrubby and herbaceous plants.

An interesting ecological aspect of this type of community is that forest fires are necessary for it to continue as a pine forest. If protected from fire, the pines are often succeeded by broadleafed trees. (This situation was referred to in Chapter XXI under the topic of succession.) Forestry studies in the 1920s indicated how fire affects longleaf pines. The seedling of this pine is covered by a bushy canopy of needles and is always in danger of being shaded by rapidly growing broadleafed competitors. In addition, it is susceptible to a fungus growth on its needles. If fire passes through the area, it usually destroys the competing hardwoods as well as the fungus growing on the pine seedlings.

The dense covering of needles protects the bud of the seedling so that the plant survives. The young pine grows extremely rapidly for two or three years finally becoming tall enough to escape damage from the next ground fire. Thus, with periodic burning, a pine flat-woods or forest can maintain itself.

This situation is not peculiar to southern pine forests. The jack pine of Michigan, Wisconsin, and Minnesota and the knobcone pine of California apparently require heat from a fire to open tightly closed cones. Some weeks after the fire the seeds fall into the bed of ashes, which are ideal for germination. The seeds of competing species have been destroyed. Here we see an adaptation dependent on the presence of periodic fires! Specialists in forest management have utilized this concept so that controlled burning is a useful tool in certain situations.

Tropical Forest Biomes

Contrary to the impression we are likely to acquire from movies and television, the tropics are not uniformly enveloped by steamy, impenetrable jungles. Instead we find a variety of ecosystems such as deserts, scrub lands, deciduous forests, rain forests, and cloud forests. In this section we consider rain forests in particular, as they constitute a sizable belt of vegetation surrounding the earth in equatorial latitudes: the Amazon and Orinoco basins in South America, a large segment of Central America, a band in central and western Africa, and much of the Indo-Malayan region.

In terms of climate, the outstanding features are year-round temperatures which are consistently high, uniform lengths of day and night, and large amounts of rainfall, exceeding eighty inches a year. In regions where the rainfall is seasonal, such as monsoons alternating with dry periods, rain forests give way to a tropical deciduous forest. Notice that the deciduous adaptation here is in relation to rainfall rather than temperature.

An outstanding vegetational feature of rain forests is that virtually all of the plants are woody and grow as trees. Bamboos, which are grasses, exemplify this. Thick-stemmed woody vines (*lianas*) and *epiphytes* abound as one of the most typical features of the biome. Some of the climbers are "stranglers" in that they gradually envelope the host plant, kill it, and then remain as free-standing plants. In contrast to temperate forests, tropical forests contain a large number of species and relatively few individuals of the same kind. The dominant trees average 100–180 feet in height and are slender and unbranched except at the crown or top. Palms and tree ferns are often abundant. The thick crown presented by the trees casts a heavy shadow so that the forest floor is frequently dark, humid, and open. Dense, junglelike growth is found only in an opening and where succession is occurring, or along river and stream banks where sunlight can penetrate. Many of the earlier accounts described tropical forests as being junglelike, possibly because the observers always traveled in these areas by boat.

Rain forests are well stratified in the sense that there are distinctive layers of vegetation at various heights in the forest. The thick canopy formed by the tops of the taller trees constitutes one layer, and is inhabited by a characteristic assemblage of arboreally adapted organisms. Another layer, in contrast to the canopy, is the forest floor where an entirely different set of physical conditions prevail. Intermediate strata exist between these and have their own specialized forms of plant and animal life (Figure 24.8).

In the American tropics, an epiphyte group called *bromeliads* are notable because they hold a gallon or so of rainwater in their nested leaves. In these small pools live many insects, frogs, and other tiny organisms.

Animal life in this biome is exceedingly varied in number of species. Table 24.1 shows the richness of two types of fauna as compared with those of other regions. As with plants, there are fewer *individuals* of each species than would be found in temperate areas. This diversity of species makes it impractical to list even typical forms; the following discussion merely points out a few noteworthy adaptations.

Table 24.1

Birds		Snakes	
Region	Number of Species	Region	Number of Species
Labrador	81	Canada	22
New York	195	United States	126
Panama	1100	Mexico	293
Colombia	1395	Brazil	210

A visitor to a rain forest might be disappointed in the apparent absence of animal life, because many of the forms are either nocturnal or dwell in the treetop canopies. Many animals are adapted for fruit eating and nectar feeding. Many of the canopy dwellers build

Figure 24.8. Tropical rain forest. (Russ Kinne, Photo Researchers, Inc.)

hanging nests possibly as a solution to the competition for nesting sites or as protection against ants and other marauders. Most mammals and birds inhabiting rain forests tend to be smaller than their temperate-zone relatives. Reptiles and arthropods (insects, spiders, etc.), however, reach their largest size in tropical areas.

The soil in the tropics is not well suited to farming or grazing for domestic animals and is quickly damaged by these activities. Ecologists and students of animal husbandry have urged Africans to treat their wildlife as a crop to be managed and harvested with care; one elephant is equivalent to about eighty sheep as a protein source, can be "harvested" without great difficulty, and does far less damage to the ecosystem than cattle or sheep. So far, these suggestions have

been ignored and increasing attempts are being made to practice agriculture in the conventional way. P. W. Richards, a student of tropical forests, believes that these forests will disappear in less than a hundred years unless the present rate of their destruction by man is reduced.

Grasslands

Grasslands occur on all continents and are frequently similar to one another in climate, physical features, and fauna. Grasslands have localized terms wherever they occur: *prairie* for the tall grasslands of western North America and *plains* for the short grasses of that region; *pampas* and *savanna* in South America; *veld* in South Africa; and *steppe* in Russia. In tropical regions the term savanna is also applied to

Figure 24.9. Grassland. (Dade W. Thornton, Photo Researchers, Inc.)

grasslands containing scattered trees.

A major climatic feature leading to the formation of grasslands rather than forests is the uneven seasonal distribution of rainfall. Grassland areas may have as much rain as forty to sixty inches a year, but it falls either erratically, or, as in the tropics, interspersed with long dry periods. Trees cannot survive these droughts and the frequent fires which accompany them (Figure 24.9).

A large proportion of the animals of this biome are adapted for running, leaping, or burrowing. In North America, these include the jack rabbit, antelope, bison, fox, wolf, coyote, cougar, ground squirrel, prairie dog, and pocket gopher. Many ecological equivalents are noted over the world: Australian kangaroo and North American antelope; Australian marsupial mole and North American pocket gopher; North American wolf and Asiatic cheetah; and many more. Each of these "pairs" performs a similar role in its respective grasslands area.

Man has made extensive use of this community. The richer grasslands of North America and Europe are major cereal-producing centers. The poorer grasslands over the world are frequently over-used as grazing lands, often to the point of exhausting the land. In all parts of the world grasslands have served as vast pasturelands for nomadic people with their cattle, sheep, goats, camels, and horses.

Deserts

As moisture becomes less available, grasslands give way to deserts. About one-fifth of the surface of the earth consists of desert, and all major continents contain a biome of this type. The Old World deserts include the Sahara and those found in Asia Minor, India, Tibet, China, and Mongolia. Much of the interior of Australia is a desert. Prominent deserts also occur in southern Africa, as a strip along the west coast of South America, and, of course, our own southwestern desert which extends into Mexico (Figure 24.10).

The major controlling climatic factor in this biome is low annual rainfall, generally less than ten inches, unevenly distributed during the year. Intense sunlight, hot days, and cold nights (an 80° F range in some cases), high evaporation rate, and constant winds are characteristic of this generally inhospitable environment. Winter months are much milder than summer months and may even be cold in the northern deserts. The highest temperature ever recorded (134° F) by a standard observation station was in Death Valley, California, which is probably the hottest desert on earth.

Figure 24.10. Desert. (© Walt Disney Productions.)

Figure 24.11. A scorpion feeding on a spider. (© Walt Disney Productions.)

When rain occurs in the desert it usually takes the form of a cloudburst, often resulting in destructive flash floods and sheet erosion. At other times, sand and dust storms constitute hazards for desert-dwelling organisms.

Plants adapted for survival under extremely arid conditions are known as *xerophytes,* and as we describe some of the typical desert vegetation we shall review a few of their adaptations. Eugene Odum has concisely summarized the forms adapted to deserts. These are annual plants which grow only when adequate moisture is present, succulent plants—such as cacti—which store water, and shrubs with numerous basal branches and small, thick leaves which are shed during extremely dry times. The seeds of the annuals lie dormant in the soil for long periods of time, then, during a rainy period quickly germinate, grow, flower, and produce new seeds. The seeds, in other words, provide the organism's surviving link between two widely separated rainy periods. There is nearly always wide spacing among desert plants, which, in some instances, is known to be caused by a chemical released from the roots. This substance inhibits other plants from growing nearby (see p. 107). In addition, some desert plants release inhibiting substances from fallen leaves.

Since plants lose water through their leaves, many adaptations involving leaf structure exist in desert plants. Hairy leaves and stems are commonly found; they aid in catching and retaining moisture from the surrounding air. Leaves with a thick, leathery epidermis or a waxy covering are also common. The stomata in the leaves are often small, sunken, protected by hairs, and sometimes closed by valves. A number of larger plants lost their leaves during the course of evolution and the stem has taken over the photosynthetic function. In many of these instances, the leaves remain, but are in the form of spines or stiff hairs. Spines are perhaps an adaptation which prevents plants from being eaten by herbivores, although this is speculative. In North American deserts familiar plants include the creosote bush, sagebrush, bur sage, giant Saguaro cactus in some areas, and a number of grasses.

Reptiles and rodents are the most characteristic animal life of the deserts. Most of the animals, including insects, are active at night and spend the daylight hours either underground or in shaded nooks. Many forms are burrowers. Most desert dwellers are lighter in color than their relatives in moister climates. This protective coloration camouflages them on the desert floor. Birds, insects, and many reptiles excrete nitrogenous wastes as concentrated uric salts which further aids them in conserving water. An interesting physiological adaptation is the ability of some of the rodents to exist solely on water from their internal metabolic processes. (See Figure 24.11.)

When infrequent rain pools are formed, frogs and toads, aquatic insects, and crustacea pass quickly through their breeding cycles. Estivation enables some forms to survive long periods of drought, and hibernation occurs during the winter among those forms of life found in more northerly deserts.

Ecological Principles and Biome Distribution

All biomes consist of assemblages of producers, consumers, and decay organisms; in other words, they possess the ecosystem structure described in Chapter XXI. The shape of the food pyramids in each may vary somewhat, and the organisms composing them may be different, but all function in a similar manner. One example is given by the many kinds of ecological equivalents which exist among similar but widely separated ecosystems.

Energy flow is the most important functional feature in all communities and, of course, plants are the photosynthetic or energy-capturing agents in every case. As noted previously, biomes are based on typical assemblages of plants because they accurately reflect the broad, climatic features of the earth. Since the success of vegetational units depends on a combination of solar radiation, precipitation, and temperature, these factors are major ones in determining the distributional patterns of major ecosystems. The plants characteristic of each biome, being a product of natural selection and evolution, show many adaptations related to the special conditions of their specific environment. Conifers in the boreal forest are one example. Vegetation also modifies the climate in an environment. This reciprocal reaction is important in succession and in providing suitable living conditions for animals.

Since animals ultimately depend on plants for energy, the nature of the fauna of a biome is strongly influenced by the vegetation found there. Many of the adaptations described in this and other chapters involve features that enable animals to function efficiently with the vegetational complex in which they live. In a biome such as the grasslands, animals can be responsible for many of its major characteristics. In this instance burrowing, grazing, and even trampling strongly influence the kinds of plants which live in the community.

Principles

1. The major terrestrial ecosystems (biomes) are categorized by a distinctive biotic composition and are usually named according to their dominant plant forms.

2. The distributional pattern of biomes is determined largely by a combination of the factors of solar radiation, precipitation, and temperature.

Suggested Readings

Amos, William H., "The Life of a Sand Dune," *Scientific American,* Vol. 201 (July, 1959).

Barnett, L. and editors of *Life* Magazine, *The World We Live In.* Time, New York, 1955.

Cooper, C. F., "The Ecology of Fire," *Scientific American,* Vol. 204 (April, 1961).

Darling, Fraser F., "Wildlife Husbandry in Africa," *Scientific American,* Vol. 203 (November, 1960).

Jaeger, E. C., *The North American Deserts.* Stanford University Press, Palo Alto, California, 1957.

Odum, Eugene P., *Ecology.* Holt, Rinehart and Winston, New York, 1963, pp. 123–135.

Questions

1. Make a list of the biomes described in the chapter, then name one or more indicator plants and animals for each.

2. Why are biomes named according to their dominant plant forms rather than their major animal forms?

3. In what biome type do you live? What are some of the community types in the biome where you live?

4. Can you state some ecological principles that apply to both desert and tropical forest biomes? Can these principles be applied to *all* biomes?

5. List the major factors that determine where the various biomes are located on the earth. Which of these factors, if any, plays a dominant role in your area?

Ecological Geography of Freshwater and Marine Environments

Ecological Geography of Freshwater and Marine Environments

This final chapter describes the two major habitats, freshwater and marine, in which water dominates the environment. Aqueous environments present some features not shown by terrestrial communities, although the same basic ecological concepts of ecosystem structure and function apply to both.

Some Major Features of Aqueous Environments

Heat. Thermal energy (heat) has important effects on lakes, seas, and other bodies of water owing to the high specific heat of water. That is, water absorbs tremendous amounts of heat and releases it slowly. Bodies of water accumulate heat during warm seasons and release it during cold ones. This process is vital to organisms living in water where extremes of temperature rarely occur. Water dwellers, in fact, live in a narrower range of temperature than land inhabitants. Moreover, land areas adjacent to large bodies of water undergo less extremes of temperature than other land areas. This is illustrated by citrus trees in mid-Florida. Following a severe freeze, the citrus trees bordering large lakes are not damaged, although the remainder of the grove suffers. On a larger scale, oceanic currents like the Gulf Stream influence the temperature and entire climate of continental coastlines.

Sunlight. As in terrestrial habitats, sunlight is the energy source for photosynthesis but water filters light waves as they pass through it. For example, red, orange, and ultraviolet waves are absorbed first, leaving only green, yellow, and blue to penetrate deeper. Even in the clearest water with the sun directly overhead, 300 feet appears to be the limit of effective photosynthesis. Usually photosynthetic zones are shallower. Consequently deep lakes and all oceans contain only a small zone which will support producer organisms. Nevertheless, the entire biotic economy depends on these producers as do land areas.

The laws of energy and the concept of energy flow apply to freshwater and marine communities in the same way as they do to the land ecosystems.

Dissolved Gases. Oxygen is present in much smaller amounts in water than in the air. Air has the equivalent of 210 cubic centimeters (cc) of oxygen per liter (irrespective of temperature); at 15° C fresh water holds only 7.2 cc per liter, and sea water 5.8 cc per liter at saturated conditions; often the amount is less. Animals that breathe in water exist on these relatively small amounts of dissolved oxygen by virtue of their reduced metabolic rates and specially adapted breathing structures. Carbon dioxide dissolves readily in water and hence is present in greater amounts than in air, although in various forms: dissolved carbon dioxide, carbonic acid, carbonate, and bicarbonate. It is important in photosynthesis, regulation of pH, and other reactions.

Chemical Substances.   Sea water contains over forty chemical elements, largely in the form of ions. This "ionic soup" provides an excellent chemical environment for life. Chloride and sodium ions are the most abundant. Other principle ions are calcium, magnesium, potassium, carbonate, sulfate, and bromine. Many of these also occur in fresh water but in smaller amounts. The dissolved materials most important to organisms are nitrogen compounds, phosphates, calcium salts, and silicates. Nitrates and phosphates are valuable nutrients for phytoplankton, and calcium is required by shellfish, corals, and other marine life. The use of nutrient salts by plants was discussed in Chapter XXI.

In both fresh and salt water, organisms facing osmotic problems in retaining or excreting ions from their cells have evolved osmoregulatory organs to live only in one habitat. Most marine organisms cannot live in fresh water, and vice versa.

In discussing marine habitats the term *salinity* is often used. Salinity refers to the number of grams of dry salts per 1000 grams of water (thus, parts per thousand, ‰). This measure, in reality, includes a number of salts, but in practice only the amount of chloride ions is determined. A mathematical factor is then applied to convert this amount to salinity. The salinity of oceanic waters approximates 35 ‰, whereas freshwater bodies generally have less than 1 ‰.

Major geochemical cycles frequently involve freshwater and marine environments, as illustrated by the phosphorus cycle described in Chapter XXII.

Freshwater Environments

Streams, rivers, ponds, lakes, and marshes are all freshwater habitats. These are sometimes divided into flowing-water and standing-water communities. The general structure of a pond ecosystem was presented in Chapter XXI.

Rivers have been utilized by man for travel, commerce, irrigation, and waste disposal. This last use has been abused to the point that many major rivers are now unsuitable for recreation or as sources of drinking water. Pollution, in fact, is a major ecological problem today. Water pollution usually results from domestic sewage (organic matter) or toxic chemical wastes from industrial sources. Organic matter in moderate amounts can be disposed of in streams and rivers by organisms of decay. In large amounts organic wastes cause a severe depletion of oxygen so that only anaerobic forms can survive. Toxic industrial wastes act either as oxygen depleters or as poisons to all forms of life. Insecticides from farm lands are known to cause severe pollution in some areas. Soil erosion also produces pollution in the form of silt in streams and rivers. All these forms of pollution can be eliminated or controlled, although legislation is usually necessary to bring this about. Such legislation invariably waits until an informed and alarmed public demands it.

Lakes are not often used for waste disposal, but some areas of the Great Lakes are now badly polluted by industrial and municipal wastes. As described in Chapter XXI, we can manipulate the food-chain structure of a small lake by treating it with chemical fertilizers. This is done on many farm ponds to increase fish production. A farm pond properly managed produces more protein per acre than do ordinary agricultural efforts.

In terms of geological time, lakes have short life spans. In fact, they provide classic examples of succession as they fill with sediments and encroaching plant life, eventually becoming marshes or bogs.

Marine Environments

Oceans present the most extensive of all habitats, occupying more than two-thirds of the surface of the earth. As our example we have chosen the Gulf of Mexico. It represents an ocean in miniature in its features, and forms a convenient unit for the description of marine environments.

General Features.   Figure 25.1 is a topological map of the Gulf of Mexico showing some of its principle features. The Gulf is essentially a large basin with an opening in one side. The periphery of the basin is formed by a *continental shelf* at depths down to 100 fathoms (600 feet). As the map shows, the 100-fathom contour line indicates a wide shelf for most of the Gulf, except along the coast of Mexico. Continental-shelf areas are important in all oceans because of the abundance of life inhabiting them. Bottom-dwelling plants and animals, *plankton* (forms with limited swimming ability) and *nekton* (swimmers) form rich and elaborate food webs and pyramids. Many open-ocean fishes

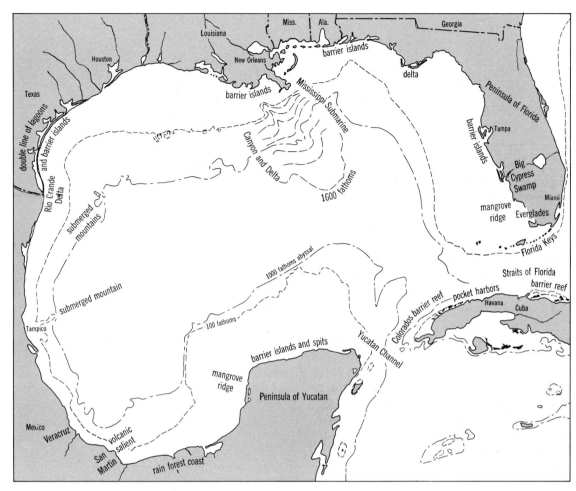

Figure 25.1. A map of the Gulf of Mexico showing some of its major features. (Modified from W. A. Price, Shores and Coasts of the Gulf of Mexico. In Gulf of Mexico: Its Origin, Waters and Marine Life. Fishery Bull. *89 of the Fish and Wildlife Service, Vol. 55.)*

return to continental-shelf areas to spawn or to use them as feeding grounds. The continental shelf and coastal communities of the Gulf include coral reefs (atolls, fringing reefs, and barrier reefs), extensive salt water marshes and mangrove swamps, numerous barrier islands built by storm action, and extensive submarine "meadows." Such variety of community types supports an enormous assortment of producers and consumers (Figures 25.2 and 25.3).

Extending across a portion of the Gulf is a large triangular area with depths exceeding 2000 fathoms. At this depth is the cold, lightless, *abyssal zone* into which all energy supplies must be imported from above. A large, submerged mountain range lies off the coast of Mexico, and a deep submarine canyon is located offshore from the Mississippi coast.

Generally speaking, the Gulf is a warm body of water. Surface readings show a summer mean temperature of 84° F and a winter mean temperature of around 70° F. In the depths it is much cooler; from 900 meters down the temperature has been measured at 40° F.

The open Gulf has a salinity of about 35 ‰, but salinities along the coastline fluctuate widely, especially near the draining areas of the rivers. Hence, off the mouth of the Mississippi, salinities of less than 24 ‰ have been recorded.

Tides and Currents. Tides are caused by the gravitational pull of the moon and, to a lesser degree, the sun. When the two are pulling together, as happens

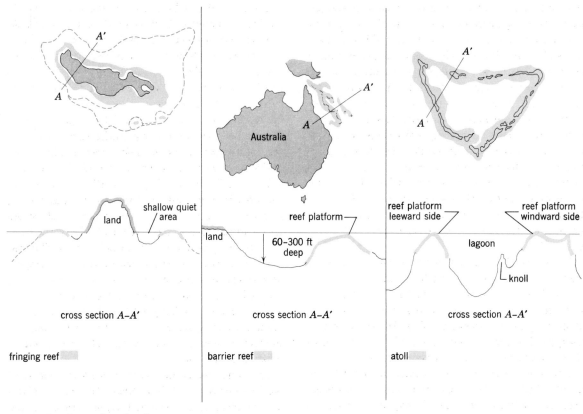

land

shallow quiet area

cross section A–A'

fringing reef

land

reef platform

60–300 ft deep

cross section A–A'

barrier reef

reef platform leeward side

reef platform windward side

lagoon

knoll

cross section A–A'

atoll

Figure 25.2. Types of coral reefs.

Figure 25.3. Exposed coral.

twice a month (full moon and new moon), the largest extremes of high and low tides occur. When these influences are opposed, the least amount of flow and ebb takes place. Additional influences on tidal movements are those of wind and change in barometric pressure. This is especially true in the Gulf with its relatively small ranges of tides and shallow coastal waters. The mean annual tide on the Gulf coast does not normally exceed two or three feet (compared with ten feet along the Atlantic coast). This small tidal fluctuation is enough to alternately flood and drain extensive areas of salt marsh, mangrove swamp, and mud flats. One of the dangers of hurricane-type storms in the Gulf is the possibility that large amounts of water will pile up against the low-elevation coastline, resulting in flooding.

The study of oceanic currents is complicated by the many variables involved, such as tidal movements, winds, density of the water, rotation of the earth, and so on, not to mention the vastness of the areas. Many of the major currents like the Gulf Stream determine the type of climate of coastal areas, although the forces that produce the currents are poorly understood.

The Gulf of Mexico contains currents of great complexity. Little is known of them other than surface velocity readings and general mappings at certain seasons. Especially during storms, Gulf currents can erode or deposit a beach in a short time.

Community Structure and Function. The sea in most aspects offers a hospitable environment for living things; organisms are bathed in salts and minerals, temperature variations are moderate, dessication is not a problem, food is frequently abundant, and heavy skeletal supports are unnecessary. Generally speaking, marine communities share some features with the pond ecosystem described previously, that is, algae form the producers, zooplankton are the primary consumers, and so on. There are also major differences. Some algae (seaweeds) that are important producers are macroscopic. In many marine communities insects are absent, their ecological equivalents being small crustaceans. There is a greater variety of life forms than in fresh water. In contrast to fresh water, the sea contains many *sessile* (attached) organisms such as sponges, corals, and sea anemones which may be ecologically important. In fact, major groups such as the sponges, coelenterates, echinoderms (starfish and sea urchins), and annelid worms are abundant and important in the sea but are minor groups in freshwater communities. (See Figures 25.4–25.7.)

Plankton play a large role in the energy flow in marine communities both as producers (phytoplankton) and as consumers (zooplankton). Producer plankton are mostly *diatoms* and *dinoflagellates*. Diatoms are unicellular algae encased in two halves or valves which are impregnated with silica, an important feature (to biologists) since these forms may be represented in fossil formations. Their significance to marine and freshwater communities is that they are the most abundant microscopic plants, and hence the major component of the producer level (Figure 25.8).

Dinoflagellates, small photosynthetic forms, are also abundant in plankton. Some are luminescent and give rise to spectacular displays at night. Others like *Gymnodinium brevis* cause the death of marine creatures by the production of toxic substances. The consequences, known as red tide, may assume catastrophic proportions in some areas. A notable feature of all phytoplankton is their occasional tremendous increase in numbers, a so-called plankton "bloom." This may occur seasonally, for example, in the spring and late summer, or may result in some areas from a welling up of nutrient minerals.

The other major microscopic plankton consist of the *Foraminifera* and *Radiolaria* (Figure 25.9). Members of these groups live in tiny, sometimes ornate, shells which they secrete. Their numbers are so great that portions of ocean bottoms may consist of foraminiferal or radiolarian oozes of great thickness.

The small crustacea, particularly copepods, are among the most important and abundant primary consumers, which in turn are utilized by secondary consumers such as small fish. Other important crustacea are ostracods, amphipods, and small shrimp and prawns (Figure 25.10).

The following paragraph from a paper by Gunter et al. (1948) summarizes the kind of chain reaction which plankton may exhibit.

"There was first the appearance of numbers of *Gymnodinium brevis* mixed in with other normal plankton types, mostly diatoms. . . . Locally, or over large areas there then appeared a "bloom" of *Gymnodinium,* and in these areas the mortality occurred. This was then followed by the decomposition of many dead organisms, with the consequent release into the water of much nutrient material. Bacteria and/or phytoplankton utilized this nutrient material and then were themselves utilized, especially by the *Copepoda,* which consequently increased enormously in the plankton. . . . The *Copepoda* devoured all the suitable diatoms, and left only the species of *Rhizosolenia,* which would be very difficult for the copepods to handle. . . ."

Figure 25.4. Kelp, a large marine alga.

Figure 25.5. Close-up of a living coral. (Kitchen/Kinne, Photo Researchers, Inc.)

Figure 25.6. A sea anemone.

Figure 25.7. Starfish and sea urchins.

Figure 25.8. Some forms of plankton.

A common technique in studying plankton is to count the numbers in a small sample of water (one milliliter, for example) and then use this finding to calculate the number in larger volumes. Hence, biologically "poor" waters might have a hundred or less plankton per liter, whereas during a plankton bloom these waters might contain many thousands per liter. Quantitative studies have indicated that an increase in phytoplankton may be followed by an increase in zooplankton, a reasonable expectation. On the other hand, zooplankton have been observed to be abundant when phytoplankton were few in number, which seems contradictory to our concept of food pyramids. Recent investigations have shown that sea water frequently contains a considerable amount of organic detritus (tiny bits and even molecules of organic matter) concentrated on the interfaces of bubbles at the surface. Presumably, microcrustacea and smaller zooplankton feed on these.

Nekton, the large consumers, consists of fishes, marine mammals, sea birds, molluscs (squid), and turtles. Although members of these groups may range the open sea, they are found in the largest concentrations near their energy sources, over continental shelves and along coastlines. These are important as well as frequently spectacular members of marine communities. Some of the fishes, mammals, and turtles are of economic value to man, a situation which often means they are being unwisely utilized. But in this case, with the exception of a few of the mammals and turtles, man has not apparently damaged these marine crops. (See Figures 25.11 and 25.12.)

Example of a Marine Community

Marine communities along the Gulf coast frequently form extensive underwater meadows of grasslike seedplants such as turtlegrass and manateegrass. Green algae may also contribute to this photosynthetic layer. These extensive underwater grasslands constitute a region of rich marine life, with burrowing and filter

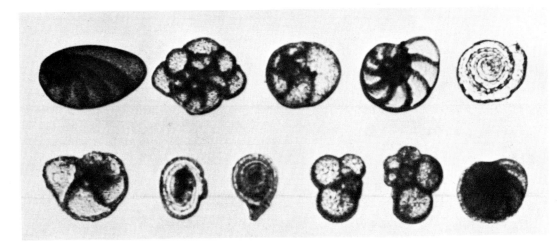

Figure 25.9. Foraminifera.

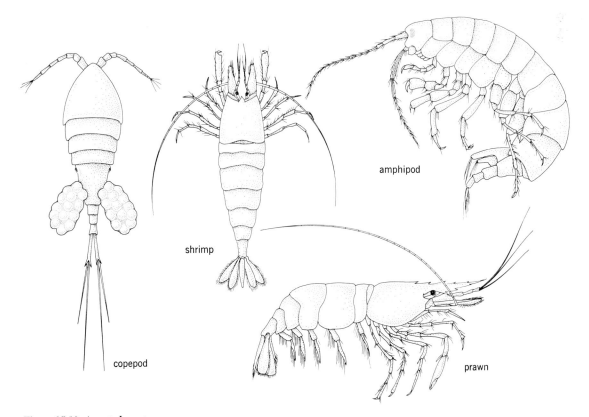

amphipod

shrimp

copepod

prawn

Figure 25.10. Assorted crustacea.

309

(a)

(b)

Figure 25.11. Killer whales. The insert shows a captive female; the large photograph shows a male. (Insert—Dr. Merrill P. Spencer, Life Sciences Company.)

feeding perhaps the commonest adaptations.

Many varieties of shellfish (pelecypods), burrowing worms, starfishes, marine snails, and crabs are the dominant forms of animal life. Bacteria probably reach their greatest abundance in the mud bottoms, and in turn provide a food source for many protozoans and zooplankton. In addition to filter feeding, many organisms are "deposit-feeders" in that they sift bottom sediments for bits of organic material, bacteria, and various plankton. Larger consumers such as fishes, porpoises, sea turtles, and birds feed extensively over these communities. Studies on the Gulf coastal area indicate that these shallow-water areas serve as nurseries for a number of larger fishes—their young dwell and feed there until they are large enough to enter deeper waters.

Extensive organismic interaction is found here, as in many marine communities. These communities change (undergo succession) as do land and freshwater ecosystems. One application of this idea is utilized along the Gulf coast to improve fishing. Debris like concrete blocks and old auto bodies are dumped offshore to create artificial reefs. Small marine life soon inhabit the reef which in turn attracts large consumers. The final consumer in this case is, hopefully, the fisherman!

Many additional communities, of course, exist in the sea, such as the organisms of the open sea, those dwelling in abyssal areas, coral reef inhabitants, and so on. (The Suggested Readings provide a detailed account that we cannot provide here.)

Concluding Remarks

In the Preface to this book we suggested that an informed citizen should be able to make an intelligent evaluation of the discoveries and issues in science. We have attempted to contribute to this objective by presenting some of the important topics in modern biology. If this helps you to read scientific articles in magazines and newspapers with greater understanding and intellectual enjoyment, or helps you better to assess the issues in local controversies involving sewage disposal, air pollution, fluoridation, and the like, this book has fulfilled a major part of its intention.

Figure 25.12. Brown pelicans.

We conclude the book by proposing the question, "What are some of the major lessons or guidelines the field of biology offers mankind for tomorrow?" The most basic issue pertains to the relationship between energy and life. Energy considerations are basic to life from the level of molecules to that of biomes. This becomes particularly crucial to man since as his populations increase, his demands for carbon compounds (food) also increase. The source of these compounds are plants; photosynthesis is the vital energy-providing reaction. In the sections on ecology we noted that a community in nature is composed in such a way that its energy producers are also its energy bottleneck. In other words, there is a limit to the number or amount of photosynthesizers in an ecosystem: hence there is a limit to the amount of energy available for life. Man changes the energy relations in ecosystems. He may increase the energy output temporarily for his own use by replacing the natural community with an artificial one (crops). Eventually, though, even man encounters the inevitable photosynthetic bottleneck. What happens when all available lands on the earth are farmed efficiently?

Man often changes the energy relations in his environment unwittingly, that is, as a by-product of some other activity. Perhaps this is the greatest danger we face. Pollution, industrialization, urbanization, and farming each plays a role in disturbing or destroying natural habitats. Pollution of all kinds from cities and industries must be better controlled because it is a destroyer of producer organisms, not to mention its other undesirable powers. Smog, for example, is detrimental to all organisms that breathe it. Severe atmospheric pollution can even completely denude the landscape (see Figure 25.13). Pollution can and must be controlled, but this will require large expenditures of money and, in some instances, legal enforcement. Hopefully we may someday see river systems like the Potomac or Hudson restored to a state where they can safely be used for recreation and water consumption.

Man's industries and dwellings often wipe out natural communities. There is little that can be done about this in most instances although there are a few encouraging signs across North America. In the pulpwood industry, for example, large acreages of forests are carefully managed so that a supply of pulpwood

Figure 25.13. Areas around smelters at Copperhill, Tennessee, have been turned into waste-lands by fumes from the smelters.

will always be available. This management not only protects the woodland but also provides a refuge for wildlife and, in some cases, recreation areas. This is in sharp contrast to the activities of the lumber industry a few decades ago. At that time vast areas of forest land were completely stripped of trees and abandoned. Fires and erosion often followed.

The development of suburbs proceeds rapidly in most parts of the United States, unfortunately for the natural communities they replace. Seldom are even small portions of the natural suburban landscape preserved as parks. This is the sort of thing that can be changed only by the action of citizens working through planning and zoning committees.

The wholesale destruction of natural areas by farming and home building has often brought on drastic consequences. A common consequence is flooding because the normal watersheds that absorb or contain excess rainfall are no longer present. Efforts are then made to retain the water artificially as by dams and dikes; then the problems multiply. Thus in southern Florida, efforts to drain swampland for use in farming were so successful that much of the Everglades were destroyed. As a by-product, the Everglades National

Park is at this time in serious difficulty and quite likely is doomed.

Our growing populace descends on the countryside during the summer months seeking relaxation. Most of the national parks fill to capacity with campers and visitors. It is evident that much larger recreation areas of this type must be provided soon, not only for the benefit of people but also to keep certain unusual portions of the country from being ruined. Areas like Yellowstone National Park or the Cape Cod National Seashore have educational, aesthetic, and recreational value. There appears to be considerable interest in creating more areas of this type—hopefully this is a trend for the future.

One of the key factors in man's ultimate survival or failure on this planet depends on his treatment of natural communities, biomes, and natural resources in general. Conservation once meant preservation; now it is more meaningful to think of it in terms of *wise use,* in the sense of practices consistent with empirically derived biological concepts rather than personal, political, or economic dictates or desires. In this light we must think in terms of the conservation of entire ecosystems, not just certain species in it or parts of it.

Principles

1. The same basic ecosystem concepts of structure and function apply to aqueous and terrestrial environments, despite their different physical and chemical features.

2. Marine environments occupy approximately two-thirds of the surface of the earth and contain the majority of the earth's producer and consumer populations.

Suggested Readings

Bates, Marston, *The Forest and the Sea*. Vintage Books, Random House, New York, 1960.

Carson, Rachel, *The Edge of the Sea*. The New American Library of World Literature, New York, 1963.

Carson, Rachel, *The Sea Around Us*. The New American Library of World Literature, New York, 1964.

Coker, R. E., *This Great and Wide Sea*. Harper and Row, Publishers, New York, 1962.

Deevey, E. S., Jr., "Life in the Depths of a Pond," *Scientific American,* Vol. 199 (August, 1958).

Galtsoff, Paul S., coordinator, "Gulf of Mexico. Its Origin, Waters, and Marine Life," *Fishery Bulletin* 89, Vol. 55, United States Department of the Interior, Fish and Wildlife Service, 1954.

Gunter, G., R. H. Williams, C. C. Davis, and F. G. W. Smith, "Catastrophic Mass Mortality of Marine Animals and Coincident Phytoplankton Bloom on the West Coast of Florida, November 1946 to August 1947," *Ecol. Monographs,* Vol. 18, 1948, pp. 309–324.

Hutner, S. N. and J. J. A. McLaughlin, "Poisonous Tides," *Scientific American,* Vol. 199 (August, 1958).

Long, Capt. C. John, USNR (ret.), *New Worlds of Oceanography*. Pyramid Publications, New York, 1965.

Murphy, Robert C., "The Oceanic Life of the Antarctic," *Scientific American,* Vol. 207 (September, 1962). Offprint No. 864, W. H. Freeman and Co., San Francisco.

Odum, Eugene P., *Ecology*. Holt, Rinehart and Winston, New York, 1963, pp. 112–123.

Pequegnat, Willis E., "Whales, Plankton and Man," *Scientific American,* Vol. 198 (January, 1958). Offprint No. 853, W. H. Freeman and Co., San Franciso.

Questions

1. Why do underwater movies taken at considerable depths show blue as the dominant color?

2. If 300 feet is the limit of photosynthesis, what is the energy source for animals that dwell below that depth?

3. Why is dissolved carbon dioxide important to aquatic plants?

4. What is the origin of the salts which maintain the salinity of the oceans?

5. Why, then, are lakes not also salty?

6. Describe what happens to the food pyramid in a lake when chemical fertilizers are added.

7. In what respects does the sea provide a beneficial environment for living things? In what respects is it a detrimental environment?

8. Propose a series of succession stages which could take place on a man-made reef.

9. What kinds of "crops" does man harvest from the sea at present? What additional organisms might be utilized in the future?

Classification

The following gives a commonly accepted scheme for classification of most plants and animals, along with line drawings of representative organisms in the major classes and phyla.

Kingdom *Plantae*

Subkingdom *Thallophyta*—thallus plants lack true roots, stems, and leaves. Plant body lacks differentiation; single cells, filaments of cells, and intertwining filaments are three common body types.

Phylum *Schizophyta* (bacteria)—single celled, lack a distinct nucleus and generally lack chlorophyll, three general shapes: spiral, rod shaped, and spherical.

Phylum *Cyanophyta* (blue-green algae)—single celled; lack a distinct nucleus; chlorophyll *a* and a blue pigment, phycocyanin, are not contained in chloroplasts; species frequently surrounded by a gelatinous matrix, forming colonies which often are spherical or fan shaped. Figure 1

Phylum *Euglenophyta* (euglenoids)—single celled or colonial; contain chlorophyll *a* and *b*; reproduce by cell division; flagellum present; usually lack a cell wall. Figure 2

Phylum *Chlorophyta* (green algae)—contain chlorophyll *a* and *b*; unicellular and multicellular forms; store food as starch. Figure 3

Phylum *Chrysophyta* (diatoms)—golden to golden-brown or yellowish-green; contain chlorophyll *a*; majority are unicellular or colonial; store food as an oil or a carbohydrate, leucosin. Figure 4

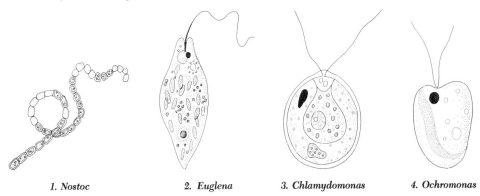

1. Nostoc   *2. Euglena*   *3. Chlamydomonas*   *4. Ochromonas*

5. Glenodinium

6. Ectocarpus

7. Chantransia

8. Marchella

9. Mushroom

Phylum *Pyrrophyta* (golden-brown algae)—contain chlorophyll *a* and *c*; dinoflagellates comprise main class; heavy cell wall divided into plates with furrows, one longitudinal and one transverse. Figure 5

Phylum *Phaeophyta* (brown algae)—plastids brown, owing to the pigment fucoxanthin; chlorophyll *a* and *c* present; usually large; food stored as an oil or carbohydrates. Figure 6

Phylum *Rhodophyta* (red algae)—plastids red, owing to the pigment phycoerythrin; chlorophyll *a* and *d* present; food stored as a starchlike compound; usually conspicuous. Figure 7

Phylum *Myxomycophyta* (slime molds)—lack chlorophyll; vegetative stage is a multinucleate mass of protoplasm. Part of life cycle is composed of single independent cells. See Figure 8.7 for life cycle.

Phylum *Eumycophyta* (fungi)—plant body is composed of tubular filaments called hyphae; lack chlorophyll.

   Class *Phycomycetes* (algal fungi)—hyphae lack cross walls.

   Class *Ascomycetes* (sac fungi)—Hyphae have cross walls. Spore that is produced after fertilization is developed in ascus. See Figure 16.6 and Figure 8

   Class *Basidiomycetes* (club fungi)—have cross walls in hyphae, spores are borne in club-shaped structures; mushrooms are familiar members of this group. Figure 9

      Lichens are composite plants made up of algae and fungi in a symbiotic relationship. Figure 10

10. Lichen

Subkingdom *Embryophyta*—mostly land plants; embryo develops in female sex organ; contain chlorophyll *a* and *b*.

   Phylum *Bryophyta* (liverworts and mosses)—generally small land plants found in moist habitats; gametophyte is the conspicuous plant; do not have true roots, stems, or leaves; sperm swims to egg in a layer of water. Contains liverworts, horned liverworts, and mosses, respectively. Figures 11, 12, and 13

11. Marchantia, a liverwort

12. Anthroceros, a horned liverwort

13. Polytrichum, a moss

14. *Psilotum*   15. *Lycopodium*   16. *Selaginella*   17. *Equisetum*   18. *Dryopteris*

Phylum *Tracheophyta* (vascular plants)—contain vascular tissue (xylem and phloem), sporophyte is the prominent plant.

Subphylum *Psilopsida* (chiefly fossil)—rare plants, usually tropical; true roots and true leaves absent. Figure 14

Subphylum *Lycopsida* (clubmosses and quillworts)—true roots present, leaves small, arranged spirally; stems not jointed; spores borne on the upper surfaces of some leaves. Figures 15 and 16 (both clubmosses)

Subphylum *Sphenopsida* (horsetails)—leaves small, arranged in whorls; stems jointed. Figure 17

Subphylum *Pteropsida*—leaves generally large and complex; all well-known plants are in this group—ferns, conifers, and flowering plants.

Class *Filicinae* (ferns)—horizontal stem bearing roots and leaves; alternation of generations; sporophyte dominant generation. Figure 18

Class *Gymnospermae* (cone-bearing seed plants)—bear naked seeds (embryo plus maternal tissue). Figures 19, 20, and 21

Class *Angiospermae* (flower-bearing seed plants)—bear seeds enclosed in the ovary.

Subclass *Monocotyledoneae*—vascular tissue of stem in scattered bundles; cambium usually absent; leaves with parallel veins; embryo with single cotyledon. Figure 22

Subclass *Dicotyledoneae*—vascular tissue of stem forms a cylinder; cambium present; leaves with net venation; embryo has two cotyledons. Figure 23

19. *Cycas*

20. *Ginkgo*   21. *Pinus*   22. *Zea*   23. *Cassia*

Kingdom *Animalia*

Phylum *Protozoa*—unicellular; usually motile.

  Subphylum *Mastigophora*—flagellate protozoa; one to many flagella for locomotion throughout life or at certain stages; generally uninucleate. Figure 24

  Subphylum *Sarcodina*—ameboid protozoa; pseudopodia for locomotion; uni- and multinucleate. Figure 25

  Subphylum *Sporozoa*—spore-forming protozoa; no special organs for locomotion; uni- and multinucleate. Figure 26

  Subphylum *Ciliophora*—ciliate protozoa; locomotion by cilia; micro- and macro-nuclei. Figure 27

Phylum *Porifera* (sponges)—central cavity with pores to the outside; no tissue organization; all aquatic; attached to a substrate. Figures 28, 29, and 30

Phylum *Coelenterata* or *Cnidaria*—aquatic; tentacles surrounding mouth, the only opening to the gastrovascular cavity; single or colonial polyp, which is sessile; or a floating medusa; nematocysts (stinging cells) present.

  Class *Hydrozoa*—both medusa and polyp forms; solitary or colonial. Figures 31 and 32

  Class *Scyphozoa* (true jellyfishes)—medusae predominant. Figure 33

  Class *Anthozoa*—polyp form only; solitary or colonial. Figures 34 and 35

Phylum *Ctenophora*—all marine; free swimming; with or without tentacles; locomotion by 8 meridional comb plates. Figure 36

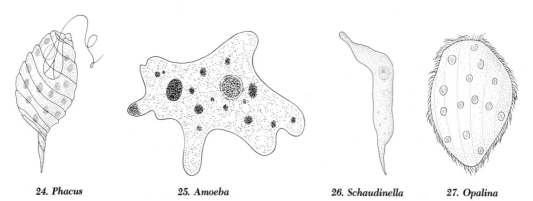

24. Phacus   *25. Amoeba*   *26. Schaudinella*   *27. Opalina*

318

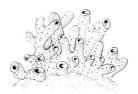

28. Scypha　　　　　**29. Euplectella**　　　　　**30. Demospongia**

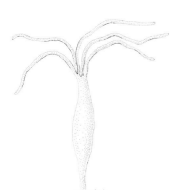

31. Hydra　　　　　**32. Obelia**　　　　　**33. Aurelia**

34. Metridium, an anemone　　　**35. Acropora, a coral**　　　**36. Pleurobrachia**

319

37. *Planaria*

38. *Fasciola*

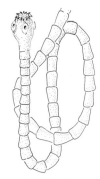

39. *Taenia*

Phylum *Platyhelminthes* (flatworms, flukes, and tapeworms)—body flattened dorso-ventrally; digestive system without anus; absence of circulatory and respiratory systems; no body cavity.

Class *Turbellaria* (free-living flatworms)—epidermis without cuticle; digestive system present. Figure 37

Class *Trematoda* (flukes)—digestive system present, epidermis absent; body covered with cuticle; suckers present. Figure 38

Class *Cestoda* (tapeworms)—epidermis absent; digestive system absent; cuticle present. Figure 39

Phylum *Nemertinea* (Rhynchocoela)—digestive system complete (mouth and anus present); lack a body cavity; circulatory system present; sexes separate; proboscis eversible. Figure 40

Phylum *Aschelminthes*—wormlike; superficial segmentation; cuticle present; body cavity a pseudocoel; number of cells or nuclei constant in a group.

Class *Rotifera*—microscopic; wheel organs at anterior end; mostly fresh water. Figure 41

Class *Nematoda* (round worms)—body elongate and cylindrical; free-living and parasitic. Figure 42

Phylum *Echinodermata*—spiny skinned; all marine; calcareous endoskeleton; pentamerous symmetry; water-vascular system.

Class *Holothuroidea*—body elongate, sausagelike; skeleton reduced to microscopic ossicles; secondary bilateral symmetry. Figure 43

Class *Asteroidea* (sea stars)—stellate shaped; arms number 5 to 50, usually not sharply set off from disc; ambulacral grooves open. Figure 44

Class *Echinoidea* (sea urchins and sand dollars)—globular or disc shaped; arms absent endoskeleton fused; ambulacral grooves closed. Figures 45 and 46

Class *Ophiuroidea* (brittle stars, serpent stars, basket stars)—arms sharply set off from disc; ambulacral grooves closed; madreporite on oral side. Figure 47

40. A ribbon worm   41. Rotifer   42. *Ascaris*

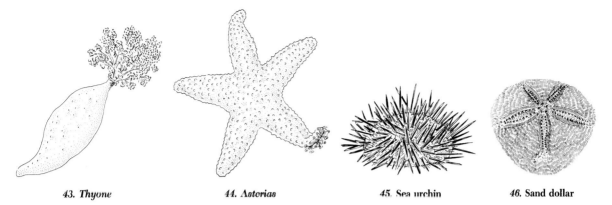

43. Thyone   *44. Asterias*   *45. Sea urchin*   *46.* Sand dollar

Phylum *Chordata*—pharyngeal gill slits; dorsal hollow nerve cord; notochord.

Subphylum *Urochordata* (tunicates)—body surrounded by tunic; unsegmented; pharynx with gill slits and endostyle; nerve cord and notochord usually absent in adults; marine; sessile or pelagic. Figure 48

Subphylum *Cephalochordata* (lancelets)—marine, sand-dwelling; dorsal nerve cord and notochord present throughout life; pharynx with gill slits and endostyle. Figure 49

Subphylum *Vertebrata*—possess a vertebral column, internal skeleton of bone or cartilage, skeleton at least partly encloses brain.

Class *Agnatha* (lamprey and hagfish, etc.)—jawless; no bone present, no appendages, vertebrae small, notochord persistent in adult.

Class *Chondrichthyes* (sharks, rays, skates, etc.)—skeleton is cartilaginous; possess jaws and paired appendages, fertilization is internal.

Class *Osteichthyes* (the bony fish)—skeleton is mostly bone; possess jaws and paired appendages.

Class *Amphibia* (frogs, toads, and salamanders, etc.)—most have a smooth, moist skin without scales; four limbs; usually have lungs.

Class *Reptilia* (snakes, lizards, turtles, crocodiles)—egg has a protective coating; skin is usually scaly; heart is three chambered.

Class *Aves* (birds)—feathered, homoiothermous; heart is four chambered.

Class *Mammalia* (mammals)—have hair; suckle the young; homoiothermous; possess a four-chambered heart.

Phylum *Bryozoa* (*Ectoprocta*) (moss animals)—mostly marine; colonial; sessile; liphophore; U-shaped digestive system. Figure 50

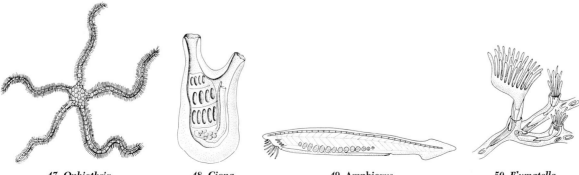

47. Ophiothrix   *48. Ciona*   *49.* Amphioxus   *50. Plumatella*

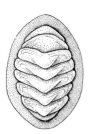

51. *Chiton*   52. *Patella*   53. *Dentalium*   54. *Mytilis*

Phylum *Mollusca*—soft-bodied; body composed of head, foot, and visceral hump; body enclosed in mantle which secretes an exoskeleton; digestive system with radular organ; respiration by gills.

Class *Amphineura* (chitons)—body elongate; shell consists of 8 dorsal plates; head reduced; tentacles and eyes absent. Figure 51

Class *Gastropoda* (snails and related forms)—visceral hump spirally coiled; with or without torsion; shell generally present; head with eyes and one or two pairs of tentacles; large flat foot. Figure 52

Class *Scaphopoda* (tooth shells or tusk shells)—slightly curved, tubular shell, open at both ends; gills absent; foot modified into burrowing organ. Figure 53

Class *Pelecypoda* (bivalved molluscs)—two lateral valves, hinged dorsally; head absent; radula absent; foot hatchet shaped, used for burrowing; mouth with labial palps; crystalline style in stomach in most species. Figure 54

Class *Cephalopoda* (squids, octopi, nautili)—head large and with tentacles; shell external and chambered or internal and reduced or not present; mouth with horny beak and radula. Figures 55, 56, and 57

Phylum *Annelida* (segmented worms)—chitinous setae; organ systems segmentally arranged; closed circulatory system; septate coelom; respiration by epidermis or gills.

Class *Oligochaeta*—primarily terrestrial and fresh water; parapodia absent; setae few per somite; head absent; obvious segmentation. Figure 58

Class *Polychaeta*—primarily marine; numerous somites with parapodia bearing many setae; head end with tentacles. Figure 59

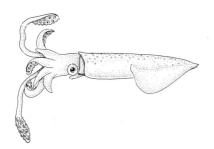
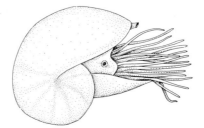
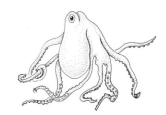

55. *Loligo*   56. *Nautilus*   57. *Octopus*

58. *Lumbricus*   59. *Nereis*   60. Leech   61. *Cyclops*

Class *Hirudinea* (leeches)—primarily freshwater parasites; parapodia and setae lacking; tentacles lacking; large posterior sucker; occasionally smaller sucker at anterior end. Figure 60

Phylum *Arthropoda*—body segmented and jointed externally; paired, segmented limbs on some or all of the segments; chitinous exoskeleton; open circulatory system.

Subphylum *Chelicerata*—body of cephalothorax and abdomen; six pairs of appendages found on cephalothorax; antennae absent. First pair of appendages are pincerlike (chelicera).

Class *Arachnida* (spiders, ticks, mites, scorpions)—simple eyes present; abdomen contains distinct segments; respiration by book lungs.

Class *Merostomata* (Horseshoe crabs)—compound and simple eyes present, abdominal segments fused, respiration by book gills.

Subphylum *Mandibulata*—body of cephalothorax and abdomen or head, thorax, and abdomen; cephalothorax or head externally unsegmented; thorax or abdomen segmented; one or two pairs of antennae on head; next pair of appendages are mandibles.

Class *Crustacea*—aquatic; two pair of antennae. This class is an amazingly diverse group that contains copepods (Figure 61), barnacles (Figure 62), isopods (Figure 63), amphipods (Figure 64), and crabs (Figure 65).

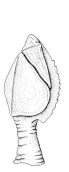

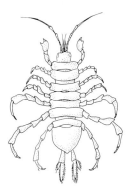

62. *Lepas*   63. *Asellas*   64. *Gammarus*   65. *Uca*

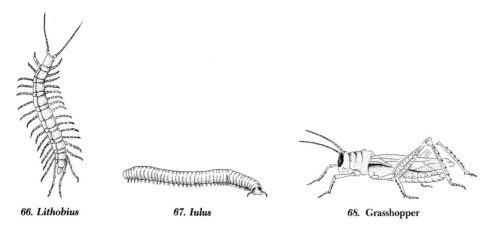

66. Lithobius   *67. Iulus*   *68.* Grasshopper

Class *Chilopoda* (centipedes)—terrestrial; respiration by tracheae; one pair of antennae; one pair of walking legs on each segment of body except the first one and the last two. Figure 66

Class *Diplopoda* (millipedes)—terrestrial; respiration by tracheae; one pair of antennae; each abdominal segment bears two pair of walking legs. Figure 67

Class *Insecta* (hexapoda, insects)—respiration by tracheae; three distinct body regions, head, thorax, abdomen; one pair of antennae and three pair of walking legs. Figure 68

Index